D1093812

PRODUCT DESIGN 2

PRODUCT DESIGN

INTERNATIONAL AWARD-WINNING SELECTIONS OF THE MID-EIGHTIES

by Sandra Edwards and the editors of *ID* Magazine

2

PBC International, Inc. ■ New York

Distributor to the book trade in the United States:
PBC INTERNATIONAL, INC.
P.O. Box 678
Locust Valley, NY 11560

Distributor to the art trade in the United States:
Letraset USA
40 Eisenhower Drive
Paramus, NJ 07653

Distributor to the trade in Canada:
General Publishing Co. Ltd.
30 Lesmill Road
Don Mills, Ontario M3B 2T6, Canada

Distributed throughout the rest of the world by:
Hearst Books International
1790 Broadway
New York, NY 10019

Library of Congress Cataloging-in-Publication Data

Edwards, Sandra, 1941–
Product design 2.

Includes indexes.
1. Design, Industrial. I. Industrial design magazine. II. Title.
TS171.E38 1986 745.2 86-9395
ISBN 0-86636-008-5

Printed and Bound by Arti Grafiche Motta Milan, Italy

Typesetting by Vera-Reyes, Inc.

10 9 8 7 6 5 4 3 2 1

STAFF OF PBC INTERNATIONAL, INC.

Publisher:	**Herb Taylor**
Project Director:	**Cora Sibal Taylor**
Executive Editor:	**Virginia Christensen**
Editor:	**Carolyn Edwins**
Art Director:	**Richard Liu**
Art Associates:	**Pat Bertram**
	Dan Larkin

STAFF OF DESIGN PUBLICATIONS, INC.

Publisher:	**Randolph McAusland**
Editorial Assistants:	**Donna Green**
	Lauren Lambert

CONTENTS

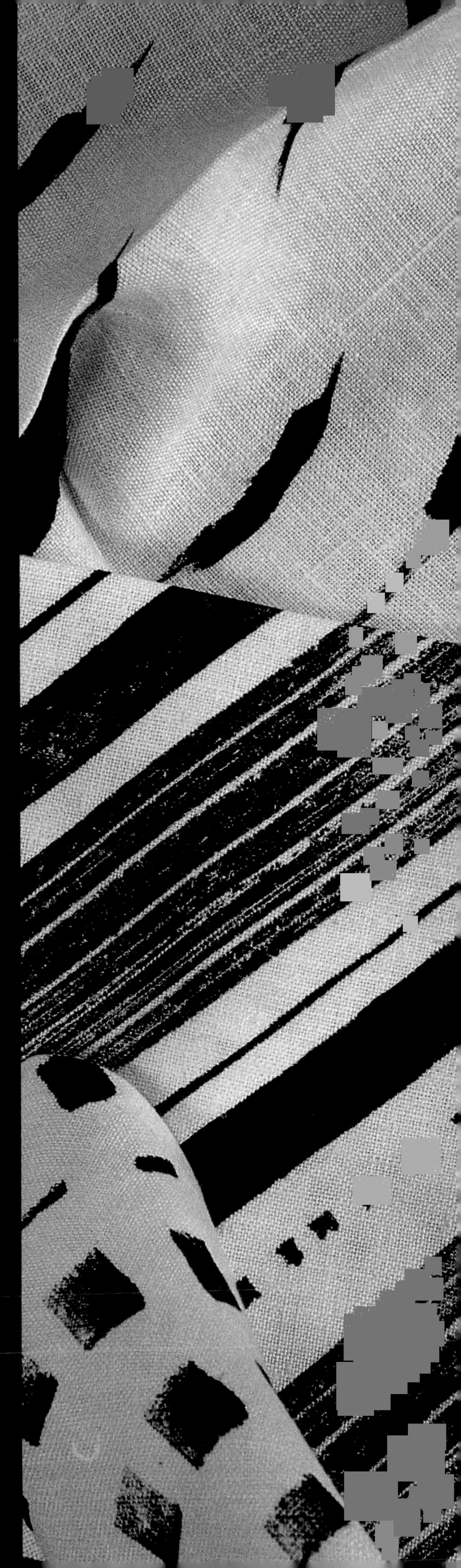

FOREWORD

Collections such as this, said Andres Malraux, are ''museums without walls.'' In effect, *Product Design 2* is a retrospective of contemporary design, and the content, of course, is not encyclopedic, but curatorial. In such categories as tabletop and furniture, we find unshackled individual visions driving the designs; these are our new ''tastemakers.'' In other categories, such as recreational and business products, what we illustrate defines the contemporary market, mid-eighties state-of-the-art design.

Here, we promote design for design's sake, first, because the forces that promote mediocrity remain so powerful, and second, because refined, thoughtful design contributes tangibly to the quality of our culture. Though many of these designs take huge risks, the majority correlate with Raymond Loewy's MAYA principle: given an assignment, a designer is duty bound to create the ''most advanced yet acceptable'' work. Manufacturers that ask less from designers squander talent and opportunities.

An important trend Sandra Edwards has isolated in *Product Design 2* is the increase in limited production— especially in furnishings, tabletop, textiles and scientific equipment. This is good news, for it correlates with Robert Reich's observation in *The New American Frontier:* ''The central problem of America's economic future is that the nation is not moving quickly enough out of high volume, standardized production. . . America must focus on precision manufactured, custom tailored, and technology driven products.'' The implication of this is that ''inherently non-routine problem solving requires close working relationships among people at all stages in the process.'' And this is why one finds many design credits associated with sophisticated products; it is collaboration in action.

However much one wants to locate bias, the editing process that yields a book like *Product Design 2* is based on much more than personal taste. In fact, the days of the genius curator are over. There is too much to know about, too many sources. No one in America is as well positioned as Sandra Edwards to undertake such a book as this one. Not only is she an *ID* contributing editor, but she has been deeply engaged in the *ID Annual* for the last two years as coordinator, moderator and editor. In addition, Edwards compiled and wrote the highly acclaimed *Office Systems* (PBC International, fall 1985), and is writing another groundbreaking book, *Designing Childhood.* Moreover, working out of *ID's* headquarters, she had access to the hundreds of design projects submitted to *ID* and the *ID Annual Design Review,* the world's largest and broadest design recognition program. In this edition alone, there are products created by more than five hundred designers from around the world. Finally, to help gather and review material, Edwards was assisted by Donna Green and Lauren Lambert, and received input from *ID* editors Steven Holt, Annetta Hanna and Chee Pearlman.

In addition to material from *ID,* Edwards drew on most of the international design competitions. Most important, however, rather than rely on the hyped, haute-design products that are promoted regularly, she took pains to explore the world of design and discover products that otherwise might have gone unnoticed. In this sense, *Product Design 2* is an important piece of design criticism.

''There is no such thing as criticism, there is only history,'' Italian architectural historian Manfredo Tafuri told the *Design Book Review.* What should interest historians, he says, are the *cycles* of design, how a work fits in its own time. ''To do otherwise is to impose one's own way of seeing.'' He believes it is essential to understand the ''mental structure'' of a period and recreate its intellectual context—evaluate all the elements that surround a work, all of its margins of involvement. Only then, says Tafuri, can we ''discover the margins of freedom or creativity that were possible.''

An editor faces the same problem when trying to comprehend and select current work. ''Distance is fundamental,'' says Tafuri, ''and those who examine current work must create *artificial* distance, because through the differences we can better understand the present.'' Though he attributes such discipline to historians, much the same process is used when jurying the *ID Annual* or selecting projects for this book.

Finally, says Tafuri, ''One of the greatest problems of our own times is dealing with the uncontrollable acceleration of time, a process that began with the 19th century industrialization; it keeps continually disposing of things in expectation of the future of the next thing. All avant garde movements were in fact based on the continual destruction of preceding work in order to go on to something new.''

The collection captured in *Product Design 2* is one way to ''save the present,'' to postpone its destruction, to prevent it from being crushed by the hype of the next trend, the next new wave; for, like Tafuri, we believe that the media's habit of destroying the present ''contributes to the nihilism of our times.'' Too many thoughtful designs are overlooked because they will not fit into trendy schemes.

It is ironic that ten years from now many of the products illustrated here will be forgotten, the entire collection mere footprints on a beach. Though individual items may be irrelevant, the collection will have meaning in the way it relates to the problems of living and designing in the mid-1980s. In the end, *Product Design* and now *Product Design 2* will tell us something about our current design cycle—and about ourselves.

RANDOLPH MCAUSLAND
Publisher, ID magazine

INTRODUCTION

Design, craft, and art have meshed with past and present to set up a lavish smorgasbord of design elements and philosophies from which designers may choose. Textures and materials combine in manners that both defy and exalt conventional forms. Color, perhaps the most striking departure of this collection, is served up in larger portions and with greater variety than ever before, adding the finishing touches to visions that range from grandeur to whimsy.

The ranks of industrial designers—historically the providers of product—have been joined in record numbers by architects, craft artists, and even fine artists. Not surprisingly, an architectonic composure or craft's Oriental-rooted love of beauty, marks the objects created by these allied disciplines. Architects, who have previously undertaken the design of furniture to preserve an aesthetic purity with their architecture, have now discovered whole new industries open to their smaller scale imaginings.

While the record prices commanded by architects for their earlier products reinforced a hierarchy within the design profession, similar historic price hikes have legitimized the coming of age of an entire discipline—the American craft movement. Designs suitable for limited edition or, in the case of artists such as Dorothy Hafner, for mass-production techniques, alert the design world that this new influence is not likely to be a fleeting presence. Feverish collecting in this area by museums and individuals underlines the notion. Craft artists, working in a tradition rich in experimentation with shape and color, are well-suited to take on the post-Modern challenge.

While it may be less apparent as to exactly who is responsible for a particular design, so too design distinctions of geographic origin have become less pronounced. American manufacturers, inspired by Europe's co-option of an increasingly large percentage to the product market, are now competing with the sleek, recognizable design known as ''Eurostyle.'' Meanwhile, and not without irony, Europeans are modifying their approach to reach new segments of the coveted American market. In addition, bolstered by a growing nationalism on their own front, American companies appear to have finally rebounded from the swift turnaround in public opinion on goods from Japan and are matching the high-performance image that Japanese manufacturers enjoy.

If we have multiplied the creative sources for design, likewise, the recipients of design's many benefits have dramatically expanded. Design has become more accessible to a greater proportion of the populace, cropping up in every ritual of our daily living, from the shape of our toothbrush and how we make our morning coffee, to the tools we use to sustain, and save, our lives. The decorative and the functional—present throughout history—co-exist today in unprecedented fashion. Product designers are combining sensitivity and beauty, creating real solutions for real lives.

Contemporary designs incorporate influences from every major design tradition, representing styles that span the entire design spectrum: avant-garde, late Modernism, post-Modernism, and revivals. Each style exists out of a specific set of expectations relating to cultural requirements or transitions. We see in the voluptuous lines of Hollein's ''Marilyn'' the credence the post-Modern doctrine lends to sensuality, while avant-garde's flamboyance is evident in the exaggerated, elegant forms of the Zabro table/chair by Studio Alchimia and in the ribald application of color on Arquitectonica's ''Madonna.''

Refinements that adhere to the principles of a specific doctrine are included in the collection. However, the overriding design message of the mid-80's is the sampling of elements and the cross-referencing of styles. Randolph McAusland, publisher of *ID,* postulates on the composite elements of New Design: ''Maybe it comes down to this: the Bauhaus provides forms based on principles of functionality, post-Modern graphics and architecture provide styles full of flair and Memphis provides creative license.''

But, if this creative feed is stimulating for some, it is unsettling for others. What we have is a product *Amazon* with design streams reflecting or persuading consumers at every level—a new mobility of taste. We have broken up ''good design,'' and conventional design approaches do not always work anymore. Peter Wooding (Providence, Rhode Island) while jurying the furniture category of 1986 *ID Annual,* voiced some of the conflicts that have arisen: ''There is a whole set of conditions that art furniture cannot meet, and should not be made to. The problem is this: all the criteria that industrial designers use as the basis for solving design problems no longer apply. We lose our common reference points, the things we have been educated in, our understanding about what good design is.''

Concerns, like the designs, vary. Products can serve as symbols of an upwardly mobile rise in lifestyle. When forms and colors once reserved for the ''top of the heap'' are applied to mass-marketed wares, it causes consternation for high-end users quite accustomed to the exclusive rights to ''good design.'' But, no need to fret. That age-old delineator, the price tag, safeguards elitism (at least in some areas), for if design options are expanded, so also have prices.

In our age, inculcated with the idea of specialization, removing obvious distinctions between the work of allied disciplines can reek further havoc with the categorization process. Take, for example, the recent experience of Beth Forer at the Accent on Design Show in New York. ''They thought my pieces were beautiful and wanted to give them some kind of recognition. However, according to their previously established guidelines, they couldn't determine exactly *where* I fit in. So, what happened was they created a new design award.''

While relishing the challenge and opportunity inherent in the new design polemics, many designers remain sensibly cautious in awarding primary jurisdiction to any single school of thought. Neither form nor function should be sacrificed. Their goal is balance. ''I would be very reluctant to encourage design for art's sake while the fundamentals of 'people-machine' interface is at stake,'' said Robin Chu, Director of Industrial Design, ID Two, San Francisco. Philippe Starck, French furniture designer, puts it another way. ''For an object to be worth anything, it must be functioning in one way or another. People talk of a Starck style. I prefer a Starck logic.'' (*New York Times,* 12 Dec. 1985) But still, even after the rationale is determined, the aesthetic choices remain wide open.

Whether designers (or consumers) choose to dive in head first, step in gradually, or just walk around the edges of the new design, there is no disputing that the temperature of the design waters has changed. (Granted, depending on the area one comes from, it can still seem either warm or cold.) However, most would agree, the outlook for design awareness and appreciation has warmed considerably.

Unquestionably, the contemporary consumer is more *design literate* and has more disposable income—a fertile combination indeed for design acceptance. Chances have also jumped markedly that a particular consumer will be either older or younger. The elderly constitute the fastest-growing segment of the population, while those adolescent allowances are adding up—often to significant purchasing power. Product designers are beginning to target the needs of these newly expanded markets.

Again, we are reminded that successful design does not happen in a vacuum. The atmosphere for design is created by the repeated interplay, not only between the designer and production techniques, but between the object itself and the constants of popular culture and the marketplace. *The climate of consumption.*

It appears to be fact that people no longer want a homogeneous setting. What remains more difficult to assess is whether this desire is the cause or the effect of current product offerings.

A profound sense of individualism and risk-taking is pervading our society and is mirrored in the products being designed. In the current mood, it is now possible to create products that seduce us personally. Enter the new retail outlets for design. Design ''galleries'' (or in larger department stores, storewide product promotion galas built on the idea of *design*) typify the circular current necessary for the present product design renaissance. Born out of the steamy design atmosphere, these outlets provide a lifeline for new designers and, almost, guarantee that the recent design exploration will stay around for a while longer. Designers' ability to embody in their product designs the images we *need* or *want* to hear translates, manufacturers are slowly realizing, into that profit-generating competitive edge.

Yet, perhaps nothing has forced us to examine our collective beliefs in both design and the prevailing culture as much as the group of designers known as Memphis. In a way, this book stands as testament to the far-reaching impact a sincere exploration of design can evoke. It is a testament, not to a changing look, but to the polemics behind them—and to the many designers who, upon being startled by Memphis, joined in and carried forth the conversation. They have fulfilled what Nelson referred to as design's potential to "serve as a catalytic agent for constructive change."

No longer the screaming infant that burst onto the scene five years ago demanding our attention, Memphis continues to provoke our imaginations (and, our ire). Even if not all its designs, this Milanese studio's presence is generally accepted, having been given the official plum of design approval, museum recognition. However, a welcome into the mainstream having never been its objective, Memphis continues on creating disquieting reflections of our current state of social affairs. It defines its new designs as "barbaric"—the value judgment, like the designs, unmistakable.

Unfortunately, there are many people who misunderstood the Memphis message. Richard Horn elaborates, "Its designs have fallen prey to the twin idiocies of a culture that distorts their meaning and a consumerism that gobbles them up regardless." Memphis is an influence, not a style. Cheap imitations are killing the thought and excitement that are the soul of Memphis design, and turning Memphis into "one more dumb new look."

Sadly, the knock-off dilemma may ironically prove to be Memphis' most biting and accurate reflection of our society. Plagiarism is running rampant and travels in both directions across the water; it is a cross-cultural activity. And, its financial consequences are serious. A report from the International Trade Commission estimates that U.S. business loses $8 billion and 130,000 jobs annually to counterfeiting. In his call to the design community to support proposed Congressional law, HR 1900—which would extend copyright protection to designs—McAusland notes, "Americans may still be a nation of inventors, but our creativity and technology is being borrowed with a vengeance." In sharing a collection of designs, such as this book, the purpose is to stimulate thoughtful exploration, not license duplication.

Finally, when all the rhetoric is silenced and the lengthy discussions are concluded, the fact remains that the selection process is only one part intellectual to two (or more) parts visceral. This applies to the designer who creates a product, and the consumer who buys it. Similarly, it accurately defines the act of putting together this collection. After reviewing thousands of products, what is it that makes these designs stand out? Sometimes that cannot be articulated, it can only be felt. George Nelson said, "Design is not a science and it never will be, for the simple reason science deals with process, like an earthquake or a star going nova, which is observable, measurable and even predictable sometimes, while design deals with human activity." So too, the designs that follow are—like the human activities they serve and the human spirit that produces them— full of surprise and vision.

TABLETOP

For an industry long-slumbering, it appears that suddenly the alarm has gone off. And, whether the response is relief or rude awakening, one cannot deny that the end result is certainly a change of state.

Tableware designers have served up a palette of color ranging from subtle to riotous. A renaissance in the studio craft movement is spilling over the boundaries, inspiring and instructing the mass-market tableware industry. This is aided by craft artists who, no longer confined by one-of-a-kind designs, are finding manufacturers to produce their work for a commercial market. Meanwhile, established companies are encouraging in-house designers to be more creative, or—like Copco—hiring industrial design consulting firms to jazz up their products . . . and their images.

The tabletop is a theatre of design. In showcasing some of the profession's brightest stars and producing wares that reflect the breadth of contemporary design trends, the industry is staging a brilliant production. It promises to be a long run.

Product: Picnic Flatware
Designer: David Tisdale, New York, New York
Distributor: Rogers & Tropea, New York, New York; Clodagh Ross, Williams New York, New York
Awards: American Craft Museum Design Award
1986 *Industrial Design* magazine Design Review honorable mention

Product: Demitasse Spoons
Designer: David Tisdale, New York, New York
Distributors: Rogers & Tropea, New York, New York; Clodagh Ross Williams New York, New York
Awards: American Craft Museum Design Award

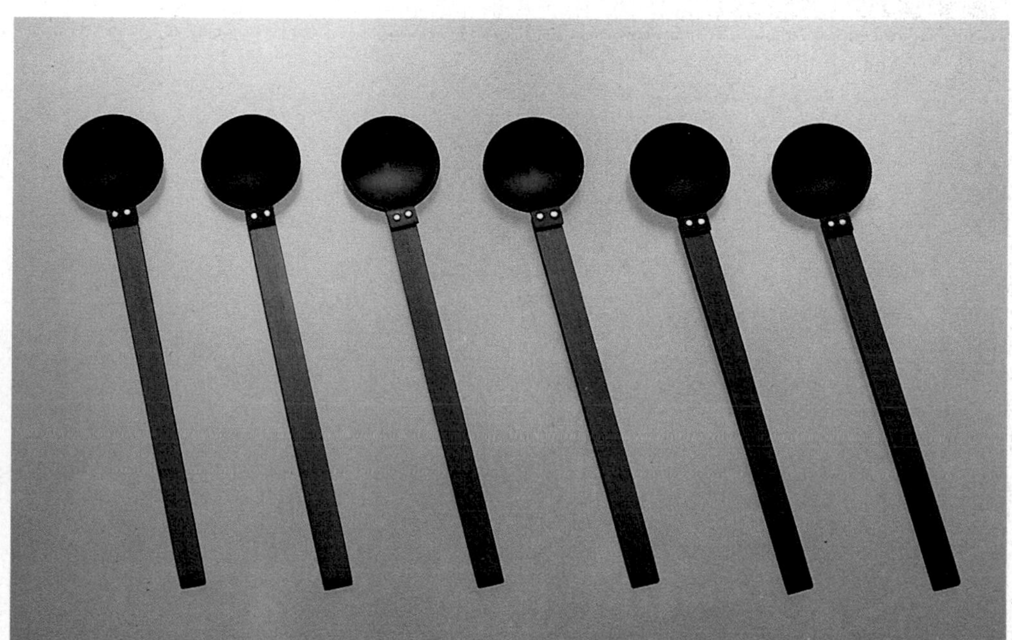

Product: "Joined" Glass Series
Designer: Robin Mix
Manufacturer: Tunbridge Glassworks, Tunbridge, Vermont
Photo Credit: Susie Cushner, Boston, Massachusetts
Materials: Spun Glass

Product: "CHEVRON" Dinnerware
Designer: Dorothy Hafner, New York, New York
Client: Tiffany & Company, New York, New York
Materials: Handpainted porcelain

Product: Egg Cup with Built-in Salt Shaker
Designer: Maya Kissoczy
Manufacturer: Bodum, Horsham, Pennsylvania

Product: Stripe Pattern Bowl
Designer: Beth Forer, New York, New York
Awards: 1986 *Industrial Design* magazine Design Review, Best of Category

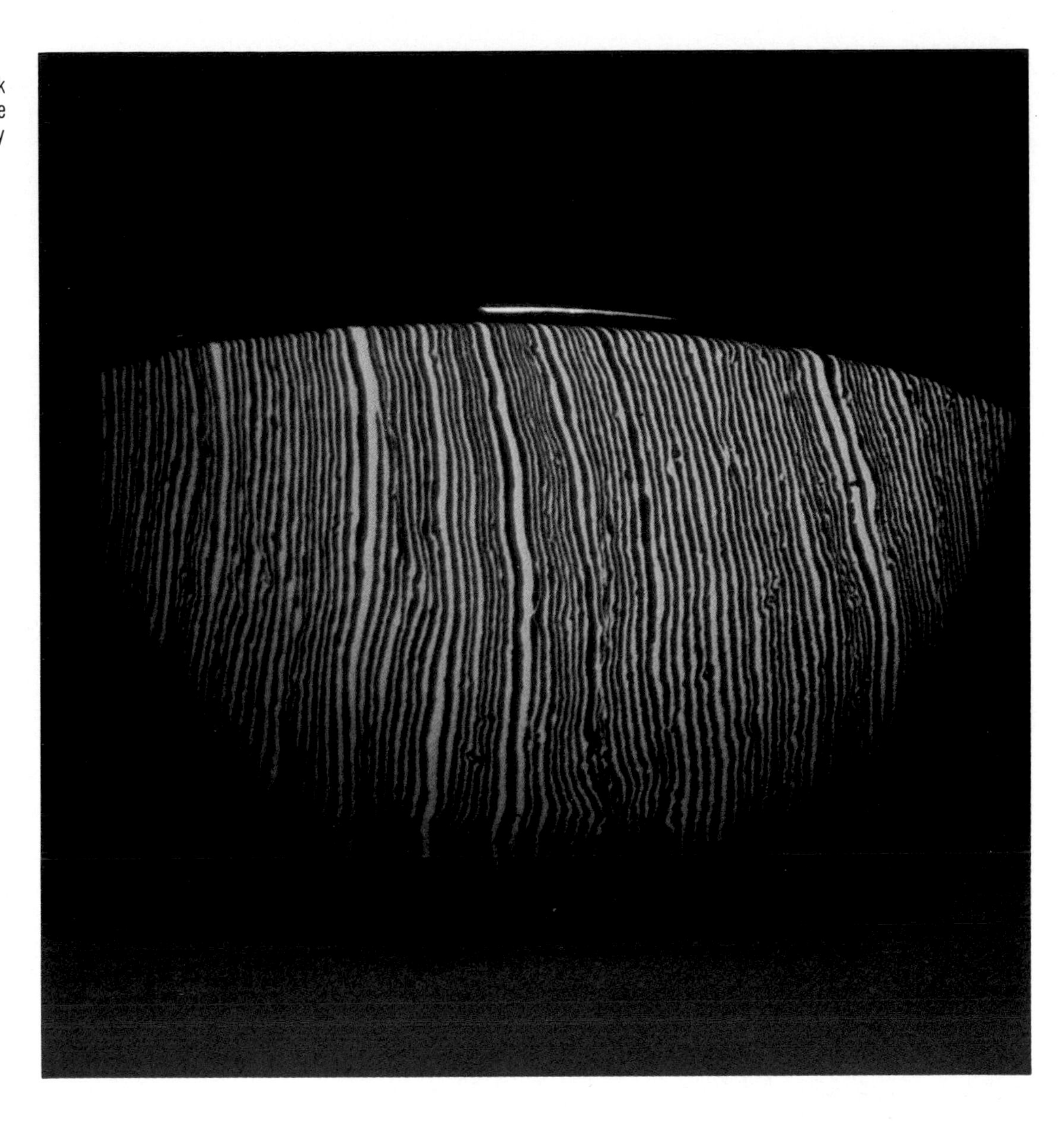

Product: Scallop Pattern Bowl
Designer: Beth Forer, New York, New York
Awards: American Craft Museum Design Award, "Designed and Made for Use";
1986 *Industrial Design* magazine Design Review, Best of Category
Materials: Technique: nerikomi; 11-in. diameter, 4-in. high

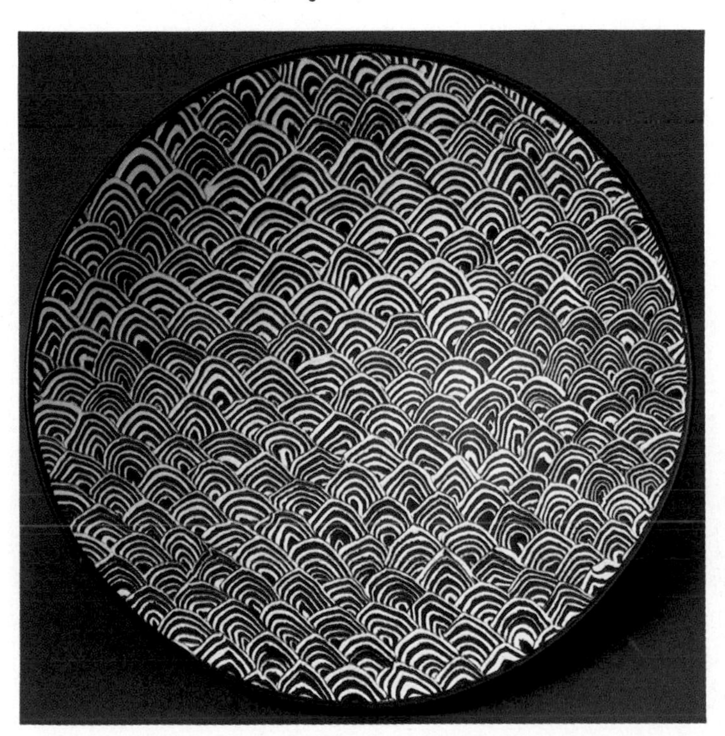

Product: 17-in. Platter
Designer: Beth Forer, New York, New York
Materials: Clay; technique: nerikomi

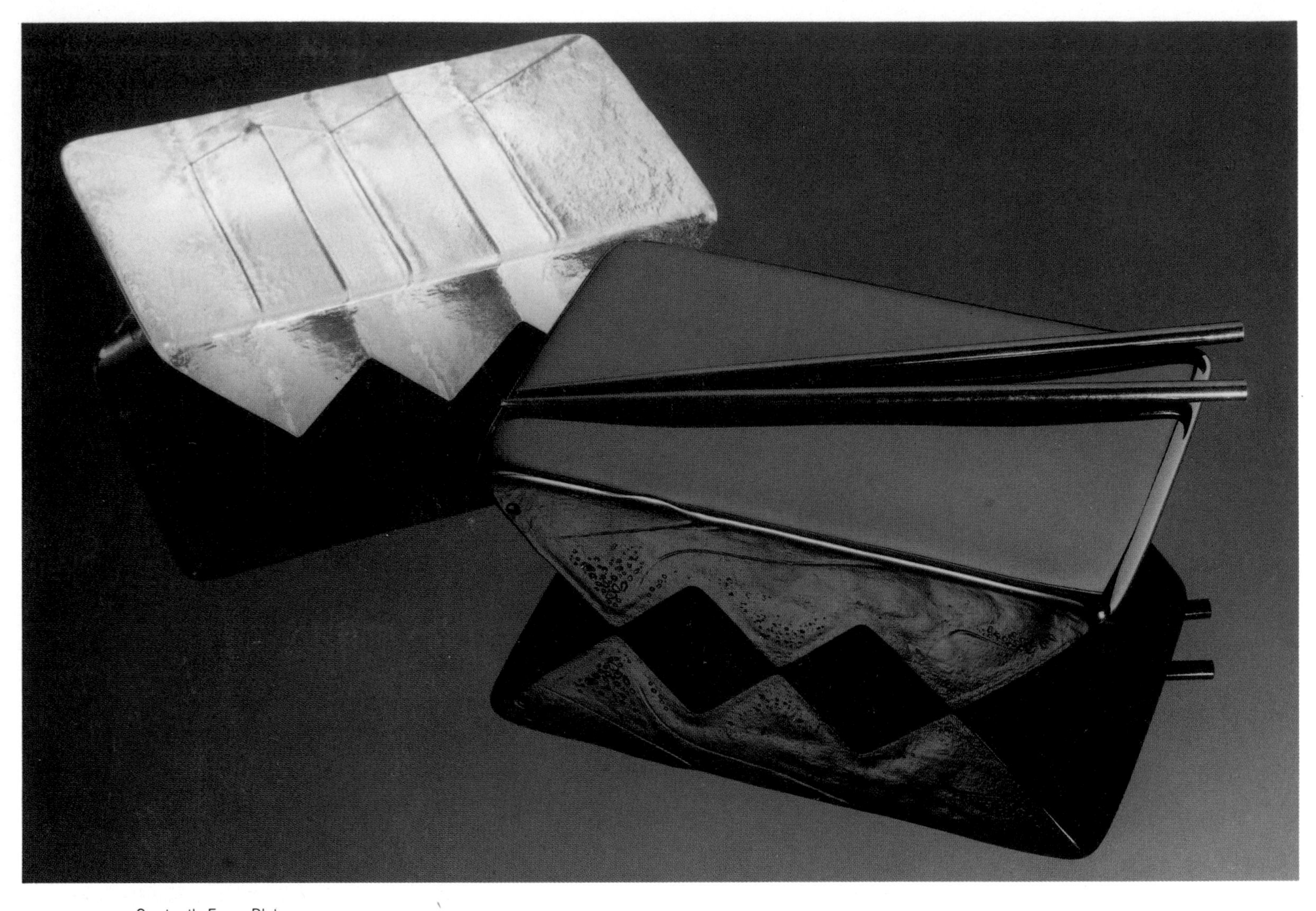

Product: Sawtooth Form Plates
Designer: James Harmon, New York, New York
Distributor: Sointu, New York, New York
Materials: Cast glass available in crystal or black

Product: Salt/Pepper
Designer: Noriaki, Nikura
Courtesy: Gallery 91, New York, New York

Product: Lettuce
Designer: Ettore Sottsass, Italy
Manufacturer: Memphis, Milan, Italy

Product: Asymmetria
Designer: Bjorn Wiinblad
Client: Rosenthal AG, Selb, West Germany

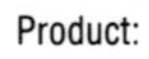

Product: Ogee
Designers: Lella and Massimo Vignelli; David Law
Design Firm: Vignelli & Associates New York, New York

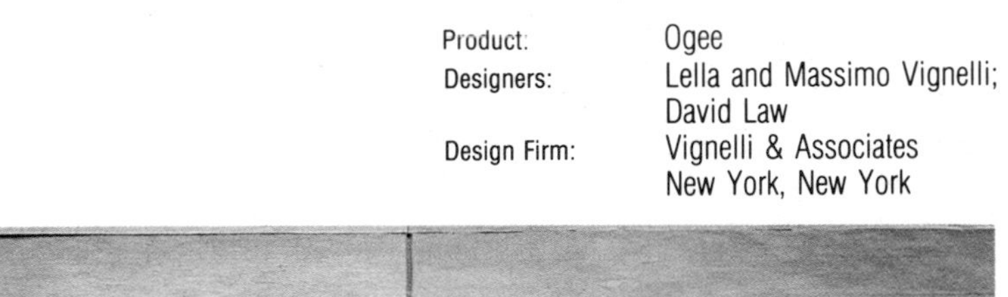

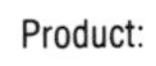

Product: Diu
Designer: Ettore Sottsas, Italy
Distributor: Global Furniture, New York, New York
Materials: Marble: Rosa Portogallo, Nero Marquinia, and Bianco Carrara Statuario

Product: Frame
Designer: Richard Meier
Client: Swid Powell, Inc., New York, New York

Product: Pedestal Bowl
Designer: Susan Hamlet, San Diego, California
Distributor: Clodagh Ross Williams New York, New York
Materials: Stainless steel, anodized aluminum, brass, and rubber

Product: Square Platter
Designer: Angelo di Petta, Ontario, Canada
Materials: Earthenware clay

Product: Coasters
Designer: David Tisdale, New York, New York
Distributor: Rogers & Tropea, Inc., New York, New York
Awards: American Craft Museum Design Award

Product: Damascened Cutlery
Designer: Frei Otto, West Germany
Courtesy: Golden Eye Exhibit, Cooper-Hewitt Museum

Product: Decanters
Designer: A. Castiglioni
Client: Alessi s.p.a., Italy

Product: "The Campidoglio" Decorated Oval Tray
Designer: Robert Venturi
Client: Alessi s.p.a., Italy
Materials: Engraved electro plated stainless steel with gold plate inlay

Product: Bowl
Distributor: Clodagh Ross Williams
New York, New York

Product: "Mint Grid," "Black Silhouette," and "Black Lattice"
Designer: Dorothy Hafner, New York, New York
Photo Credit: S. Baker Vail
Materials: Porcelain with underglaze decoration

Product: Super Package
Designer: Makoto Komatsu
Available: Gallery 91, New York, New York
Photo Credit: Masao Ueda

Product: "Glasses for Alice," flower vase and bowls
Designer: Sergio Asti, Milan, Italy
Manufacturer: Salviati Vertrerie, Italy
Materials: Aquamarine and black glass

Product:	Carrot Vase
Designer:	N. du Pasquier
Design Firm:	Memphis, Milan, Italy

Product:	Neomurrini
Designer:	Ercole Barovier, Italy
Client:	Barovier & Toso, Italy
Distributor:	Avventura, New York, New York
Materials:	Handblown Murano glass

Product:	Triad
Designer:	Robin Mix, Tunbridge, Vermont
Manufacturer:	Tunbridge Glassworks, Tunbridge, Vermont
Photo Credit:	Susie Cusher, Boston, Massachusetts
Awards:	Corning Museum of Glass-included in their Corning New Glass Review, 1985
Materials:	Handblown glass with glass thread edge

Product: Colonna
Client: THOMAS, Branch of Rosenthal AG
Selb, West Germany
Materials: Lead crystal glass

Product: "Calice" Goblet, Double Glass
Designer: Achille Castiglioni, Italy
Client: Danese Milano, Italy
Awards: 5th Arango International Design Competition, "Glass That Works" 1984, Honorable Mention
Materials: Full lead crystal glass

Product: Cartoccio
Designer: Carlo Moretti, Italy
Manufacturer: Carlo Moretti, Italy
Distributor: Avventura, New York, New York
Materials: Handblown Murano glass

Product: Set of Glasses, Ovio
Designer: Achille Castiglioni
Client: Danese Milano, Italy
Awards: 5th Arango International Design Competition, "Glass That Works" 1984, Honorable Mention
Materials: Full lead crystal glass

Product: Oktett Glasses with Plastic Stems
Client: Bodum Design, Bodum, Inc. Horsham, Pennsylvania

Product: Salad Servers and Bowls
Designers: Davin Stowell, Tucker Viemeister, John Lonczak, Annie Breckenfeld, Brent Markee, and Linda Celentano
Design Firm: Smart Design, New York, New York
Client: COPCO, Woodridge, Illinois
Materials: Bowls: enameled steel or styrene; servers: melamine or styrene

Product: Melamine Dinnerware
Designers: Davin Stowell, John Lonczak, Tom Dair, Annie Breckenfeld, and Cindy Gerow
Design Firm: Smart Design, New York, New York
Client: COPCO, Woodridge, Illinois
Photo Credit: Stowell
Materials: Melamine plastic, injection molded

Product: Cabin Cup
Client: Western Airlines

Product: Meridiana Series
Designer: Bruno Gecchelin, Milan, Italy
Client: Rede Guzzini, Recanati, Italy

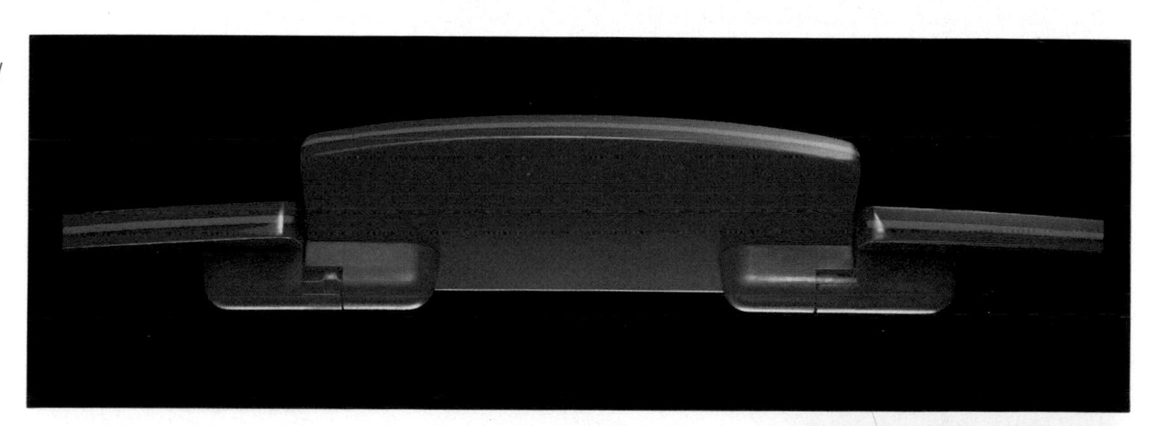

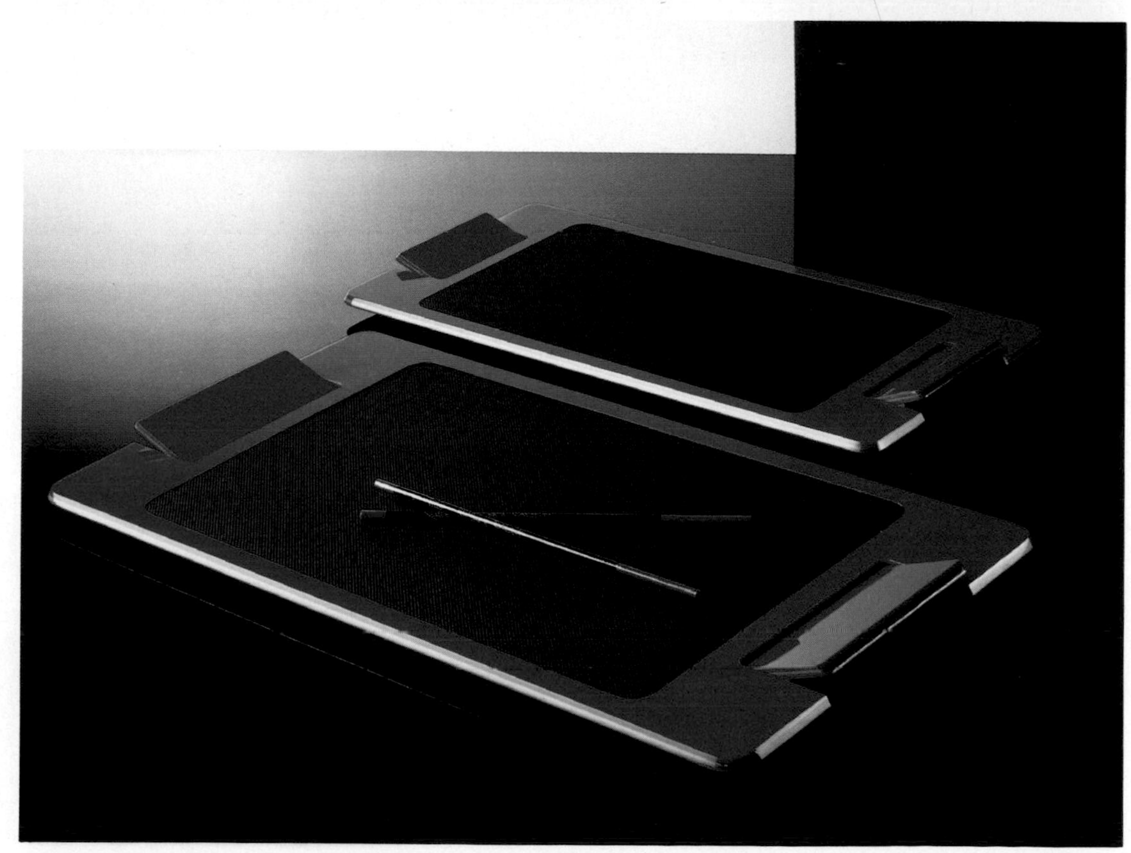

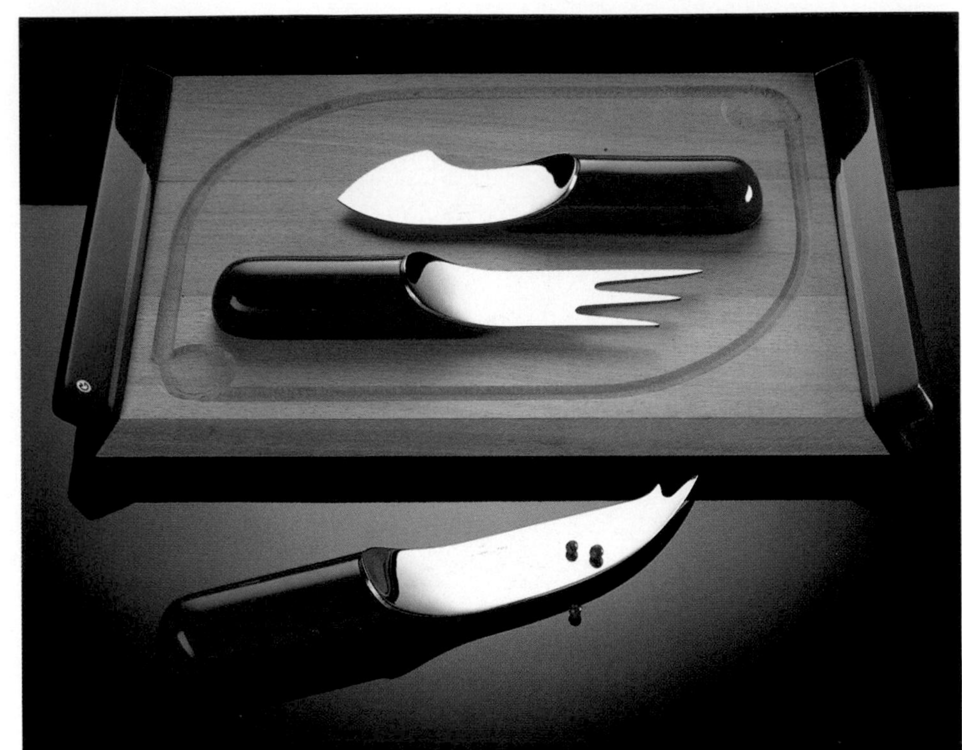

Product:	Cutlery
Designer:	Bruno Gecchelin
Manufacturer:	Rede Guzzini, Recanti, Italy

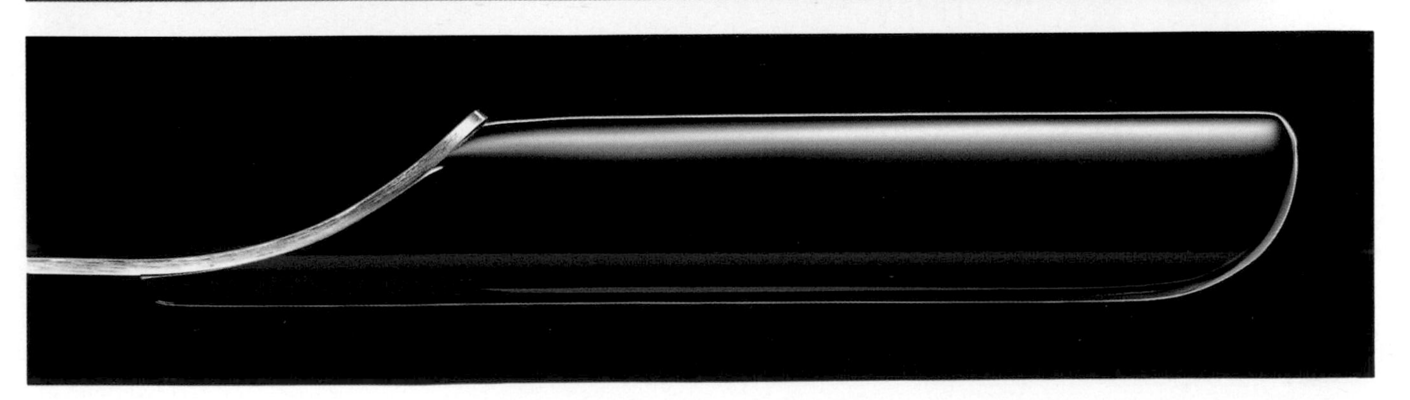

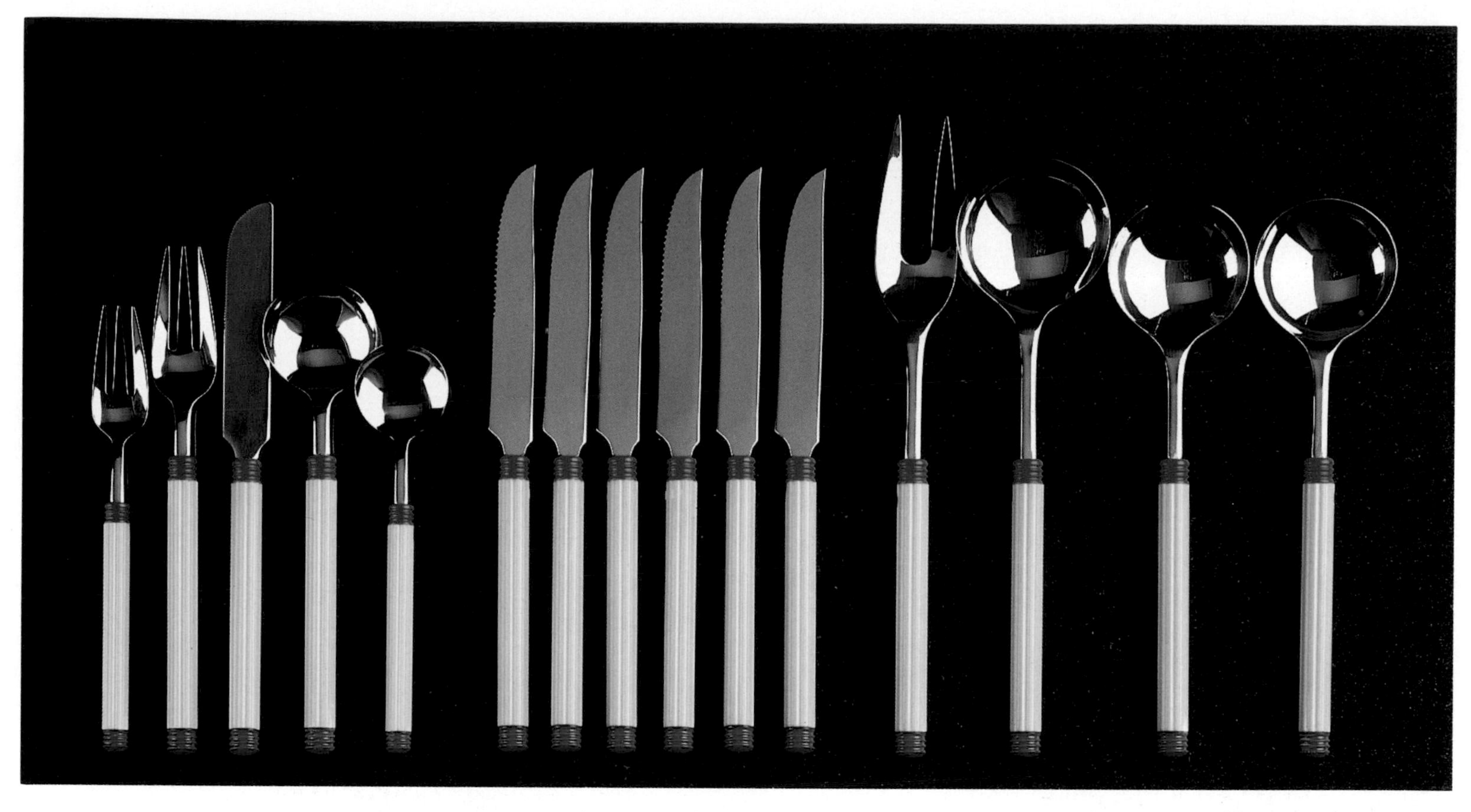

Product: Colori 20 Piece Set
Manufacturer: Crown Corning, Los Angeles, California

Product: Ferarri 20 Piece Set
Manufacturer: Crown Corning, Los Angeles, California

Product: Ultra Thermal Server from Colorworks Collection
Manufacturer: Crown Corning, Los Angeles, California

Product: Flash
Designer: Dorothy Hafner, New York, New York
Client: Rosenthal AG, Selb, West Germany
Awards: 1985 Westerwald Prize for Industrial Design
Materials: Porcelain; industrially produced with transfer print decoration

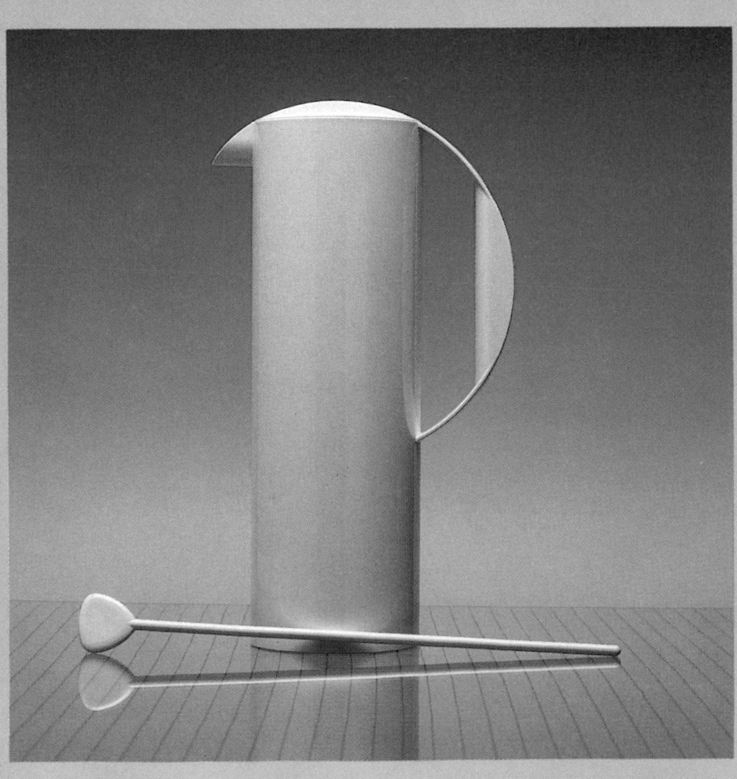

Product: Formula 2
Manufacturer: Rosti (USA) Inc., Kenilworth, New Jersey

Product: Tea Sets
Designer: Uko Morita, Japan
Courtesy: Gallery 91, New York, New York

Product: Tea Plate
Designer: Uko Morita, Japan
Courtesy: Gallery 91, New York, New York

Product: Bowl with Tall Foot
Designers: I. Teraki, J. C. Bisson
Client: Romulus Craft, Oakland, California
Materials: Slipcasted Porcelain

Product: Tuxedo Plate
Designers: Charles Gwathmey, Robert Siegel
Design Firm: Gwathmey Siegel & Associates, New York, New York
Client: Swid Powell Inc., New York, New York

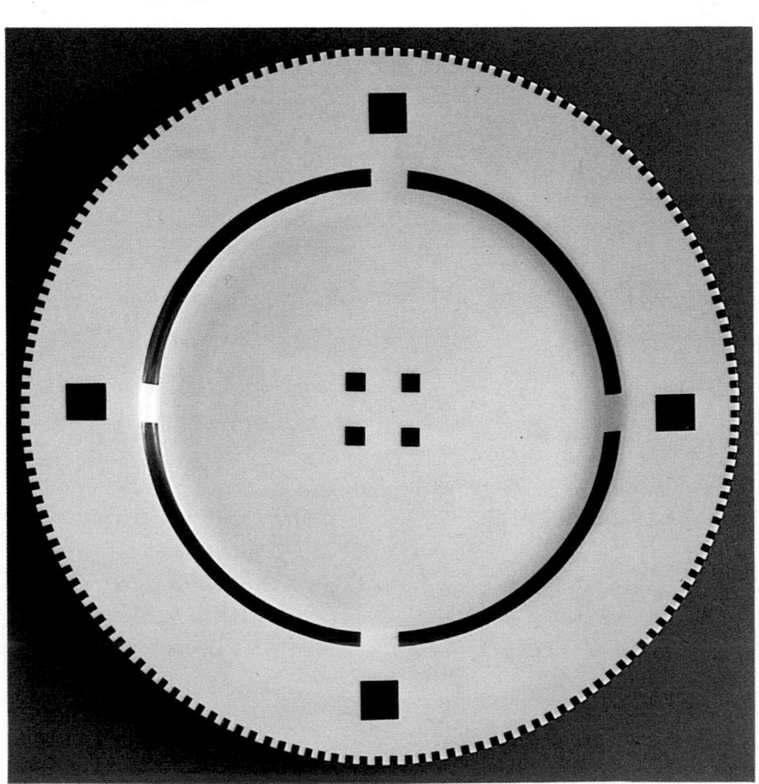

Product: Planar
Designer: Stephen Holl
Client: Swid Powell, Inc., New York, New York

Product:	Hollow Cast Bowl
Designer:	Angelo di Petta, Toronto, Ontario, Canada
Materials:	Earthenware clay; back slip and underglaze decoration; 12-in. diameter by 3¼-in. height

Product:	Bowls
Designer:	Carmen Spera
Courtesy:	Gallery 91, New York, New York
Photo Credit:	Masao Ueda

Product: Cupola
Designer: Mario Bellini, Italy
Client: Rosenthal AG, Selb, West-Germany
Materials: Porcelain

Product: Double-Lidded Teapot
Designer: Nicholas Homoky, England
Courtesy: Westminster Gallery, Boston, Massachusetts
Materials: Porcelain

Product: Angular Teapot
Designer: Marek Cecula, New York, New York
Client: Contemporary Porcelain, New York, New York

Product: Samovar
Designer: E. Saarinen
Client: Officina Alessi, Italy

Product: Tea and Coffee Service
Designer: Marianne Brandt
Client: Officina Alessi, Italy

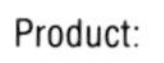

Product: Teapot
Designer: Marek Cecula, New York, New York
Client: Contemporary Porcelain, New York, New York

Product: Cup with Coaster
Designers: I. Teraki, J. C. Bisson
Client: Romulus Craft, Oakland, California
Materials: Slipcasted Porcelain

Product: Tea Set
Designer: Derek Northfield, England
Courtesy: Westminster Gallery, Boston, Massachusetts

Product: Tray with Pitcher and Goblets
Designer: Michael Lamar
Distributor: The Works Gallery, Philadelphia, Pennsylvania
Materials: Ceramic and rubber

Product: Cabbage - Radish - Pepper
Designer: Aldo Celic, Italy
Client: Memphis, Milan, Italy

APPLIANCES, HOUSEWARES, AND TOOLS

CHAPTER

The "Designs At Home" (Jan./Feb. 1986) issue of *ID* magazine describes a "revolution" in design for appliances, clocks, and housewares. The cataclysm of form and color in these tools we use to conduct our daily lives has transpired in a manner peaceful but determined, inspired by changing lifestyles and by a new courage in designers and manufacturers.

With home environments transformed by new design influences, appliances had become incompatible. The wood grained and floral-trimmed items of popular taste clashed with contemporary home designs. Clearly, the hour arrived for design to alter its form to fit the realities and aspirations of people's lifestyles.

Rather than entirely discard the past, designers have integrated familiar visual phrases into their styling to minimize consumer resistance. By presenting an attainable challenge, designers have invited broad acceptance of the new design. Nonetheless, the change is dramatic and welcome.

Moving to "Eurostyle" and beyond, these designs deliver us from the drab and predictable. In celebratory fashion, they pay tribute to the best of our cultural, work-oriented traditions. The elegance of Aldo Rossi's espresso maker for Alessi stands as a shrine to one of Italy's oldest culinary arts, while George Nelson's "Olympus" clock for Howard Miller demonstrates that the marking of time has scaled another peak.

Yet time—world famine and natural disasters remind us—is a precarious commodity running out for many whose daily task is survival. Designers creating the tools of life for the poor and third world should be acknowledged as meeting perhaps the most pressing design challenge of our age, the elimination of hunger. In this ultimate revolution, product designers are uniquely qualified and should lead the resistance.

Product: Krups Teatime
Manufacturer: Krups, West Germany
Client: Robert Krups/North America
Allendale, New Jersey

Product: Mono-Teapot
Design Firm: Tassilo von Grolman Design
Fullerstrabe, West Germany
Client: Mono-Metallwarenfabrik,
West Germany
Awards: "Haus Industrieform," Award for Outstanding Design, Essen;
Permanent Collection:
Cooper-Hewitt Museum
Materials: Stainless steel and glass

Product: Bollitore Kettle
Designer: Michael Graves
Client: Alessi s.p.a., Italy

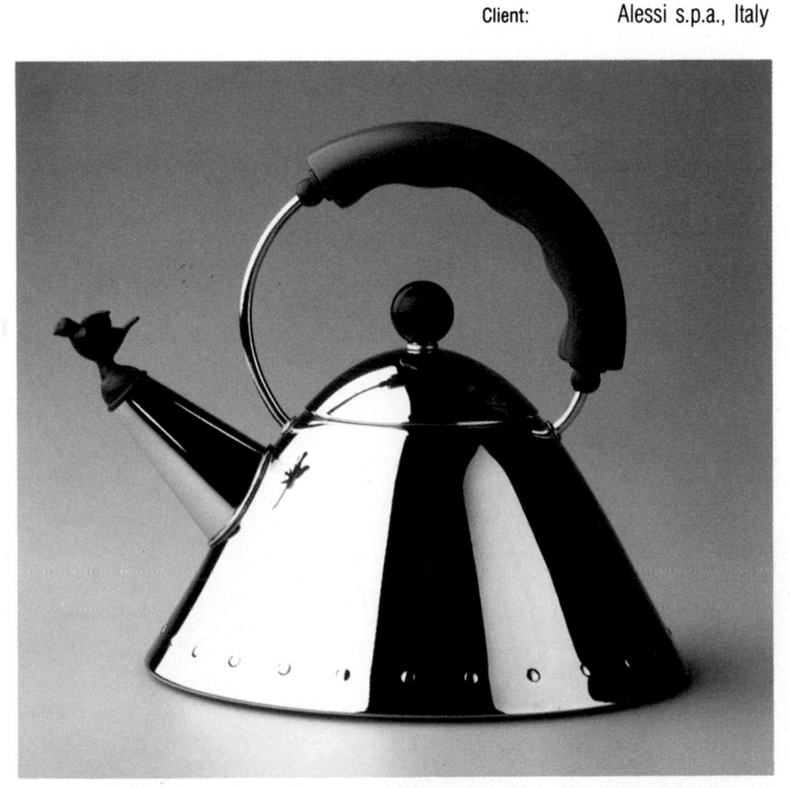

Product: Espresso Maker
Designer: Aldo Rossi
Client: Alessi USA
Cambridge, Massachusetts
Awards: 1985 *Industrial Design* magazine Design Review selection
Materials: Stainless steel body with copper bottom

Product: Euro/Brew Signal 10-cup
Manufacturer: Krups, West Germany
Clients: Krups/West Germany
Robert Krups/North America
Allendale, New Jersey

Product:	Rowenta Filtermatic Coffee Maker FK-45
Design Firm:	Rowenta, West Germany
Distributed by:	The Schwabel Corporation Cambridge, Massachusetts

Product:	Espresso Maker
Manufacturer:	Krups, West Germany
Client:	Robert Krups/North America Allendale, New Jersey

Product:	Braun Aromaster 10 plus KF 45
Design Firm:	Braun AG, Kronberg, West Germany
Client:	Braun AG, Kronberg, West Germany
Materials:	ABS plastic

Product: Oskar Food Processor
Client: Sunbeam Appliance Company
Oak Brook, Illinois

Product: 3 Mix 4000
Client: Krups, West Germany
Robert Krups/North America
Allendale, New Jersey

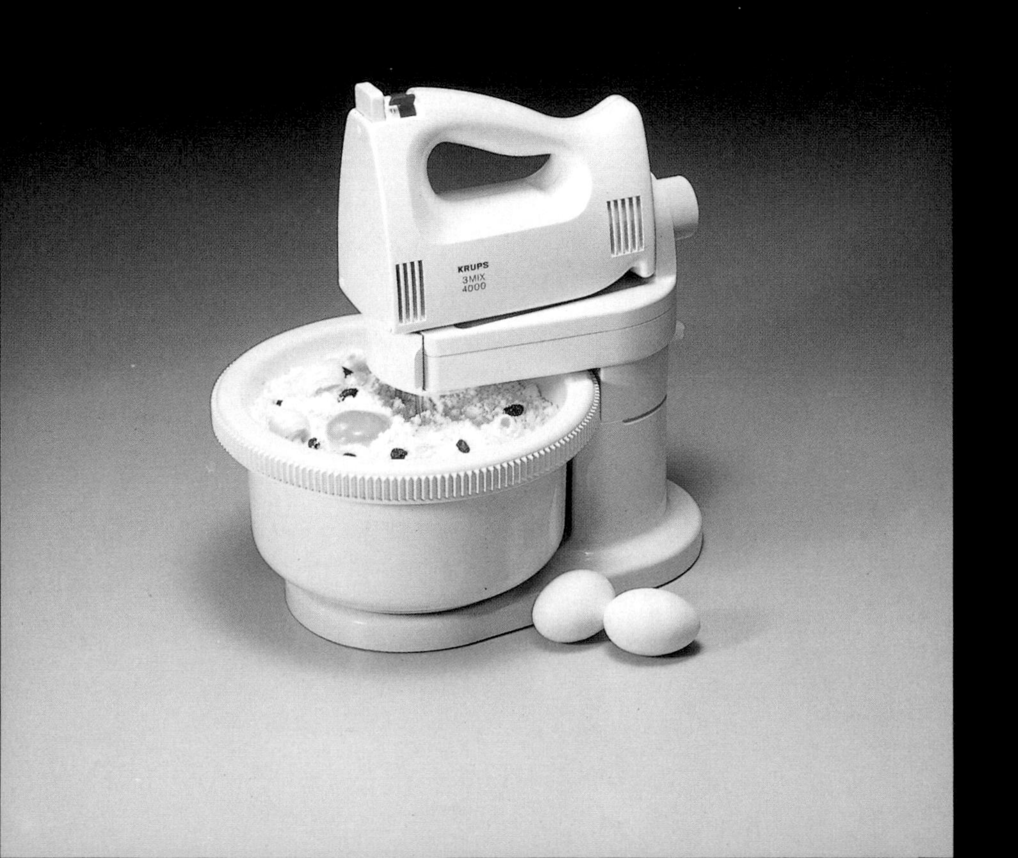

Product: 3 Mix 2000 Handmixer
Manufacturer: Krups, West Germany
Client: Robert Krups/North America
Allendale, New Jersey

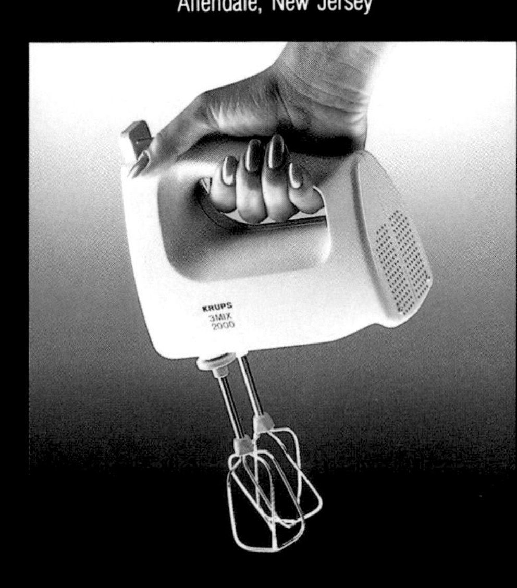

Product: Handy Mixer 9210
Design Firm: Black & Decker, Bridgeport, Connecticut
Client: Black & Decker, Bridgeport, Connecticut

Product: Multipractic Plus Electronic
Design Firm: Braun AG, West Germany
Client: Braun AG, West Germany

Product:	Pasta Set
Designer:	Massimo Morozzi, Milan, Italy
Client:	Alessi s.p.a., Italy
Distributor:	The Schwabel Corporation Cambridge, Massachusetts
Materials:	Stainless steel

Product:	Maxiskillet
Manufacturer:	Chantal
Distributor:	Lentrade, Inc., Houston, Texas

Product: Ser,vin' Saver cylinder containers
Client: Rubbermaid, Wooster, Ohio

Product: Grand Griddle
Design Firm: Cuisinart, Greenwich, Connecticut
Client: Cuisinart, Greenwich, Connecticut
Materials: Polished stainless steel with copper inlay

Product: 38 Rowenta Toast-Star
Client: Rowenta, West Germany
Distributor: The Schwabel Corporation
Cambridge, Massachusetts
Materials: White formed plastic

Product: Maxim Brunch Pan
Manufacturer: The Maxim Company, Newark, New Jersey
Client: The Maxim Company, Newark, New Jersey
Photo Credit: Jesse A. Rhines
Materials: Non-stick coated aluminum and plastic

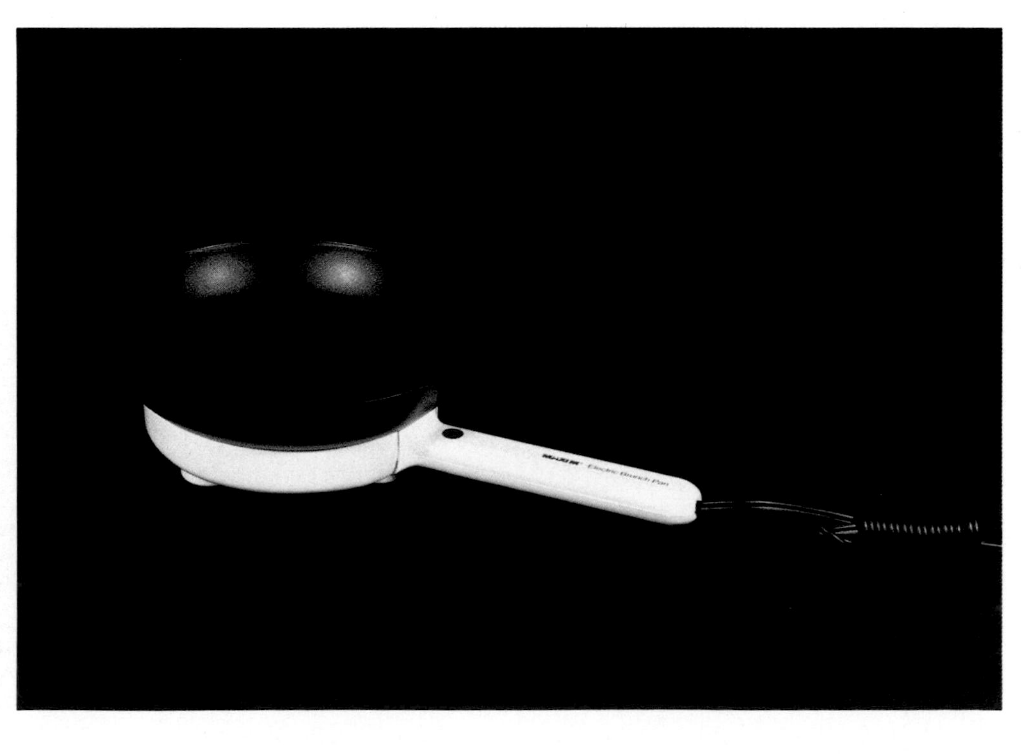

Product: Precision Portion Scale
Design Firm: Cuisinart, Greenwich, Connecticut
Client: Cuisinart, Greenwich, Connecticut

Product: Maxim Wide Mouth Toaster
Manufacturer: The Maxim Company, Newark, New Jersey
Client: The Maxim Company, Newark, New Jersey
Photo Credit: Jesse A. Rhines, New York New York
Materials: Plastic

Product: Aluminum Cookware Range
Designers: Barrie Weaver, Kerrin Lyons
Design Firm: Roberts Weaver, London, England
Client: Boots Limited, Nottingham, England
Materials: Pressed aluminum with enamel finish; handles: compression molded

Product: Compact Variable Power Microwave Oven
Manufacturer: Panasonic, Matsushita Appliance Company
Secaucus, New Jersey

Product: Electric Cook Top
Manufacturer: Panasonic, Matsushita Appliance Company
Secaucus, New Jersey

Product: Maxim Food Warming Tray
Manufacturer: The Maxim Company, Newark, New Jersey
Photo Credit: Jesse A. Rhines, New York, New York
Awards: Selected for exhibitions: Museum of Modern Art, Cooper-Hewitt Museum, and Massachusetts Institute of Technology
Materials: Mirrored glass with plastic handles

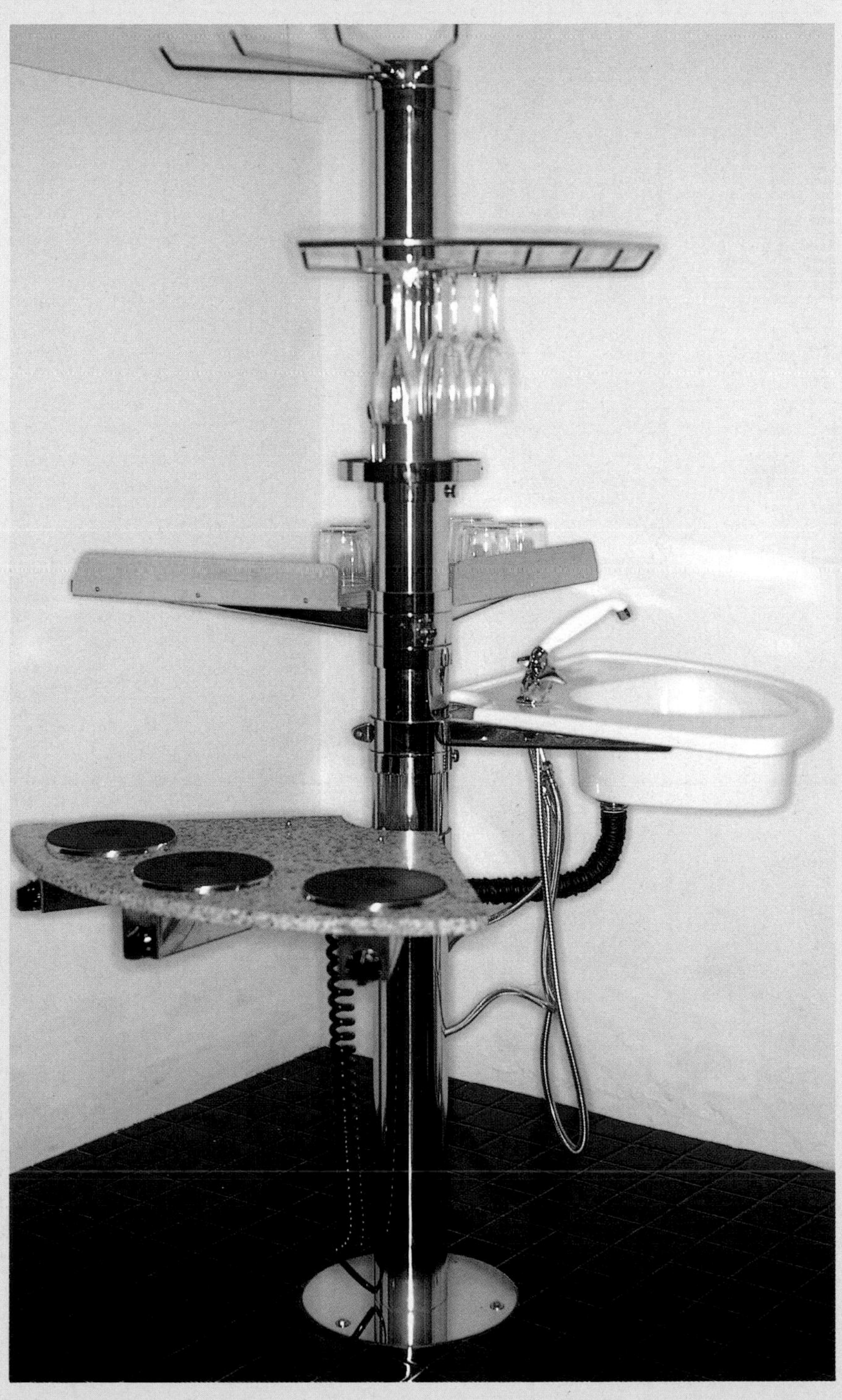

Product: Kitchentree
Designer: Stefan Wewerka
Distributor: Global Furniture, New York, New York
Materials: Chrome, granite, beechwood, and plexiglas

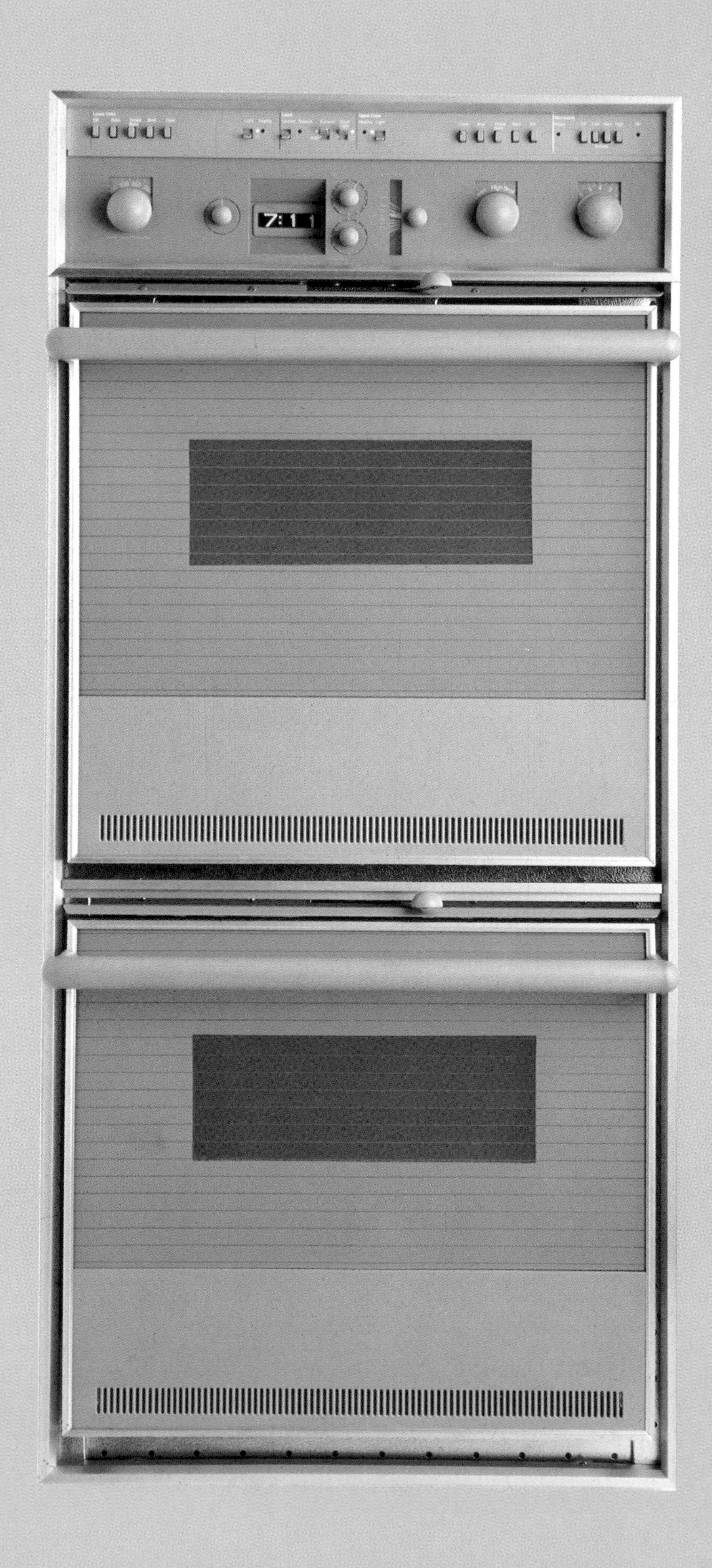

Product: Europa II, Microthermal Oven
Design Firm: Cousins Design, New York, New York
Manufacturer: Thermador - Waste King Los Angeles, California

Product: Relexor Shower/Body Massage
Client: Grohe America, Inc.
Wood Dale, Illinois

Product: Børma Lux Kitchen Faucet and Enameled Sink
Designer: Bo Anderson, Denmark
Manufacturer: CN Børma Armatur A/S, Denmark
Distributor: Abbaka, San Francisco, California

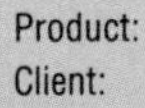

Product: White Kitchen Utensil Set
Client: Grohe America, Inc.
Wood Dale, Illinois

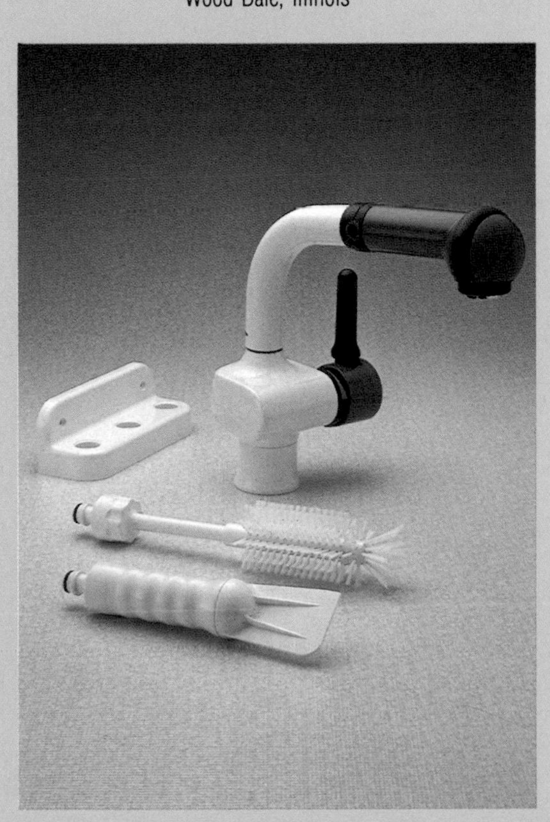

Product: Børmix 80
Designer: Christian Bjørn, Denmark
Manufacturer: CN Børma Armatur A/S, Denmark
Distributor: Abbaka, San Francisco, California
Materials: Cast brass and chrome; enamel finish

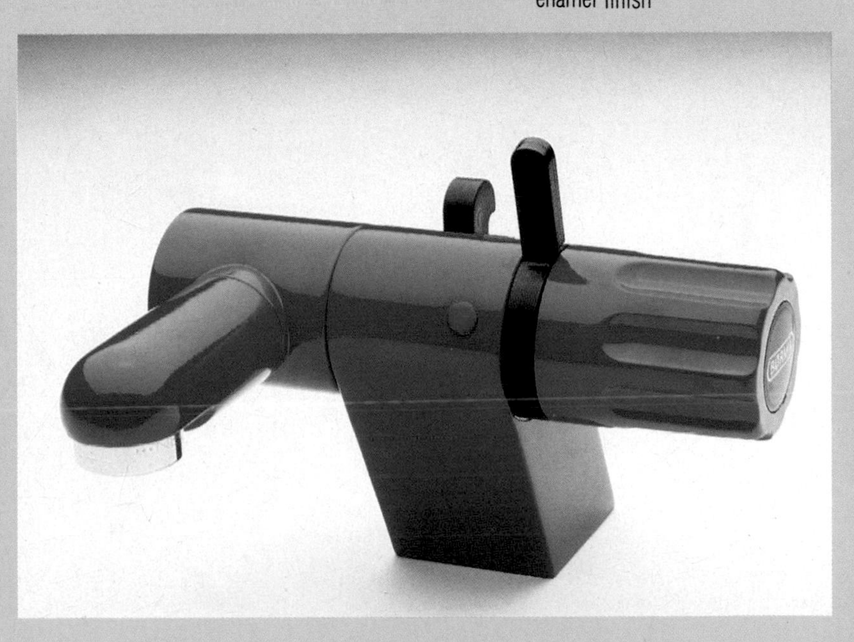

Product: UNO Basin Mixer
Design Firm: frogdesign, Campbell, California
Client: Hansgrohe, West Germany
Awards: 1986 *Industrial Design* magazine Design Review selection

Product: Tecno Brush, Razor, and Toothbrush
Manufacturer: Tecno, Italy
Distributor: Area International Inc. West Long Branch, New Jersey

Product: Cactus Cutter
Designer: Jan Axel
Client: Kohler Company Limited Editions Wisconsin

Product: Radius Toothbrush
Designer: Kevin Foley, New York, New York
Client: Radius, New York, New York

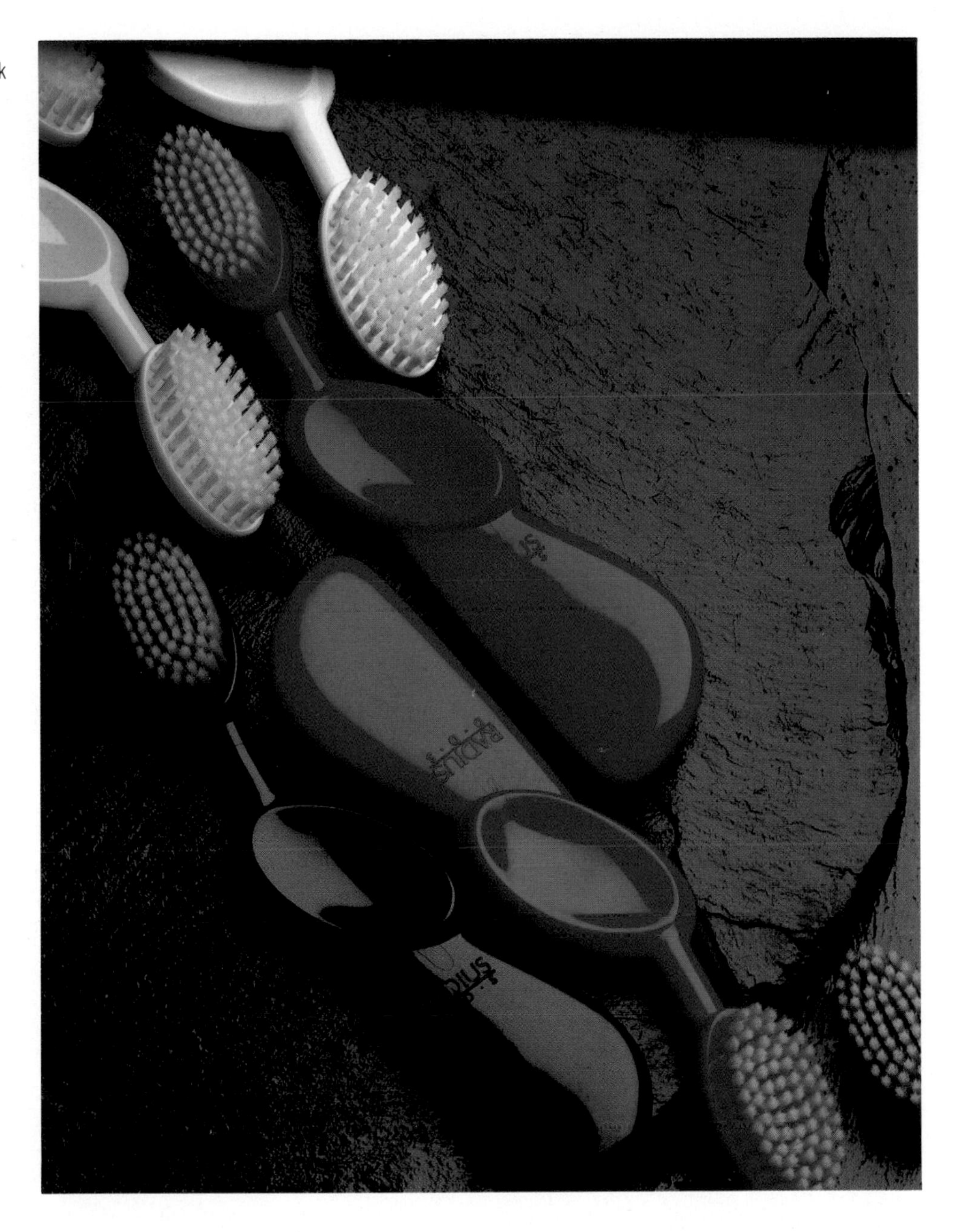

Product: Tri-Bel HandShower
Design Firm: frogdesign, Campbell, California
Client: Hansgrohe, West Germany

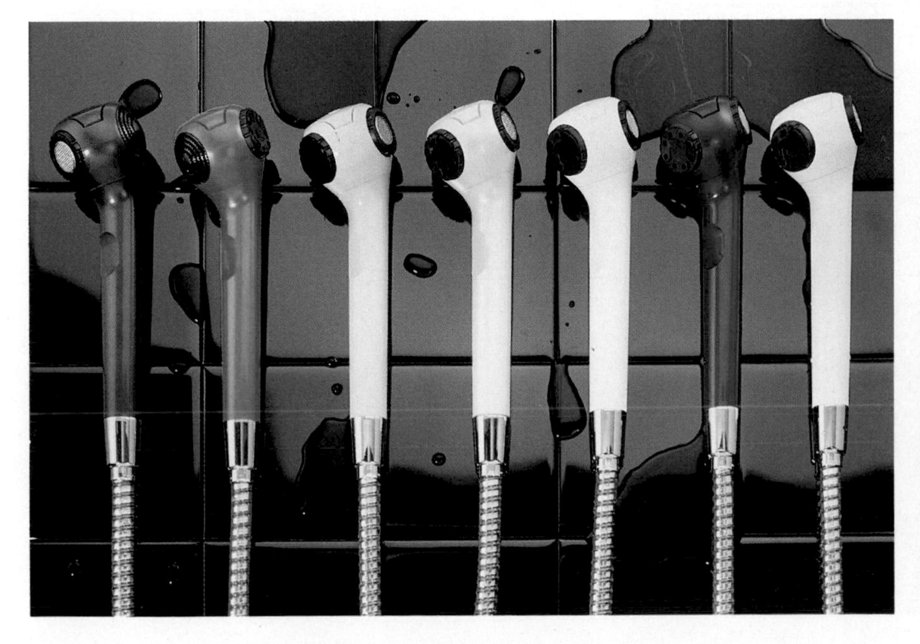

Product: The Upscale Cordless Remote Readout Scale
Client: Counselor, A member of the Newell Group, Rockford, Illinois

Product: Amanda Baines Collection – bathroom sink
Designer: David Tisdale, New York, New York
Client: Amanda Baines Company New York, New York
Materials: Anodized aluminum

Product: MicroSlim Compuscan – Electronic Digital Scale
Design Firm: Black & Decker Bridgeport, Connecticut

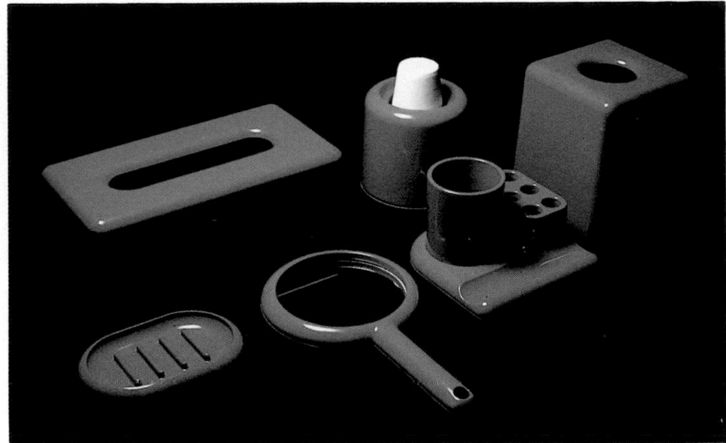

Product:	Bath Accessories
Designers:	Peter Byar, Richard Joffe, and Peter Bressler, Peter Bressler Design Associates; Don Henry, J. C. Penney Product Design Department
Client:	J. C. Penney Company New York, New York
Manufacturer:	Zenith Products Corporation Aston, Pennsylvania
Materials:	Injection molded ABS

Product:	Panasonic Lady Whisk Wet/Dry Shaver
Design Firm:	Matsushita Electric Works Ltd. Osaka, Japan
Client:	Panasonic, Matsushita Appliance Company Secaucus, New Jersey

Product: ATC 70
Design Firm: Canetti Group, New York, New York
Client: Canetti Inc., New York, New York

Product: Clock, Yellow, Red, Gray
Designer: Todd E. Noe
Courtesy: Area X, New York, New York

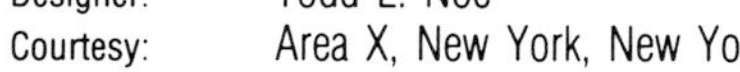

Product: Time Machine
Designer: Kenneth Grange
Courtesy: Gallery 91, New York, New York

Product: Clocks
Designer: Corporate Industrial Design Team
Philips, Eindhoven, Netherlands
Client: Nederlandse Philips Bedrijven
Eindhoven, Netherlands

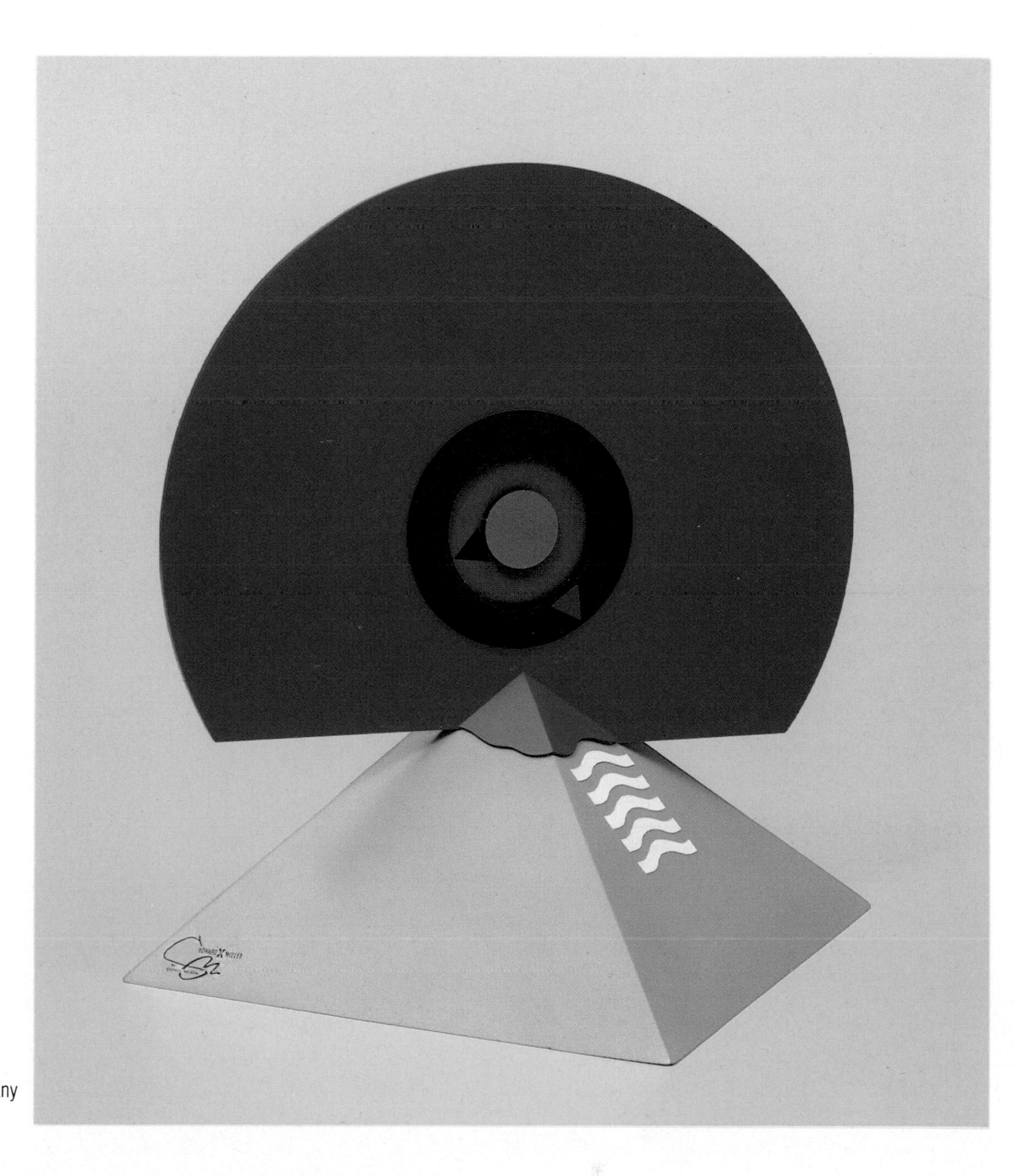

Product: Olympus
Designer: George Nelson
Manufacturer: Howard Miller Clock Company
Zeeland, Michigan

Product: Cube Clock
Design Firm: Canetti Group, New York, New York
Client: Canetti Inc., New York, New York

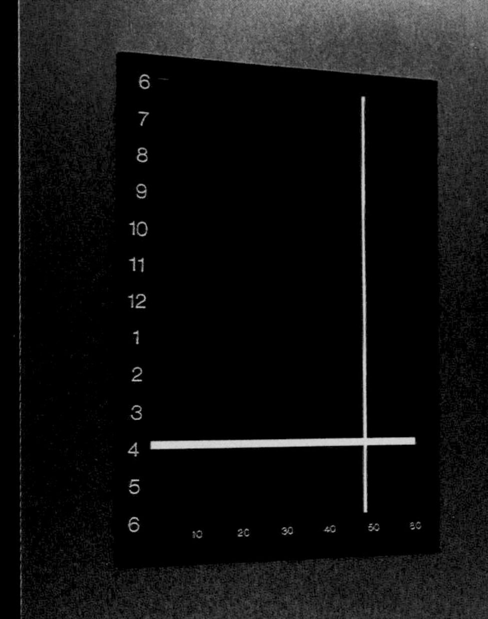

Product: Chronolog rectangular clock
Designer: James Goodchild, Glasgow, Scotland

Product: Clock
Design Firm: Matsushita Electric Works Ltd. Osaka, Japan
Client: Panasonic, Matsushita Appliance Company Secaucus, New Jersey

Product: ATC 90, Artime Collection
Designers: Gordon Naylor, Eric Bergman
Design Firm: Neophile Inc., New York, New York
Manufacturer: Neophile Inc., New York, New York

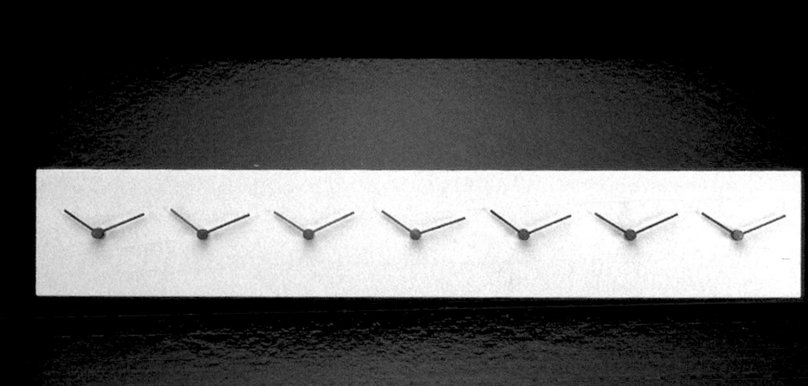

Product: Clock
Designer: Ikuyo Mitsuhashi, Japan
Courtesy: Gallery 91, New York, New York

Product: ATC 90
Design Firm: Canetti Group, New York, New York
Client: Canetti Inc., New York, New York

Product: Wristwatch
Design Firm: ninaber/peters/krouwel, industrial design, Netherlands
Client: Bruno Ninaber, Holland
Materials: Titanium case and calf leather band; Swiss quartz movement

Product: Concrete Watch
Designer: Alex Locadia, New York, New York
Distributor: Clodagh Ross Williams New York, New York

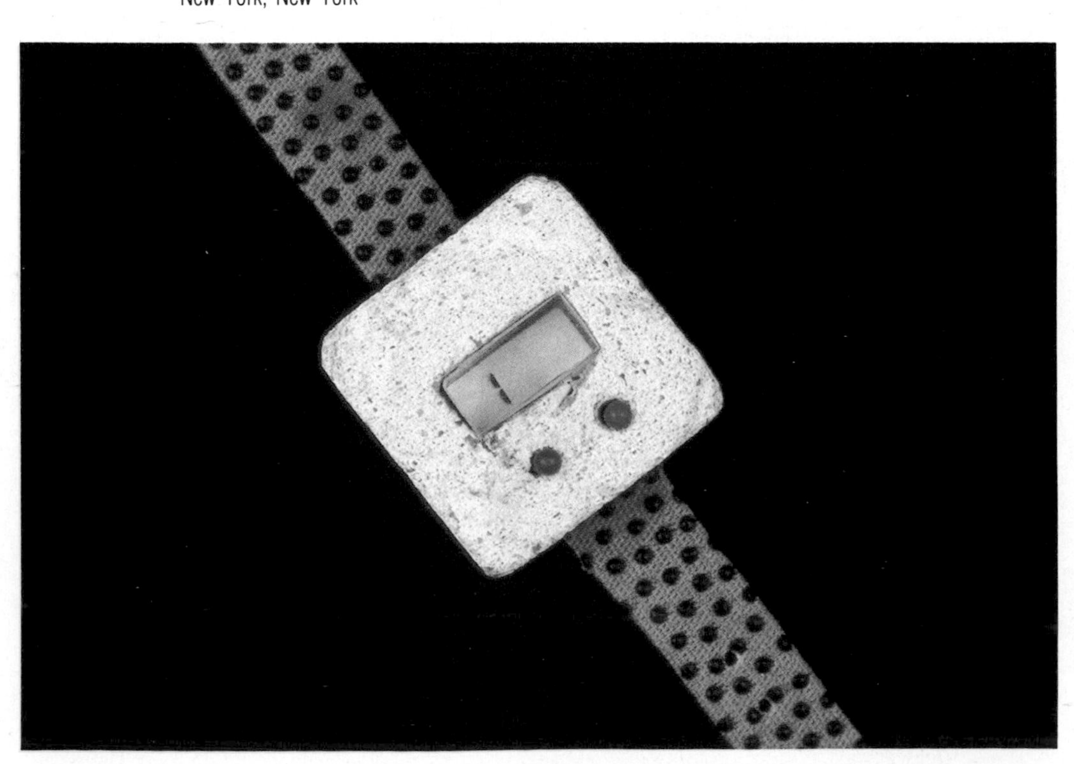

Product: Metal Vessels
Designer: Victoria, Howe, Cropseyville, New York
Materials: Stainless steel, anodized aluminum

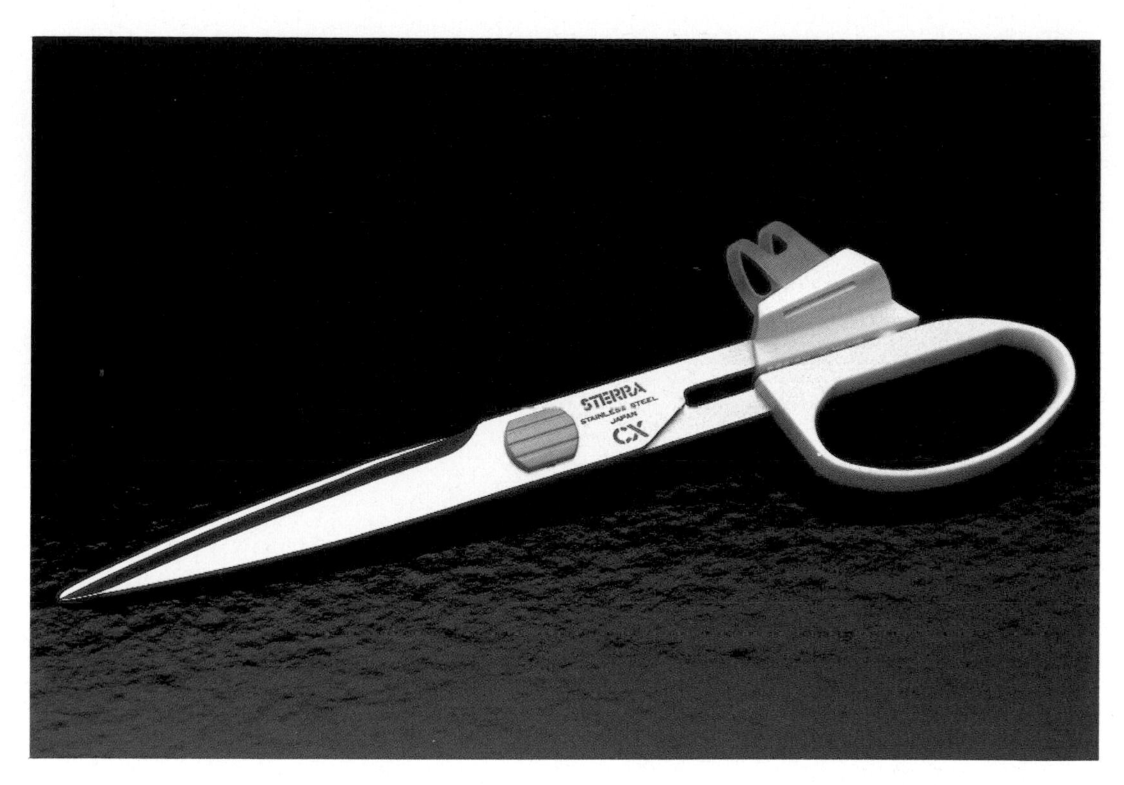

Product: Watch
Distributor: Sointu, New York, New York
Photo Credit: Jesse Rhines, New York, New York

Product: Sterra-CX Scissors
Designer: Hiroshi Yano
Manufacturer: Hasegawa Cutlery Manufacturing Co., Ltd.
Courtesy: Gallery 91, New York, New York

Product: Tropical Desk Clock
Manufacturer: Umbra USA, Inc., Buffalo, New York

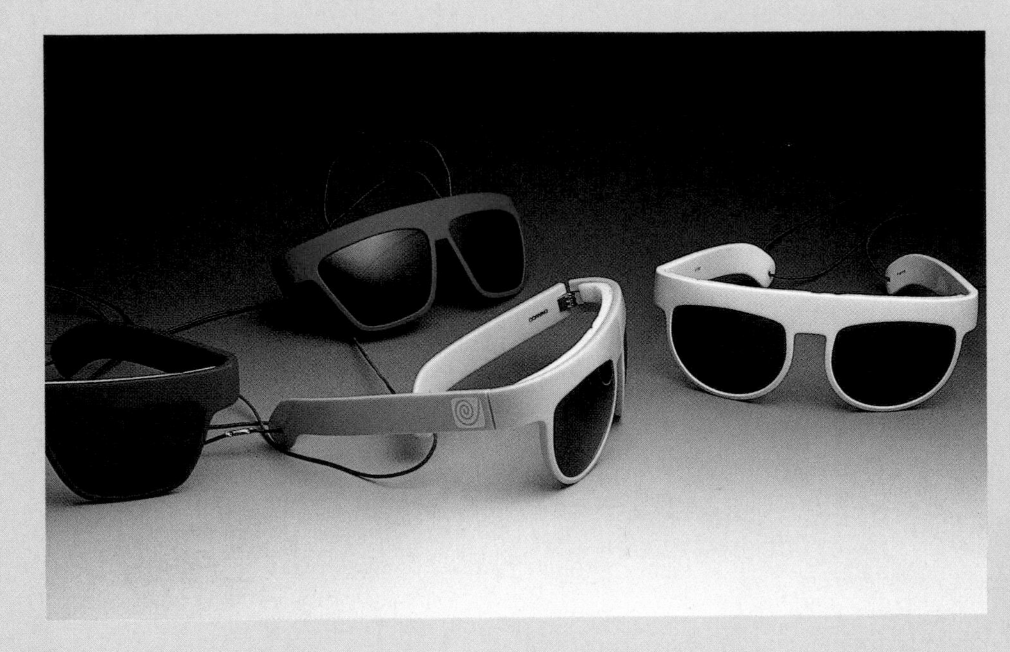

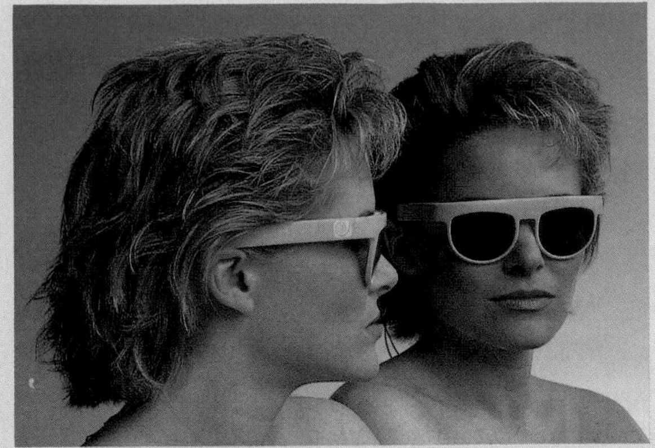

Product: Sweats
Designer: Tom Dair
Design Firm: Smart Design, New York, New York
Client: Corning Optics
Materials: Injection molded polypropinate; polyester CR39 opthomic lenses

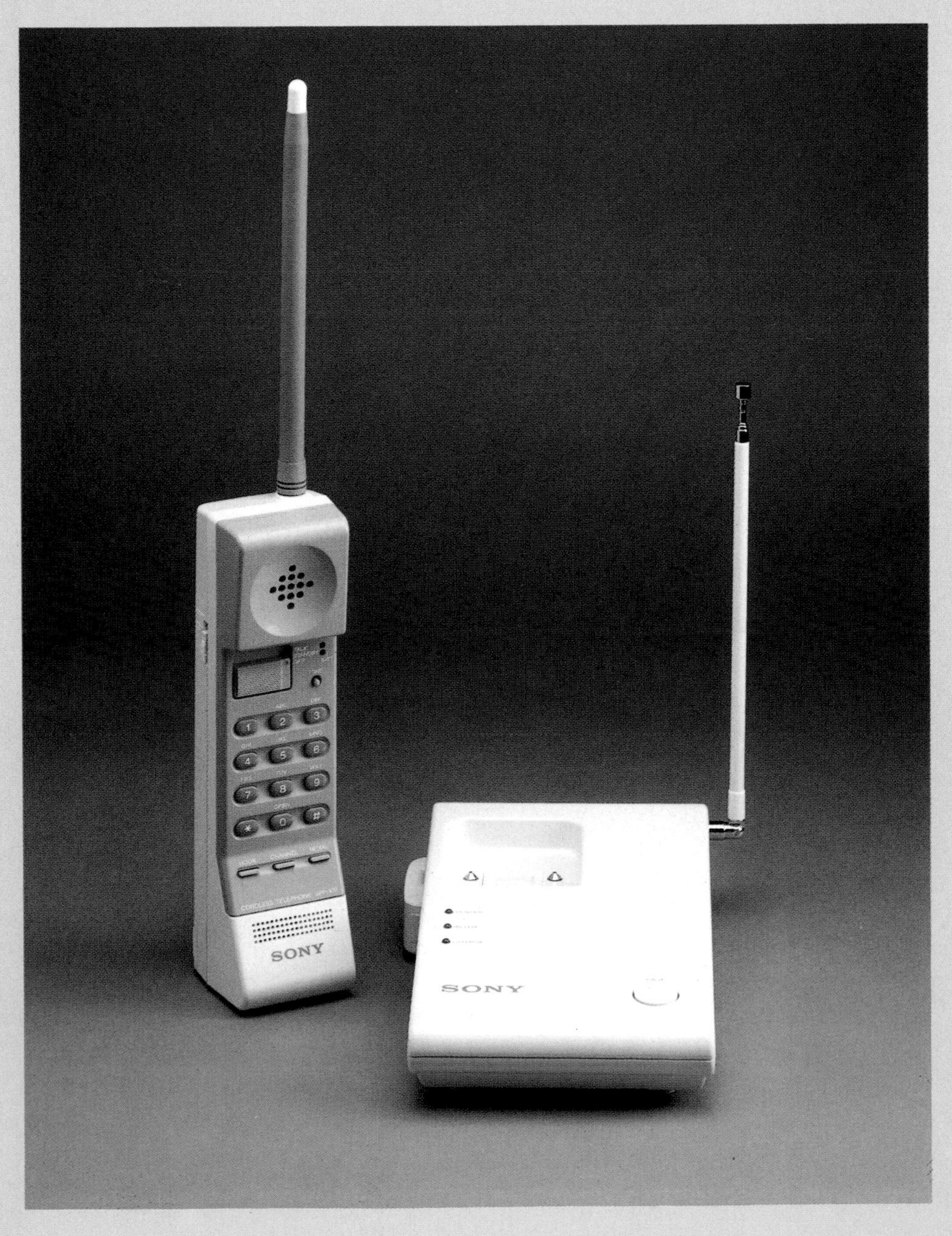

Product: Sony Telephone
Design Firm: Sony Corporation of America, Design Centers, Park Ridge, New Jersey
Client: Sony Corporation of America Park Ridge, New Jersey

Product:	Cobra
Design Firm:	Pasqui and Pasini Associates, Milan, Italy
Client:	Italtel, Milan, Italy
Awards:	SMAU Industrial Design Award

Product:	Telephone
Design Firm:	Morison S. Cousins & Associates New York, New York
Client:	ATARI-TEL Division, Warner Communications
Awards:	1985 *Industrial Design* magazine Design Review selection; Permanent Collection: Staaliches Museum, West Germany

Product: Scrim-Shim Panel Fastener
Designer: Louis Scrima
Design Firm: Louis Scrima Industrial Design
New York, New York
Awards: 1985 *Industrial Design* magazine Design Review, Best of Category, Concepts

Product: DUE Z Lever Door Handle with Spring
Designer: Cini Boeri
Client: Fusital, Milan, Italy
Materials: Metal core with elastomer coating

Product: OTTO B Lever Door Handle with Spring
Designer: Cini Boeri
Client: Fusital, Milan, Italy
Materials: Cast brass

Product: Hadajopo Hinge
Design Firm: Neville Green Design Limited
Victoria, British Columbia,
Canada
Awards: 1985 *Industrial Design* magazine
Design Review
Materials: Injection molded nylon

Product: Dustpan and Brush
Manufacturer: Bodum, Inc., Horsham,
Pennsylvania

Product: Travelaid Range Light Castors
Client: British Castors Ltd.
West Bromwich, England
Awards: 1984 Design Council Award
Materials: Nylon

Product: Black & Decker Heavy Duty Stapler
Staff Design: Robert Somers, Donald Vetter, Steven Harms, Grace Wang, Lawrence House
Client: Black & Decker, Hunt Valley, Maryland
Awards: 1985 *Industrial Design* magazine Design Review selection
Materials: ABS housing over stamped steel frame

Product: Extra Modern Deco Tool Collection
Designers: Shozo Toyohisi, Kiyoko Tanaka
Manufacturer: Koyo Sangyo, Tokyo, Japan
Distributor: Eastern Accent, Boston, Massachusetts

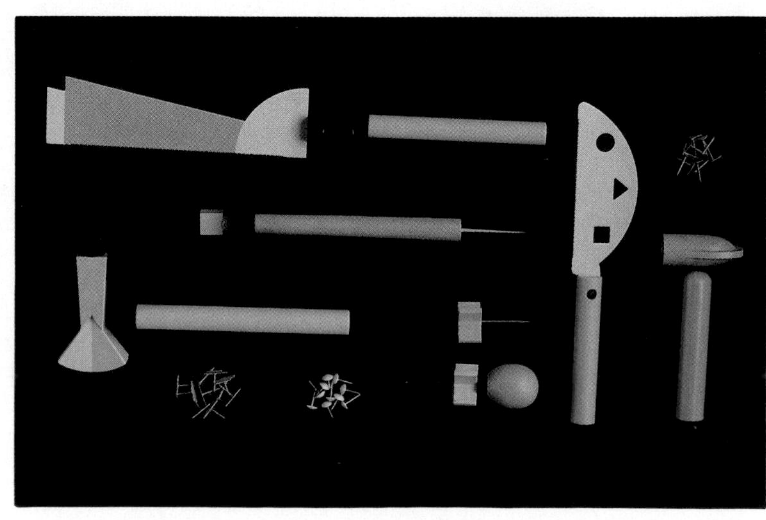

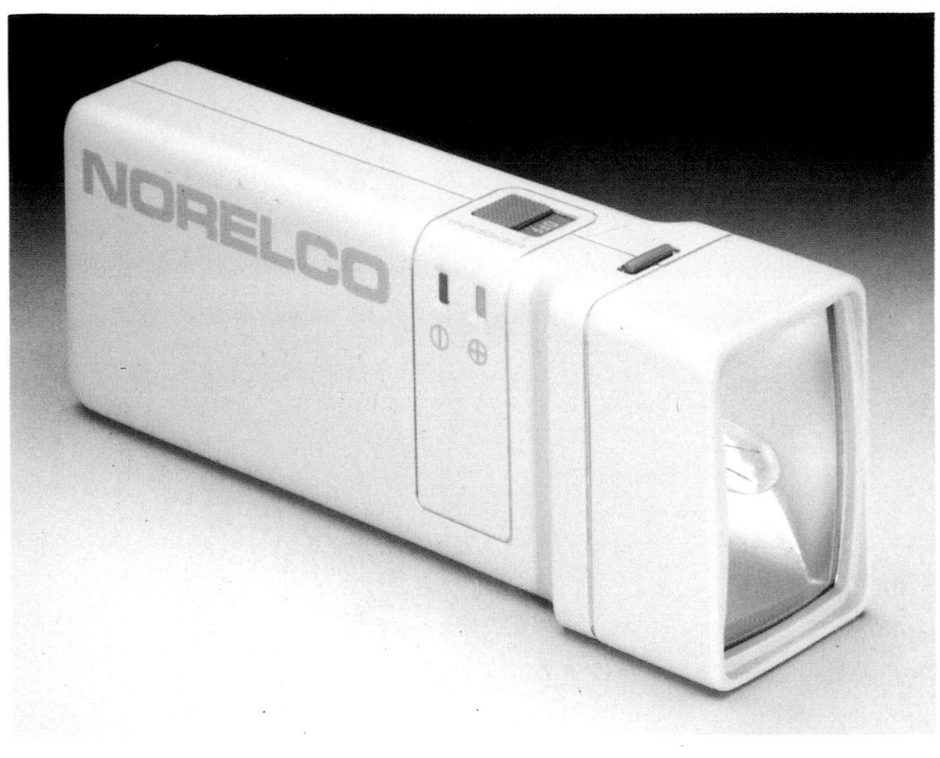

Product: Norelco Home Security RL-11 Rechargeable Light
Designers: In-house Staff Design, Essex, Connecticut
Manufacturer: Norelco, Stamford, Connecticut

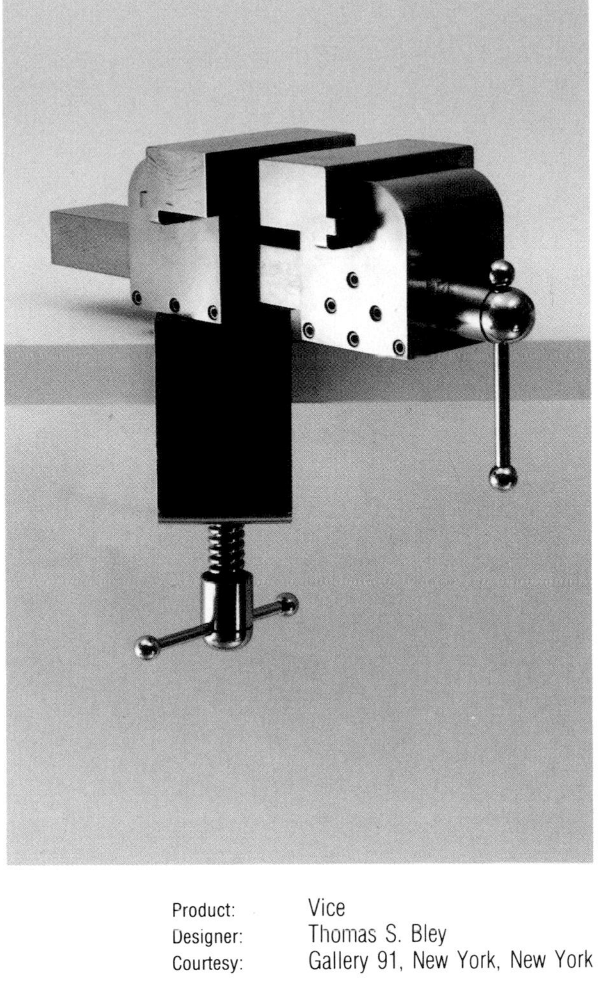

Product: Vice
Designer: Thomas S. Bley
Courtesy: Gallery 91, New York, New York

Product: ESI Air Purifier
Designers: Doug Patton, Matt Duncan
Design Firm: Patton Design Enterprises Irvine, California
Manufacturer: Electron Sciences, San Diego, California
Awards: 1985 *Industrial Design* magazine Design Review selection

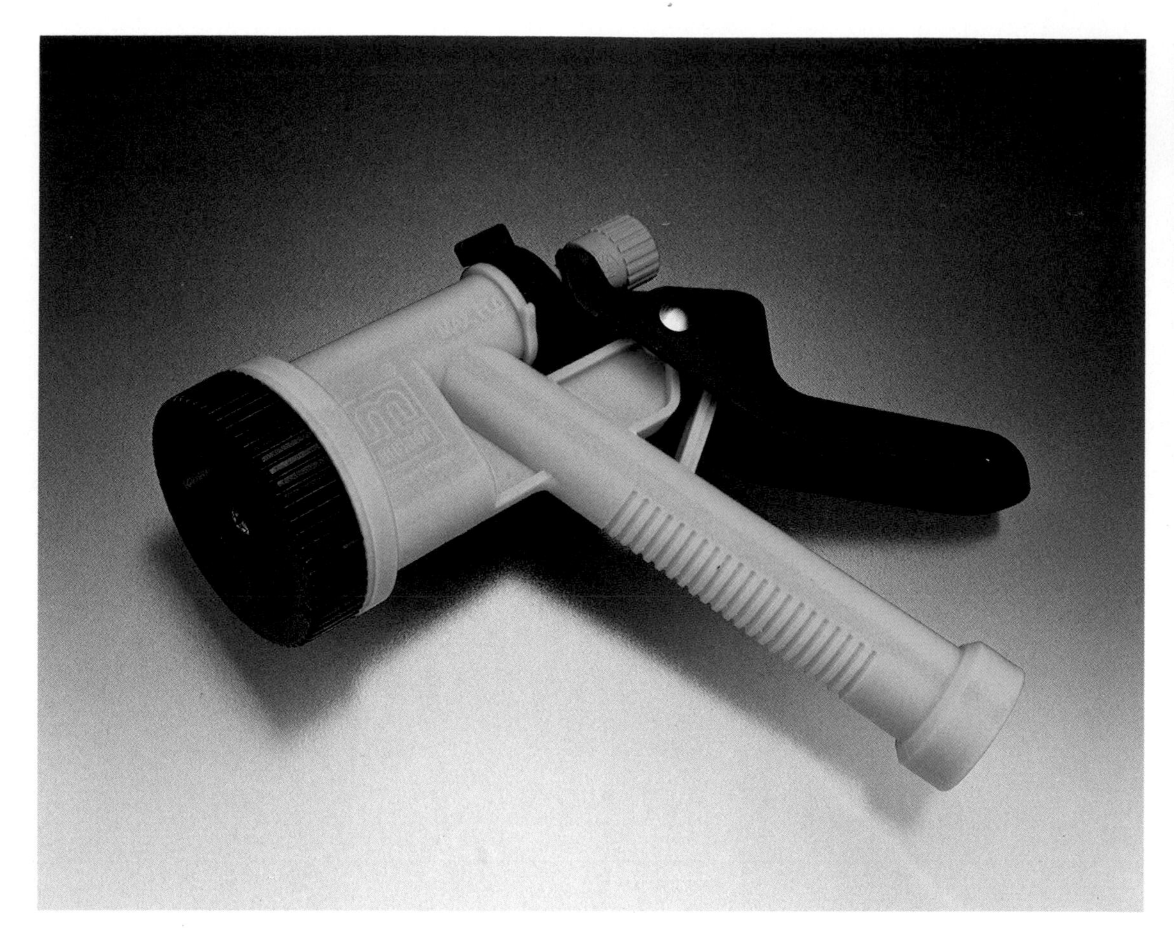

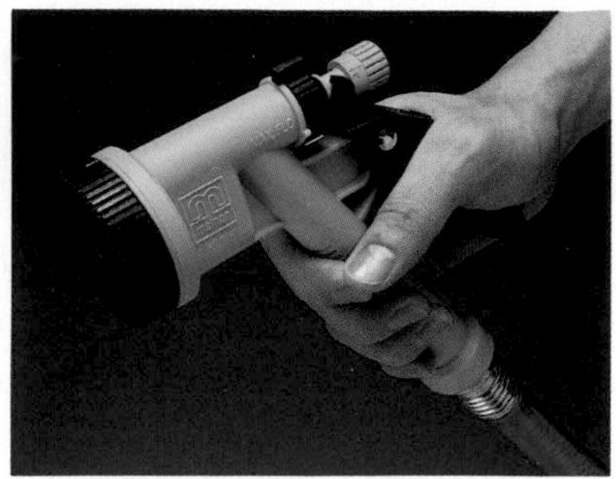

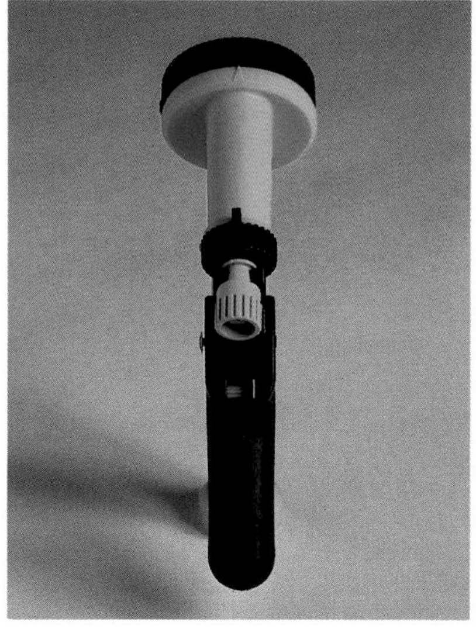

Product:	Melnor Nozzle
Designer Firm:	Tanaka Kapac Design
Distributor:	Gallery 91, New York, New York
Awards:	1985 *Industrial Design* magazine Design Review, Best of Category, Consumer Products

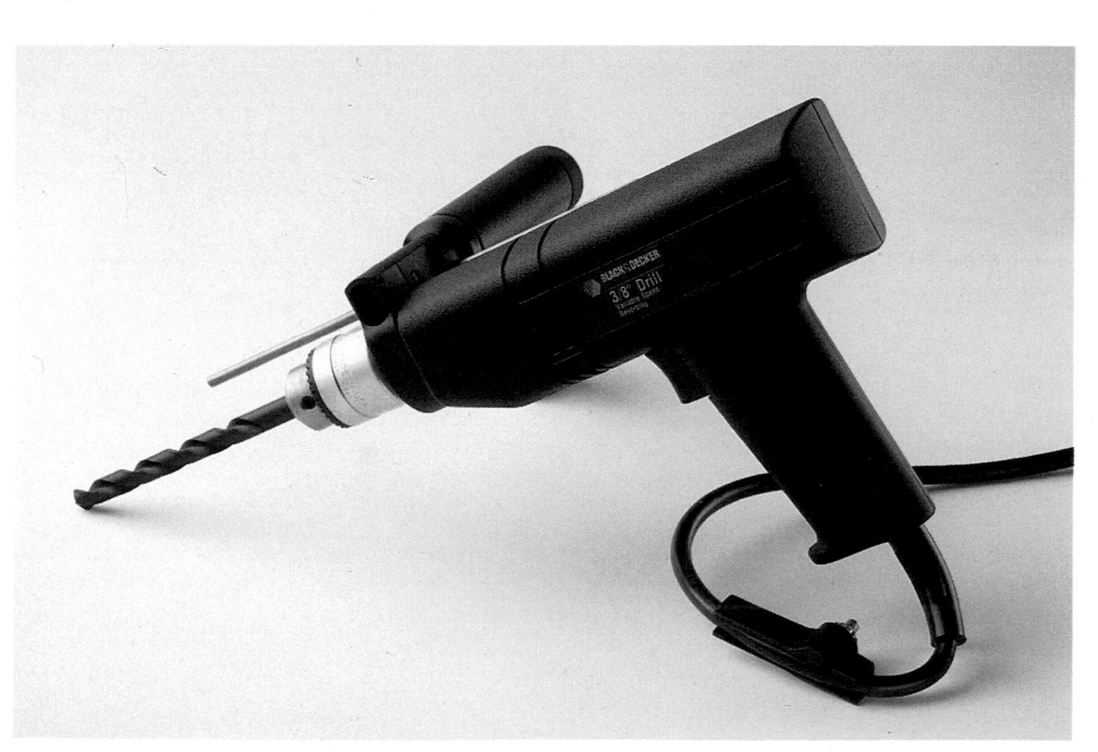

Product:	Black & Decker 3/8" Variable Speed Reversing Drill
Staff Design:	Robert Somers, Donald Vetter, Grace Wang, and Lawrence House
Client:	Black & Decker, Hunt Valley, Maryland
Materials:	Glass reinforced polypropylene housing; handles: glass-filled nylon, strong thermo-plastic rubber; check key: glass-reinforced nylon

Product: Tapmaster Steam Iron
Designer: Rowenta, West Germany
Distributor: The Schwabel Corporation
Cambridge, Massachusetts

Product: Steamship Travel Iron
Designers: Tucker Viewmeister, John Lonczak, Dan Formosa, Tom Dair, and Davin Stowell
Design Firm: Smart Design, New York, New York
Client: Sanyei America Corporation
Matorialc: Injection molded polycarbonate, non-stick coated sole, and automatic dual voltage

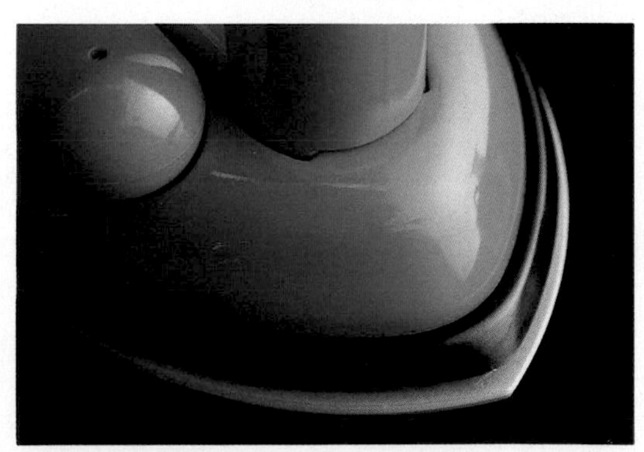

LIGHTING

CHAPTER

Never neutral, lighting will either enhance or sabotage architectural or interior design. Along with color, scale, and texture, it is a design element to be considered—and one to be used in the art of illusion as well as illumination.

Two major factors—the rising cost of energy and the visual demands that have accompanied the electronic office—are influencing contemporary lighting design and reshaping the way buildings and tasks are lit. The floodlight philosophy has been replaced by a standard of more focused and more efficient lighting schemes.

Lighting designers are imbuing the shapes they create with the wit, sophistication, and diversity that characterizes the design landscape today. They are capturing all the surprise and subtlety of nature in the synthetic worlds they bring to life.

Product:	Orgatech Bole Uplighter
Designer:	David Wales, New York, New York
Client:	Orgatech Ltd., London, England
Awards:	1984 *Industrial Design* magazine Design Review selection
Materials:	Epoxy coated steel sheet and tubing, and spun aluminum; metal halide discharge; 250W, 400W lamps

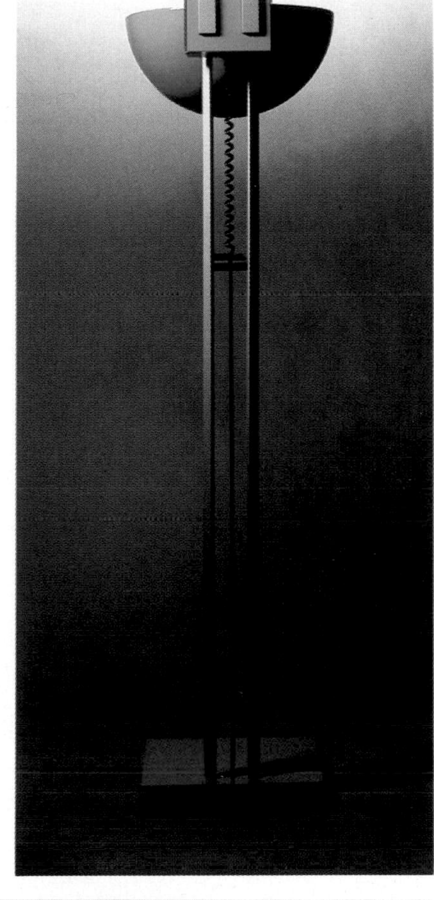

Product:	"Danger from Japan"
Designer:	Clark Robertson
Client:	Art et Industrie New York, New York

Product: Damocle
Designer: Mitchell Mauk
Client: Artemide, Inc., New York, New York

Product: Eyelamp "Argus"
Designer: Stephan Bumm, West Germany
Distributor: Global Furniture, New York, New York

Product: Crisol
Client: Atelier International
New York, New York

Product: Shogun Floor Lamp
Designer: Mario Botta
Client: Artemide, Inc., New York, New York

Product: Shogun Table Lamp
Designer: Mario Botta
Client: Artemide, Inc., New York, New York

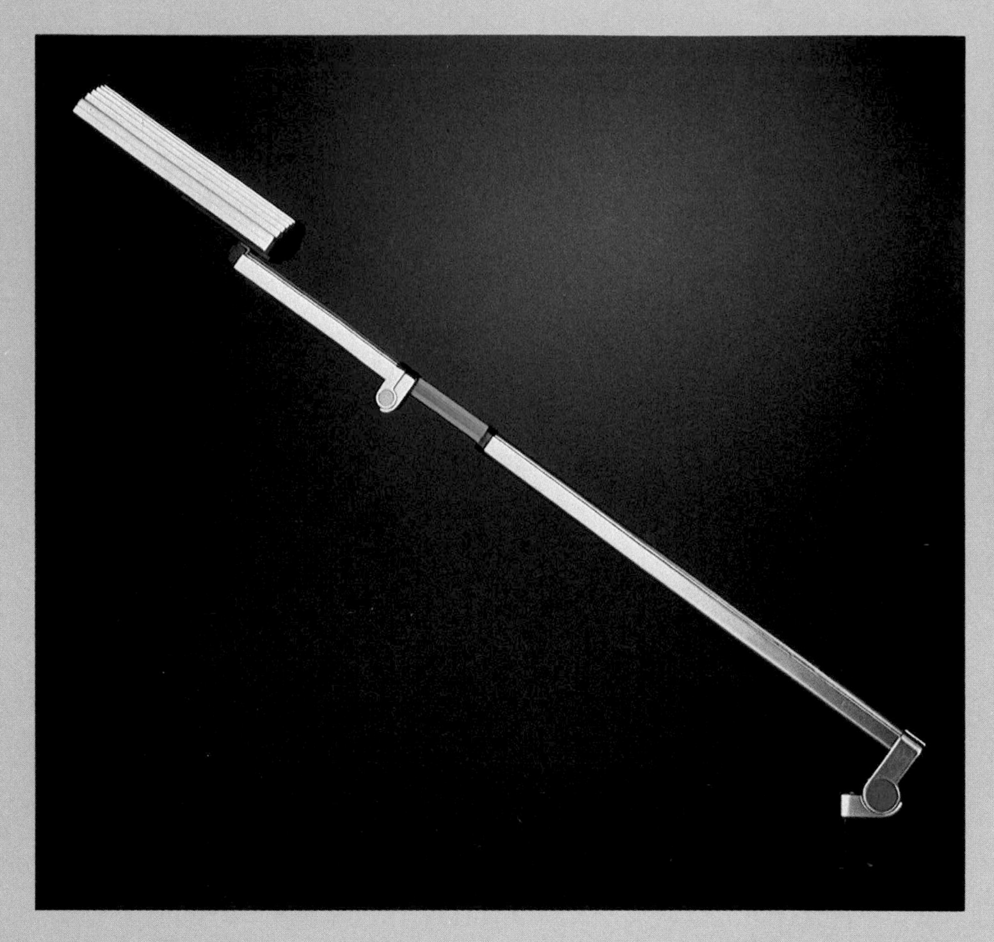

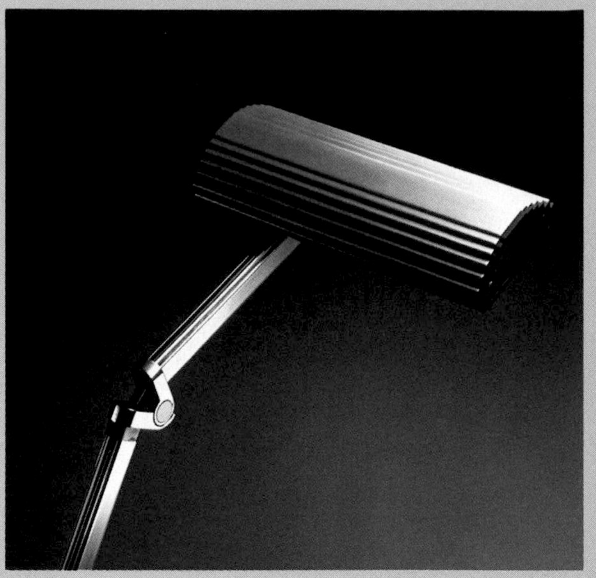

Product: "DESK"
Designer: Ezio Didone
Client: Atelier International
New York, New York
Materials: Jointed aluminum support stem; acrylic reflector; polished aluminum interior

Product: Pilade Tavolo-low voltage table spot light
Designer: Ernesto Gismondi
Client: Litech, Milan, Italy
Distributor: Artemide, Inc., New York, New York

Product: Aurora
Designers: Perry King, Santiago Miranda
Manufacturer: Arteluce, Italy
Distributor: Atelier International
New York, New York

Product: Doric
Designer: Mark Zeff, New York, New York
Distributor: Global Furniture, New York,
New York
Materials: Aluminium extrusion

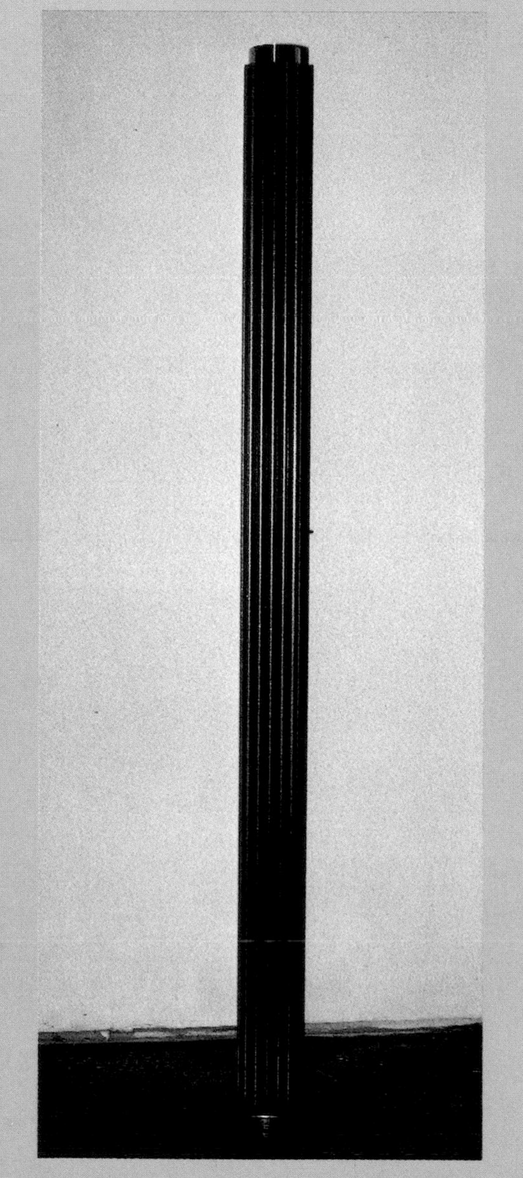

Product: Club
Designer: P. G. Ramella
Client: Atelier International
New York, New York
Manufacturer: Arteluce, Italy

Product: Falcon Eye, infrared light detection system
Designer: Fabio Fabiano, IDSA
Arlington, Texas
Client: R.P. Falconer Corporation
Fort Worth, Texas
Materials: Case: injection molded polycarbonate; built-in passive sensor; 75W reflector bulb

Product: "A 86 Ring" Task Lamp
Designer: Bruno Gecchelin,
Client: Atelier International Lighting
New York, New York
Materials: Cast aluminum with an enamel finish

Product: Cobra and Cobra Jr.
Designer: Masayuki Kurokawa, Japan
Courtesy: Gallery 91, New York, New York

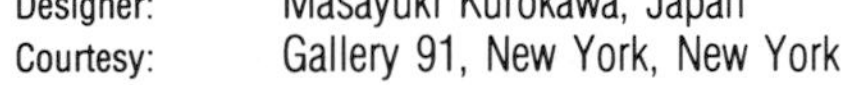

Product: Wall-Mounted Uplighter
Manufacturer: Lita, Paris, France
Materials: White-finish zamac; anodized silver sanded aluminum reflectors; protective glass cover

Product: Crepidula Table Lamp
Designer: Patrizia Belloni
Manufacturer: quattrifolio, Milan, Italy
Materials: Gray metal; 2 fluorescent bulbs

Product: Keiko
Designer: Shigeru Ban
Distributor: Gallery 91, New York, New York

Product: Geo Garden Lamp
Designers: Cristina Lancetti, Francesco Lorenzelli
Manufacturer: quattrifolio, Milan, Italy
Materials: Painted plastic; fluorescent bulb

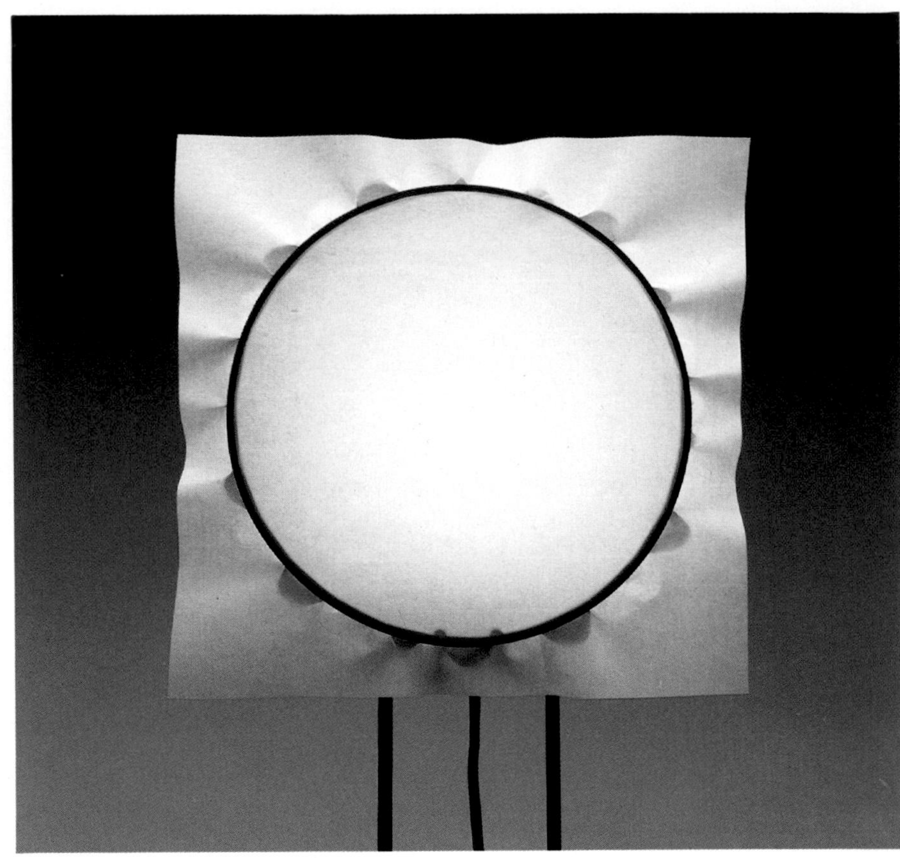

Product: Porcelli Corona Floor Lamp
Designers: V. Lorenzo Porcelli, with Carmen Basile
Design Firm: Porcelli Associates Inc., New York, New York
Client: Porcelli Associates Inc., New York, New York
Distributor: Porcelli Associates Inc., New York, New York
Awards: 1985 *Industrial Design* magazine Design Review selection
U.S.I.A.'s Cultural Exchange Exhibit: "Design in America"
Permanent Collection: Museum of Modern Art, New York
Materials: Painted steel and aluminum; solid aluminum base; Japanese rice paper shade

Product: Bascula, halogen suspension lamp
Designer: Asaharo Sigheaki
Client: Stilnova, S.p.A., Lainate, Italy
Materials: Lacquered metal; sand glass hand

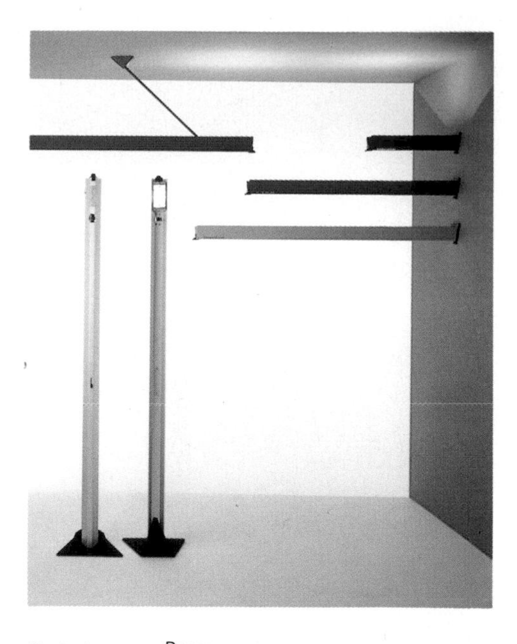

Product:	Beam
Designer:	Enrico Bona
Client:	IPI - Innovative Products for Interiors, Inc. New York, New York
Materials:	Basic manufacturing facility specializing in bent extruded aluminum and baked enamel process

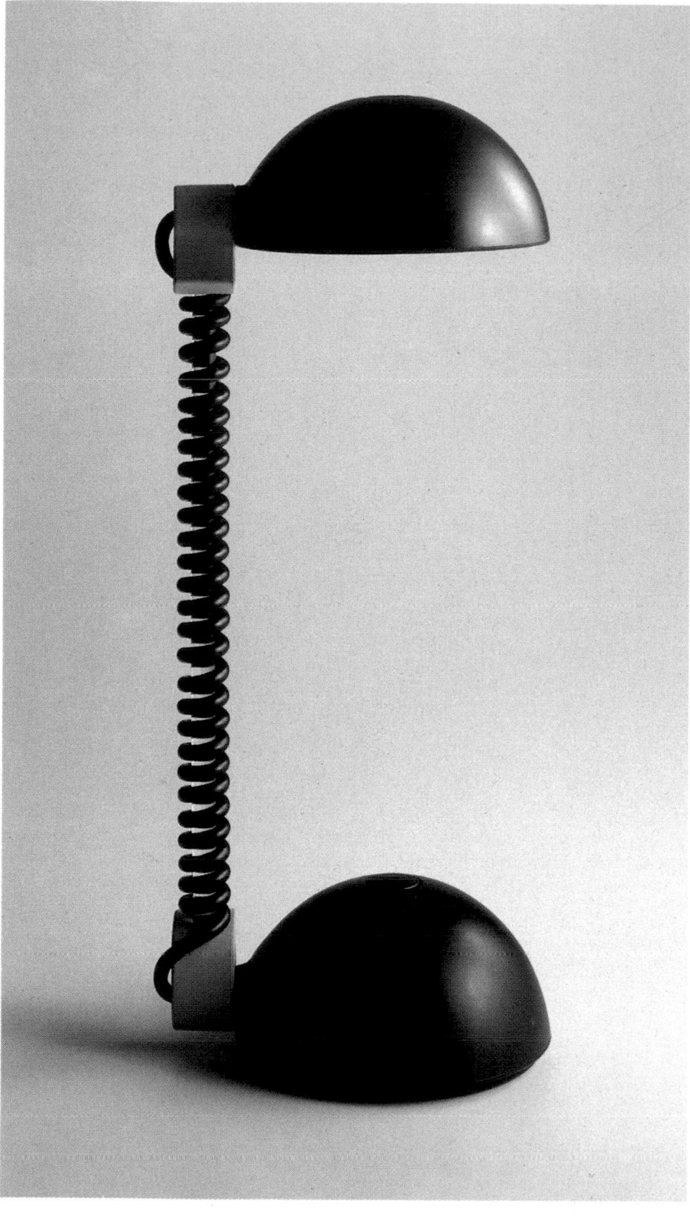

Product:	Thuja, halogen table lamp
Designer:	Damiano Alberti, Milan, Italy
Client:	YCAMI Collection
Materials:	Vulcanized rubber; round perspex connection bar; aluminum reflecting screen

Product:	Nessen/Luci "Tomo"
Designer:	Toshyuki Kita
Manufacturer:	Luci, Milan, Italy
Distributor:	Nessen Lamps Inc., Bronx, New York
Materials:	Colorful 300W halogen floor lamp, with an articulated T-shaped arm and reflector; brightness is controlled by a floor dimmer

Product: Light
Manufacturer: Studio Alchimia, Milan, Italy

Product: Police
Distributor: Gallery 91, New York, New York

Products:	Lighthouses
Designer:	James Evanson, New York, New York
Client:	James Evanson, New York, New York
Distributor:	Ivy Ross and Frank Etxaniz New York, New York

Product:	Crescent
Designer:	James Hong
Client:	Art et Industrie New York, New York

Product: Lighting Fixtures
Designer: Jerry Kugler, New York, New York
Client: Générale Banque, New York, New York
Awards: IALD Honorable Mention Award (International Association of Lighting Designers)

Product: Folding Paper Lamp
Designer: Brent Markee, New York, New York
Design Firm: Smart Design, New York, New York
Client: Smart Design, New York, New York
Materials: Black oxidized steel wire legs; 100 percent rag paper shade

Product: Rising Sun
Designer: Daniel T. Ebihara
Courtesy: Gallery 91, New York, New York
Photo Credit: Masao Ueda

Product: Sguish
Designer: F. Di Bartolomei
Client: Bieffeplast s.p.a., Padova, Italy
Materials: Halogen light made of steel with transparent and sanded perspex plate

Product: Ruhr Valley Lamp
Designer: Richard Snyder, New York, New York
Manufacturer: Richard Snyder Design, New York, New York
Distributor: Art et Industrie, New York, New York
Materials: Anodized aluminum body; case iron base

Product: Mackindiv
Client: Lazin Lighting, New York, New York

Product: Planet
Designers: Don Ruddy, Shane Kennedy
Manufacturer: Furniture Club, New York, New York

Product: Urn Sconce
Designer: Jerry Van Deelen
Design Firm: Les Prismatiques
Materials: Corian® and metal

Product: Sensu 1
Designers: Sean Corcorran, Jorge Freyer
Design Firm: Hardware Arts Group, Inc.
Distributor: Sointu, New York, New York
Materials: Aluminum base and shade; delrin caps and rubber bellows

Product: Ovuli
Design Firm: Ron Rezek Lighting & Furniture
Los Angeles, California
Distributors: Ron Rezek Lighting & Furniture
Los Angeles, California
Materials: Anodized aluminum, glass

FURNISHINGS

CHAPTER

This period of furniture design has been riddled with controversy and heated with excitement. While at the turn of the decade we wondered whether we would combine contract and residential furnishings in a single collection, now categories have multiplied and questions are raised about the appropriateness of including ''art furniture'' along with other residential designs. In the view of Sherry Williams, owner of retail gallery Clodagh Ross Williams, the current design polemic is ''only the tip of the iceberg.'' How much further is it going to go? Where do you draw the line?

The roots of such questions are sending the mass-market furniture industry running (forward or back?) to a safer time. A new emphasis on reproductions at the Fall '85 High Point Show was labeled by the *New York Times* as ''a surprising retreat from the avant-garde design featured at the last several shows.'' Not surprisingly, the bottom line was profit. Memphis did not ''sell.'' Nor, was it meant to. By its own proclamation, the radical thought-provoking designs were to exist as conceptual prototypes.

While Memphis may be more concerned with ''statement'' than ''sale,'' young designers who are traveling the road that Memphis paved show no similar qualms about cashing in on the public's expanded sensibility. They are shrewd marketers who—whether seen as perverting or supporting the new design aesthetic—stand passionately behind the legitimacy of their design solutions. Thus, while designer Bill Stumpf worries that ''purely visual ambitions'' are misleading present and future designers (''It's like all their nerve endings are connected directly to their eyes.'' [*Time* magazine, 24 March 1986]), many ''art furniture'' designers object to the categorization and take exception with the notion that their visually iconoclastic forms are not comfortable, functional. . .or purchasable.

On the other hand, few could dispute that with the creation of Equa, Stumpf demonstrated that ergonomic research can indeed spawn a new visual elegance. In doing so, he fulfilled his career ambition (and a long-awaited market demand) of combining beauty and comfort in an affordable production.

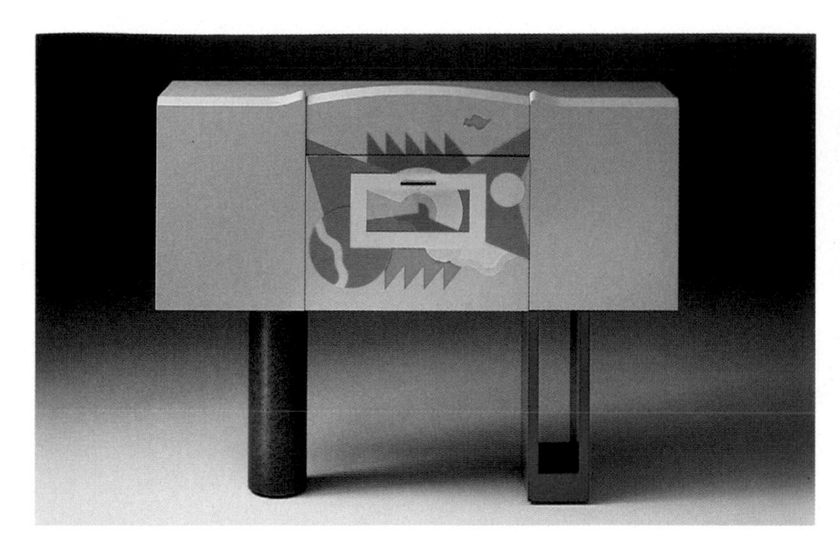

Product: Cantaride Chest of Drawers
Designers: Allesandro Mendini, Bruno Gregori
Client: Zabro, Italy
Studio Alchimia, Milan, Italy
Materials: Decorated timber; handles in silver-plated metal

Product: Orbit '84
Designer: James Evanson, New York, New York
Client: James Evanson Associates, New York, New York

Product: "Marilyn" Chaise Lounge
Designer: Hans Hollein, Italy
Client: Poltronova, Italy
Distributor: Global Furniture, New York, New York
Materials: Erable root base, plywood side; polyurethane padding

Product:	Mitzi
Designer:	Hans Hollein, Italy
Client:	Poltronova, Italy
Distributor:	Global Furniture, New York, New York
Materials:	Erable root base, plywood sides; polyurethane padding

Product:	Lullaby '85
Designer:	James Evanson, New York, New York
Client:	Art et Industrie, New York, New York

Product: Chair
Designer: Dinah Casson, London, England
Courtesy: Golden Eye Exhibition, Cooper-Hewitt Museum
Manufacturer: Golden Eye Studio, India

Product: Blongo Chair
Designer: Leo Blackman, Brooklyn, New York
Manufacturer: Jack Gavin Constructions, Brooklyn, New York
Awards: 1985 *Industrial Design* magazine Design Review selection
Materials: Birch veneer plywood with ebony stain or natural finish

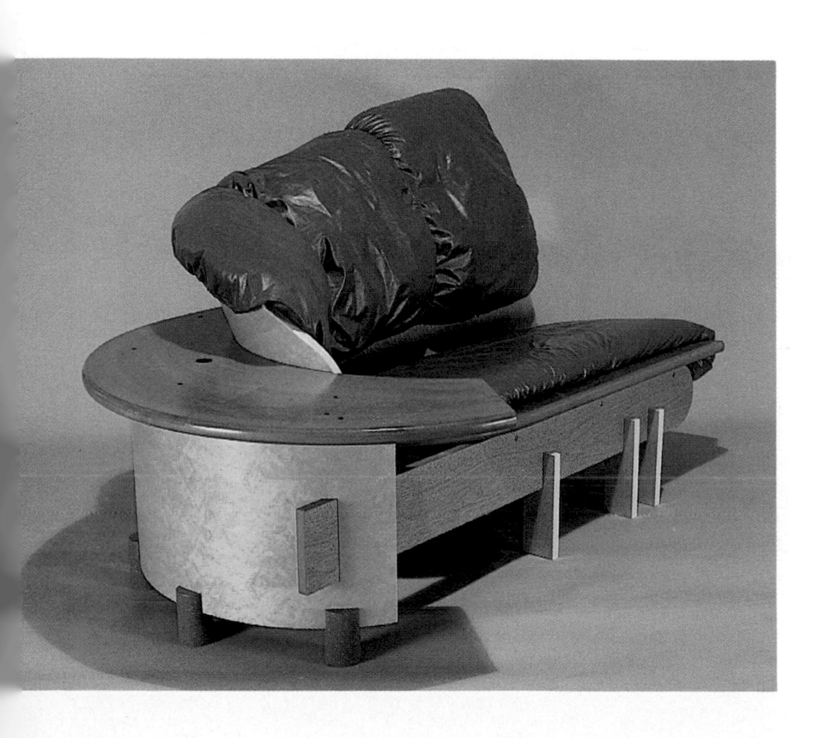

Product: I Menhir
Designers: L. Acerbis, G. Stoppino
Client: Acerbis International, Bergamo, Italy
Distributor: Atelier International, Ltd., New York, New York
Materials: Marble; top; transparent or black lacquered crystal, or black and white layered laminate

roduct: Moray Table/Desk
esigners: Bruce Keiser Don Newman
lanufacturer: Keiser-Newman, Philadelphia,
istributor: Pennsylvania
wards: Roscoe Product Design award
1986 *Industrial Design* magazine Design Review selection

Product: Sienna Table
Design: Dakota Jackson
Manufacturer: Dakota Jackson, Inc. New York, New York
Materials: Marble, glass

Product: M1 Chair
Importer: Global Furniture, New York, New York
Retailer: Clodagh Ross Williams Inc. New York, New York
Materials: Leather

Product: Pollock Table
Designers: Charles Pollock, William Jaremko
Client: Vecta Contract, Grand Prairie, Texas

Product: Zabro, Table Chair
Designers: Allesandro Mendini, Bruno Gregori
Manufacturer: Zabro, Italy
Design Firm: Studio Alchimia, Milan, Italy
Materials: Fold-down top in decorated timber; seat in leather and painted timber

Product:	Practica
Designer:	Ugo La Pietra, Milan, Italy
Manufacturer:	Busnelli, Milan, Italy
Distributor:	Greenbaum Collection, Paterson, New Jersey
Materials:	Frame and base: shock resistant gray painted steel section and solid wood; cross-elastic belt springing; feet: black injection molded PVC; padding: variable density polyurethane and polydacron

Product:	Veranda Seating
Designer:	Vico Magistretti
Client:	Atelier International Ltd., Plainview, New York
Awards:	1984 *Industrial Design* magazine Design Review selection
Materials:	Hinged steel frames with cast polyurethane foam and dacron upholstery; enameled steel base

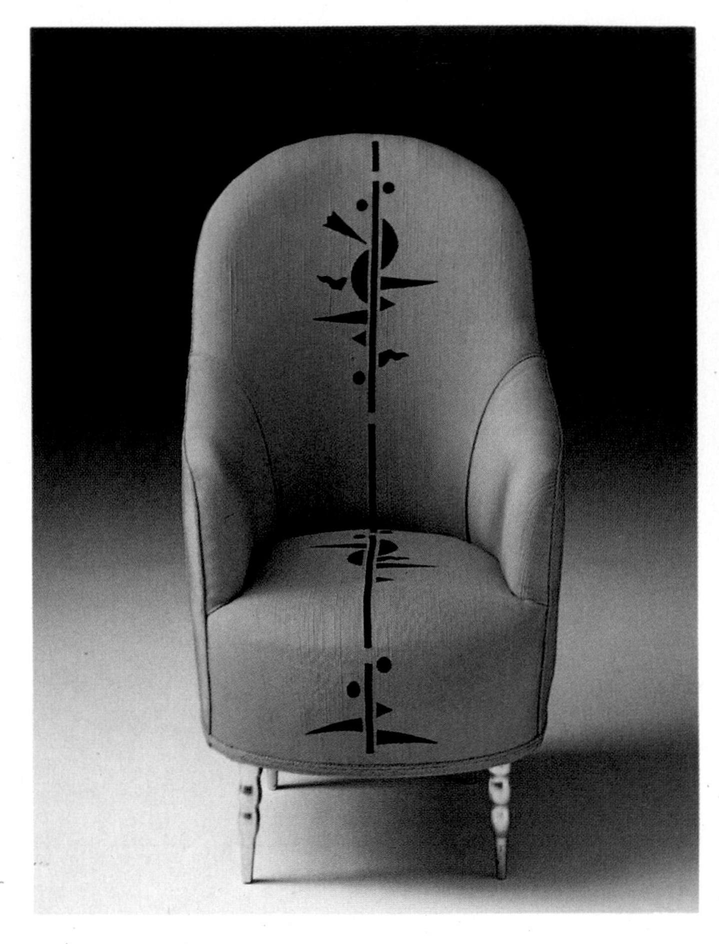

Product: Chair
Design Firm: Studio Alchimia, Milan, Italy
Manufacturer: Zabro, Italy

Product: Plant Stands
Designer: Wendy Maruyama
Client: Snyderman Gallery, Philadelphia, Pennsylvania
Materials: Lacquered bass wood, $33\frac{1}{2} \times 15 \times 15$ in.

Product: Servese
Designer: Kairos
Client: B & B Italia, Novedrate, Italy
Materials: Polyurethane; cast iron base

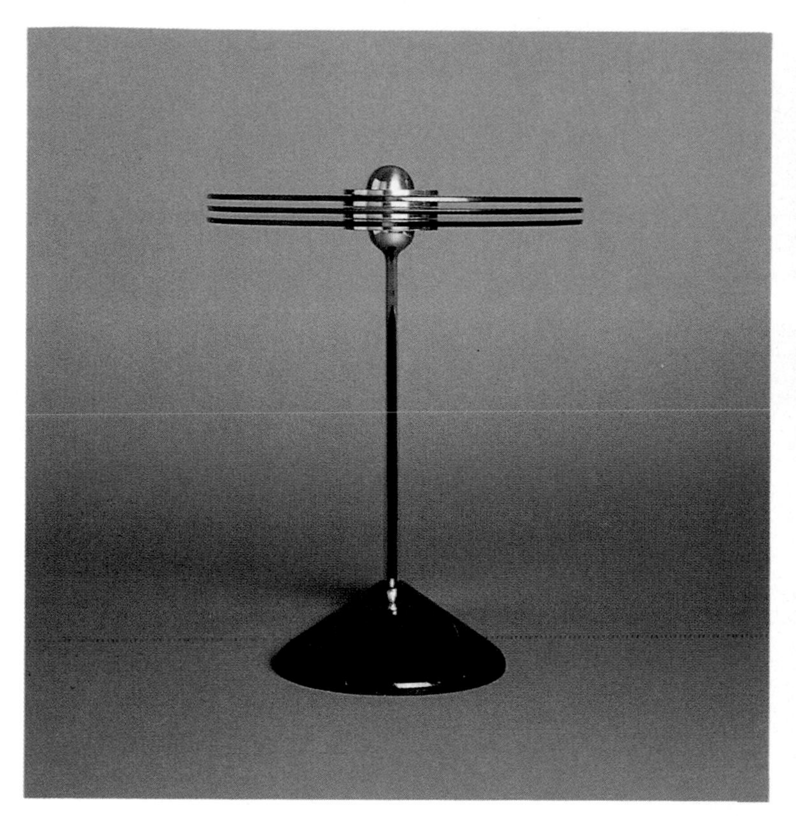

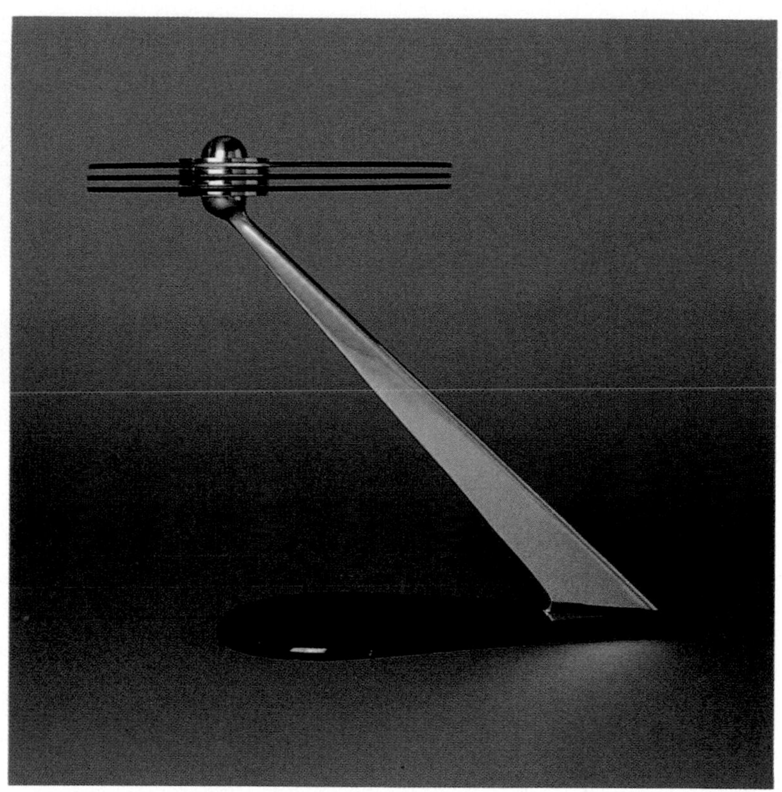

Product: K1001 Lounge Companion Table
Designer: Bruce Keiser, Philadelphia, Pennsylvania
Client: Keiser/Newman, Philadelphia, Pennsylvania
Materials: Aluminum, bronze, marble, and glass

Product: Aero Chair
Designer: Patrick Naggar
Client: Arc International, Inc., New York, New York

Product: Chair B1
Designer: Stefan Wewerka, West Germany
Distributor: Global Furniture, New York, New York
Materials: Leather or fabric seats, wood frame

Product: Comet Club, 1985
Designer: James Evanson, New York, New York
Distributor: Art et Industrie, New York, New York
Manufacturer: James Evanson Inc., New York, New York
Awards: 1986 *Industrial Design* magazine Design Review selection

Product: Humming Chair
Designer: Shinya Okayama
Distributor: Gallery 91, New York, New York

Product: PORSCHE Model 84S Reclining Chair
Designer: Ferdinand Alexander Porsche
Client: Poltrona Frau, Tolentino, Italy
Distributor: Baker Furniture Grand Rapids, Michigan
Casaform, New York, New York
Materials: Sculptural frames: one piece cast aluminum leather

Product: Venturi Collection, detail of "Grandmother's Tablecloth" pattern
Designer: Robert Venturi
Client: Knoll International, New York, New York

Product: 4310 Square Table
Distributor: Kartell USA, Easley, South Carolina
Materials: Injection molded ABS

Product: Cabriole Leg Table
Designer: Robert Venturi
Manufacturer: Knoll International, New York, New York

Product: Madonna Table
Design Firm: Arquitectonica, Miami, Florida
Manufacturer: Memphis, Milan, Italy

Product: Sheraton Chair
Designer: Robert Venturi
Manufacturer: Knoll International, New York, New York

Product: Queen Anne Chair
Designer: Robert Venturi
Manufacturer: Knoll International, New York, New York

Product: Open Staff - Board Room Table
Design Firm: Modern Design SPA, Udine, Italy
Client: Modern Design SPA, Udine, Italy
Materials: Black ash veneered, open pore lacquered

Product: Free System
Design Firm: Modern Design SPA, Udine, Italy
Client: Modern Design SPA, Udine, Italy

Product: Donahue Table
Designer: Tim Donahue
Client: Howe Furniture Corporation
Trumbell, Connecticut
Materials: Light oak, mahogany, maple or walnut; "ebonized" black wood finish

Product: Panca
Designer: Maurizio Peregalli
Client: Noto Zeus Collezione, Milan, Italy
Materials: Steel tube structure; iron rod; epoxy painted black; thousand points pirelli rubber; round extruded rubber

Product: Pianeta B
Manufacturer: G.B. Bernini SPA, Milan, Italy

Product: Imago/Figura Executive Seating
Designer: Mario Bellini, Italy
Clients: Vitra International Ltd.
Basee, Switzerland;
Vitra Seating, New York,
New York
Awards: 1st Award in "Made in Germany"
Competition Persona:
Technology Award;
1986 *Industrial Design* magazine
Design Review selection

Product: Princeton Group
Designer: Brian Kane
Manufacturer: Metropolitan Furniture
Corporation
San Francisco, California
Awards: 1985 IBD, silver award

Figura with slipcover upholstery.

Product:	LC10-P table
Designers:	Le Corbusier and Charlotte Perriand (1st release of 1928 design)
Manufacturer:	Cassina, Italy
Distributor:	Atelier International New York, New York

Product:	20/20 Seating
Designer:	Norman Cherner
Manufacturer:	Modern Mode Inc., San Leandro, California
Materials:	Wood; painted metal or stainless steel frame; upholstered

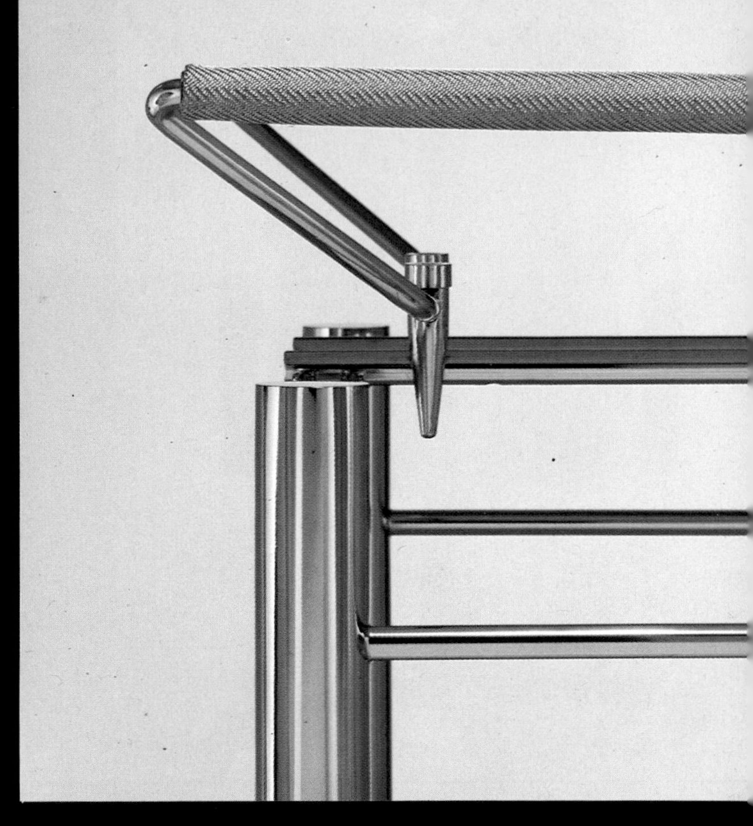

Product:	Bitsch Chair
Designer:	Professor Hans Ullrich Bitsch
Design Firm:	Harvey Probber, Inc., New York, New York
Awards:	1984 *Industrial Design* magazine Design Review selection
Materials:	Woven stainless steel fabric

Product:	Modular Table
Designer:	Giovanni Pasanella, New York, New York
Manufacturer:	Laboratorio Marmi, Lucca, Italy
Materials:	Marble

Product: Yinyang
Designer: Kengiro Azuma, Milan, Italy
Client: Morphos, Division of Acerbis International, Bergamo, Italy
Materials: Marble, glass

Product: Equa Chair
Designers: Bill Stumpf, Don Chadwick
Design Firm: Chadwick, Stumpf & Associates
Santa Monica, California
Manufacturer: Herman Miller, Inc.
Zeeland, Michigan
Awards: 1985 *Industrial Design* magazine
Design Review selection
Materials: Glass reinforced polyester resin; single piece shell cast aluminum chassis

Product: Ethospace Interiors
Designer: Bill Stumpf
Design Firm: William Stumpf & Associates
Minneapolis, Minnesota
Manufacturer: Herman Miller, Inc., Zeeland, Michigan
Awards: 1985 *Industrial Design* magazine
Design Review selection
Materials: Steel structural frames; fabric, vinyl, veneer, glazed, cork, aluminum and porcelain tiles; veneer or laminate work surfaces, with waterfall edges; veneer, vinyl, fabric and plastic components

Product: Barto Seating Collection
Designer: Dick Schultz, Barto, Pennsylvania
Client: Domore, Elkhardt, Indiana
Awards: 1985 *Industrial Design* magazine Design Review selection
Materials: Steel U-shaped member with foam and elastic webbing

Product: Director Series
Client: Gunlocke Company, Wayland, New York

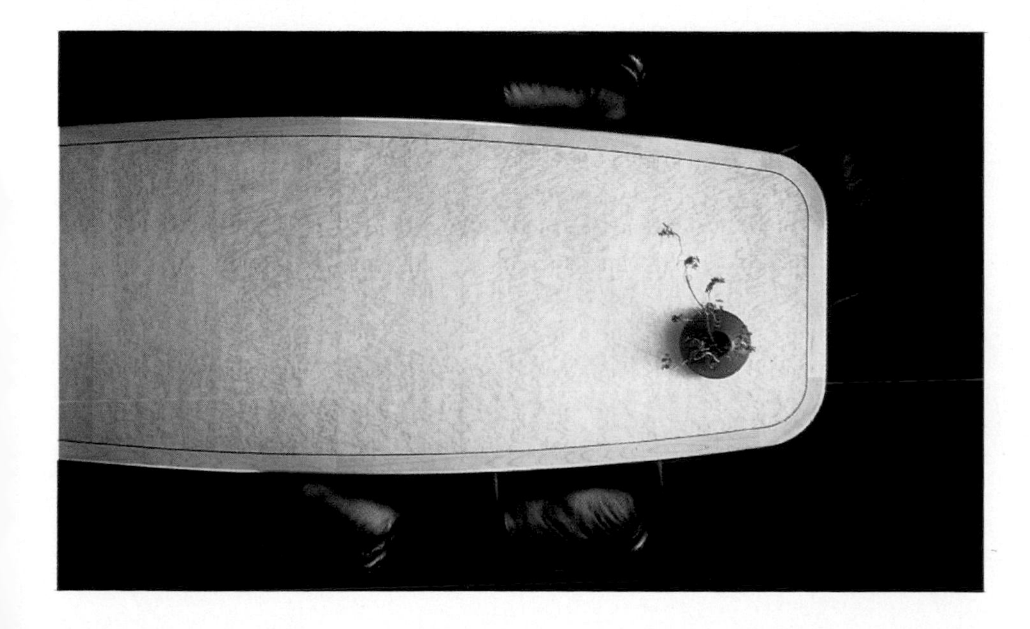

Product: Sedia Point Armchair
Designer: M. Salvato
Client: Saporiti, Milan, Italy

Product: Venturi Collection
Designer: Robert Venturi
Client: Knoll International

Product: Adjustable Work Station System
Designer: Mark Paulsen, John Rizzi
Design Firm: Niels Diffrient, Ridgefield, Connecticut
Client: Knoll International, New York, New York
Materials: Steel structural elements; paper honey comb work tops with steel and plastic laminate finish; injection molded plastic trim

Product: Chair
Designer: Jeff Kellar, Portland, Maine
Client: Gallery at Workbench
New York, New York

Product: Arcella Armchair
Designer: Paolo Piva
Client: B & B Italia, New York and
Novedrate, Italy

Product: Arm Chair Group
Designer: Brian Kane
Client: Metropolitan Furniture Corporation
South San Francisco, California
Awards: 1985 IBD Product Design, Silver
award

Product: Tables
Designers: Eric Bergman, Gordon Naylor
Design Firm: Neophile Inc., New York, New York
Materials: Birch, finished with latex and urethane coatings

Product: Oggetto Naturale Dumb-Waiter
Designer: Ugo La Pietra, Milan, Italy
Manufacturer: Busnelli, Milan, Italy
Distributor: Greenbaum Collection, Paterson, New Jersey
Materials: Turned wood; polyester lacquer finish; metal

Product: "Afternoon"
Designer: Lloyd Schwan
Client: Art et Industrie, New York, New York

Product: Attessa
Designer: Ugo La Pietra, Milan, Italy
Manufacturer: Busnelli, Milan, Italy
Distributor: Greenbaum Collection, Paterson, New Jersey
Materials: Shock resistant, painted metal framed in metallic aluminum, gray and metallic blue; spring seat and back; padding: pieces of cold injected foam

Product: Flessuosa
Designer: Ugo La Pietra, Milan, Italy
Manufacturer: Busnelli, Milan, Italy
Distributor: Greenbaum Collection, Paterson, New Jersey
Materials: Solid wood frame; crossed-elastic belt springing; base: black injection molded PVC; padding: variable density polyurethane

Product:	Bramante
Client:	Zanotta spa, Italy

Product:	Stratus
Designer:	Norman Cherner
Manufacturer:	Modern Mode Inc. San Leandro, California

Product: New Empire Desk
Designer: Jim Evanson
Manufacturer: James Evanson, Inc.
New York, New York

Product: EXA Collection
Client: Origua, Savigliano, Italy
Materials: Legs: aluminum monolithic extrusion; light gray, dark gray, and white lacquered; feet: foamed polyurethane; desks and walls: laminate, wood, lacquer, and stucco finishes

Product: Hudson Desk
Designer: Rory McCarthy, Tucson, Arizona
Materials: White oak, aluminum, steel tube, perforated stainless steel, rubber, and glass

Product: King Zet
Design Firm: frogdesign, Campbell, California
Manufacturer: König & Neurath, West Germany
Distributor: Wrightline, U.S.A.

Product: Semi-Circular Table, Rectangular Work Table
Designer: Friis & Moltke
Client: Kroin Incorporated, Cambridge, Massachusetts
Materials: Tubular steel legs; thick table top with composite wood core; surface of matched veneer or plastic laminate; solid beech edge

Product: Rubber Table Group
Designer: Brian Kane
Manufacturer: Metropolitan Furniture Company South San Francisco, California
Awards: IBD Honorable Mention 1985

Product: The Rubber Chair
Designer: Brian Kane
Client: Metropolitan Furniture Corporation South San Francisco, California
Award: 1984 IDSA Industrial Design Excellence Award
Materials: Synthetic rubber tubing over steel frame

Product: Duo
Designer: Werther Toffoloni
Client: Atelier International, New York, New York, under license from IBIS of Italy
Award: 1985 IBD Product Design Award

Product:	Handkerchief Chair
Designers:	Lella Vignelli, Massimo Vignelli, and David Law, New York, New York
Manufacturer:	Knoll International, New York, New York
Awards:	1986 *Industrial Design* magazine Design Review selection

Product: Terna
Designer: Gaspare Cairoli
Client: Industrie Secco S.p.A., Treviso, Italy

Product: Air Mail
Designers: Perry A. King, Santiago Miranda
Client: Marcatré SpA, Milan, Italy

Product: LISA
Designer: Gastone Rinaldi
Client: Thema, Padova, Italy
Distributor: D*P, Milan, Italy
Materials: Steel tube; stove epoxy colors; seat and back rest covered in rubberized fabric

Product: DAFNE 2
Designer: Gastone Rinaldi
Client: Thema, Padova, Italy
Materials: Tubular steel frame; seat: plywood or covered with rubberized fabric; epoxy colors

Product: Kick Table
Designer: Toshiyuki Kita
Client: Atelier International, Ltd., Plainview, New York
Awards: 1984 *Industrial Design* magazine Design Review, Best of Category
Museum of Modern Art Permanent Collection, New York, New York
Materials: Enameled steel and lacquered wood

Product: Raum 900 System
Client: Wilkhahn, Bad Munder, West Germany
Materials: Wool covered cushioned hung over steel tubes

Product: Ariante
Designer: Piero De Martini
Photo Credit: Aldo Ballo
Client: Cassina, s.p.a., Milan, Italy
Materials: Ash frame with natural finish and ebony stain

Product: Coat Rack
Design Firm: Centrokappa, Tiziana Violano
Manufacturer: Kartell USA, Easley South Carolina
Materials: ABS plastic

Product: Skeleton Chair
Design Firm: Minale Tattersfield and Partners
Client: Cubic Metre Furniture Ltd., London, England
Materials: Bent tubular metal-welding; upholstered

Product: POLIS Folding Chair
Designer: Michele DeLucchi
Client: Poltronova, Italy
Materials: Tubular iron pipe frame

Product: 4870 Chair
Designer: Anna Castelli Ferrieri
Client: Kartell USA, Easley, South Carolina

Product: Spass Chair, (The Joke Chair)
Designer: Walter Gerth
Client: Strässle, Kirchberg, West Germany
Materials: Aniline green dyed plywood with laquered tubular steel legs

Product: Lisitskij
Designers: A. Salvati, A. Tresoldi
Manufacturer: Saporiti, Italy
Materials: Metal structure on a cement base

Product: Soley Chair
Designer: Vladimir Hardarson
Manufacturer: Kusch & Company, West Germany
Importer: Harvey Probber, Fall River, Massachusetts
Awards: 1985 *Industrial Design* magazine Design Review selection
Materials: Welded steel frame; molded plywood seat; laminated wood back

Product: Campo Chair
Designers: De Pas, D'Urbino, and Lomazzi
Client: Zanotta SpA, Milan, Italy
Materials: Stretched fabric over a rounded metal frame to create comfortable alcave-like seating; bright red or yellow leather bolsters

Product: Servostop
Designer: Achille Castiglioni
Manufacturer: Zanotta s.p.a., Milan, Italy

Product: Servomostre
Designer: Achille Castiglioni
Manufacturer: Zanotta s.p.a., Milan, Italy

Product: Guideline 90 Barrier System
Manufacturer: Marler Haley Exposystems, England
Awards: 1984 Design Council Award

Product: Tran-Sit Contract Seating
Design Firm: OMK Designs Ltd.
Awards: 1984 Design Council Award

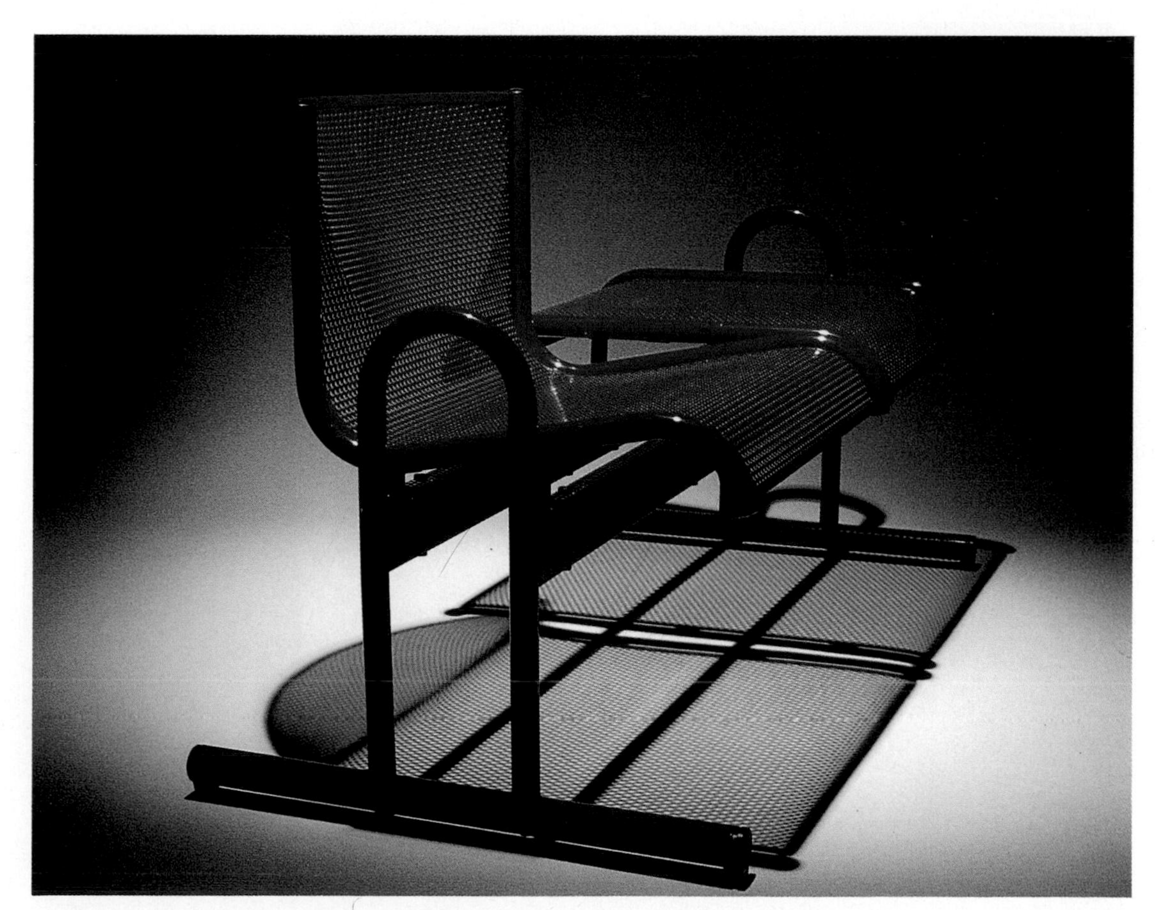

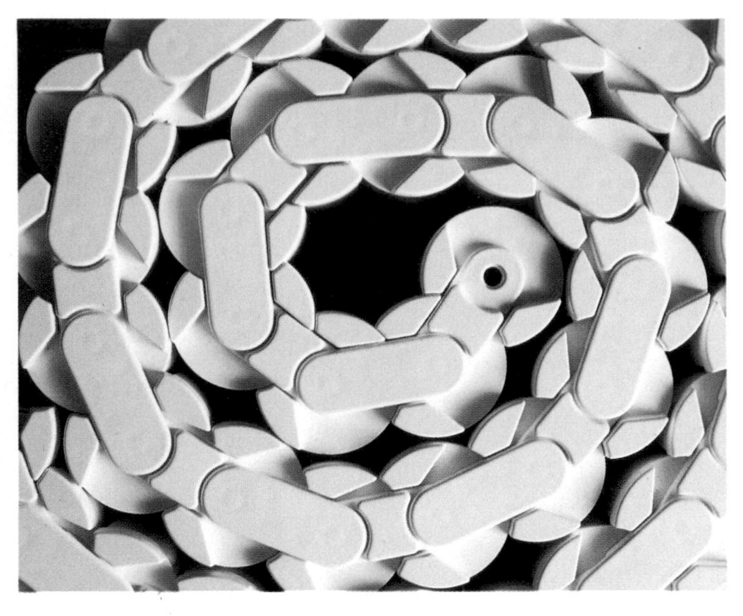

Product:	Snake
Designers:	Isao Hosoe in collaboration with Ann Marinelli, Milan, Italy
Manufacturer:	Sacea, Milan, Italy
Materials:	PVC tubes; ABS thermoplastic joints

Product: Liverpool Bench
Designer: Ronald Carter
Design Firm: Interna Designs, Chicago, Illinois
Manufacturer: Peter Miles Furniture, England

Product: Table Prototype
Designer: Michael Shannon, Englewood, New Jersey

Product: Tiles
Manufacturer: Hastings Tile Company New York, New York
Awards: 1985 ASID International Product Design Award

Product: Vertica
Design: Boccatogigante-Zambusi
Manufacturer: Industrie Secco, S.p.A., Treviso, Italy

Product: Extendible Bookcase, "Fra' Dolcino"
Designer: Paolo Palluco
Manufacturer: Palluco srl, Rome Italy
Photo Credit: Pino Abbrescia

Product: QQ Seating
Designers: Robert Taylor Whalen, Gerry Gaydos, and Stephen Brown
Design Firm: Robert Taylor Whalen Inc., Toronto, Ontario, Canada
Client: Corry Jamestown Corporation, Division HON Industries, Corry, Pennsylvania
Awards: 1985 Roscoe Annual Product Design Award
1986 Corporate Design & Realty Award
Materials: Seat and back: thermoplastic shells, plywood forms, molded polyurethane cushions; arms: molded polyurethane over steel core; base: injection molded thermoplastic

Product: Aura Seating
Manufacturer: Ahrend, Zwanenburg, Holland

Product: Jefferson Chair
Designer: Niels Diffrient, Ridgefield, Connecticut
Manufacturer: SunarHauserman, Cleveland, Ohio
Awards: 1985 *Industrial Design* magazine Design Review selection

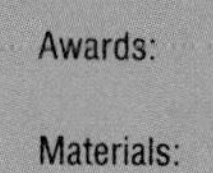

Materials: Die-cast aluminum and steel tube frame; molded polyurethane cushions with polyfoam and dacron top cover; leather, plastic, or textile upholstery

TEXTILES

CHAPTER

Color is not a new story for textiles. Changes incorporating a post-modern palette, only now manifesting themselves in other product areas, could be seen in the fiber arts at the beginning of the decade. The mid-80's has been a period of refining textile design's intelligent sensibility.

The work of ''new'' designers (those published for the first time) illustrates current directions: the superior-crafted, luxurious weaves of Anne Beetz demonstrate the use of high-quality, natural fibers and only fully reveal their essential excellence firsthand; Lori Weitzner imposes subtle variations in tone and gradation on magnificently-selected colors and juxtaposes forms to achieve an extraordinary sense of depth or undulating movement within the printed design; Heleen Heyning's block or abstract designs reflect a contemporary attention to pattern—at once meticulously controlled and intentionally informal.

Like the furnishings, tabletops, and rooms they will decorate, this collection has a decidedly eclectic feel. Texture adds richness, one that can prevent a product from falling over the line from whimsy to joke. In application, textiles often serve as a designer's closing remark.

Product: Cathedral Rose
Designer: Anne Domenech, New York, New York
Manufacturer: The Cathedral Works, New York, New York
Materials: 100 percent cotton; hand silkscreened

Product: Modern Sheers Collection
Designer: Patricia Green
Client: Groundworks Inc., New York, New York
Materials: Fine quality yarns of cotton, linen, silk, nylon, and trevira selected to allow maximum light penetration

Product: Sandstorm
Designer: David Moir, New York, New York
Manufacturer: The Cathedral Works, New York, New York
Materials: Hand silkscreened

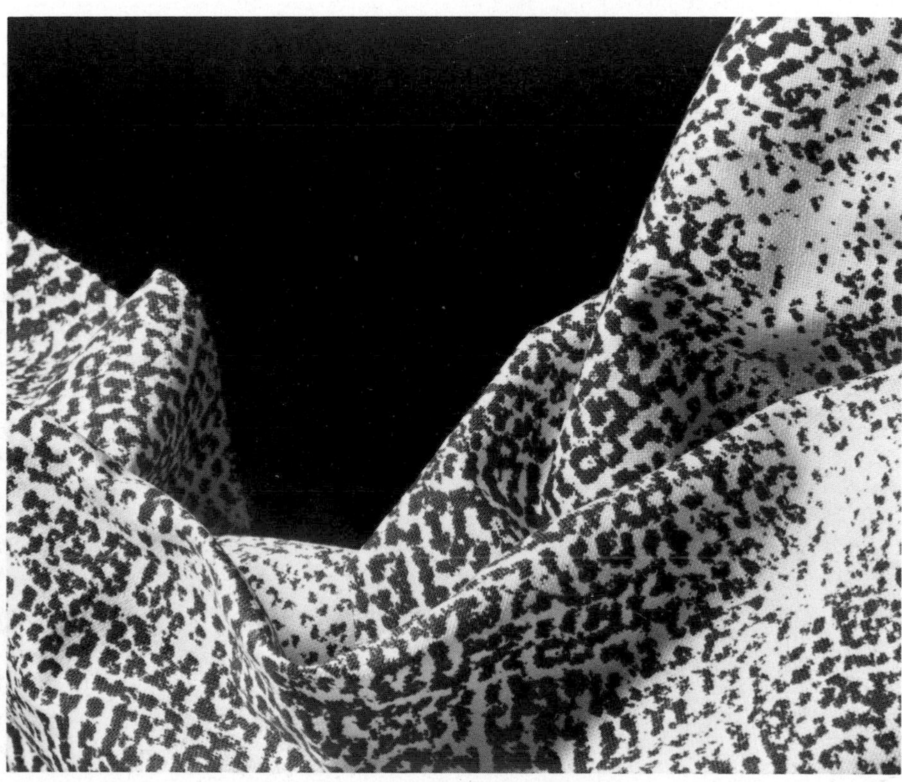

Product: Anne Beetz Collection
Design Firm: Tissus Anne Beetz, Brussels, Belgium
Materials: 47 percent linen, 33 percent natural silk, and 20 percent metallic yarn

Product: Anne Beetz Collection
Design Firm: Tissus Anne Beetz, Brussels, Belgium
Materials: 85 percent natural silk, 15 percent metallic yarn

Product:	The Nob & Non Collection
Designers:	Nob & Non Utsumi, New York, New York
Client:	V'Soske, New York, New York
Awards:	1984 *Industrial Design* magazine Design Review selection
Materials:	100 percent wool

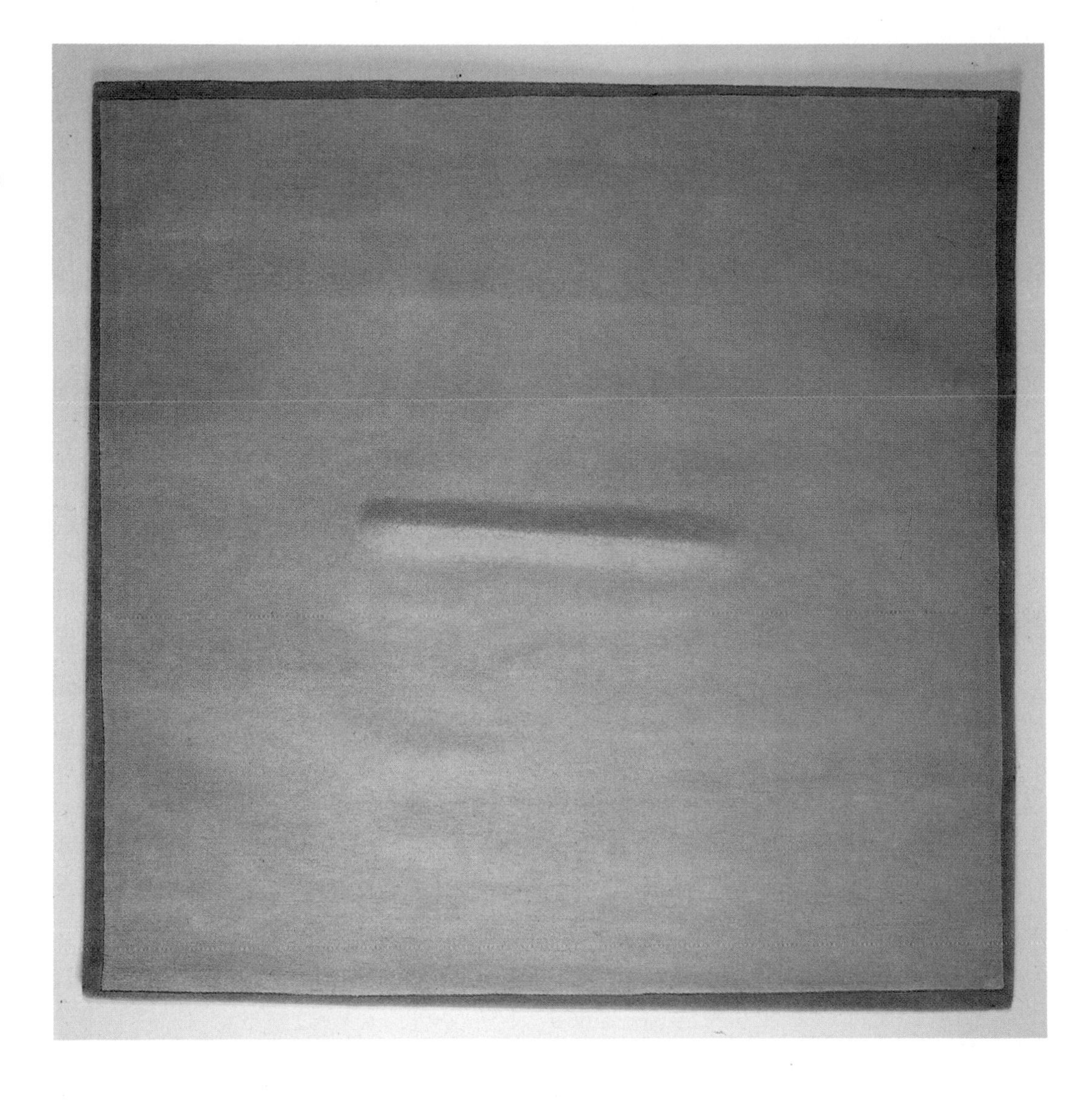

Product:	Anne Beetz Collection
Design Firm:	Tissus Anne Beetz, Brussels, Belgium
Materials:	55 percent natural silk

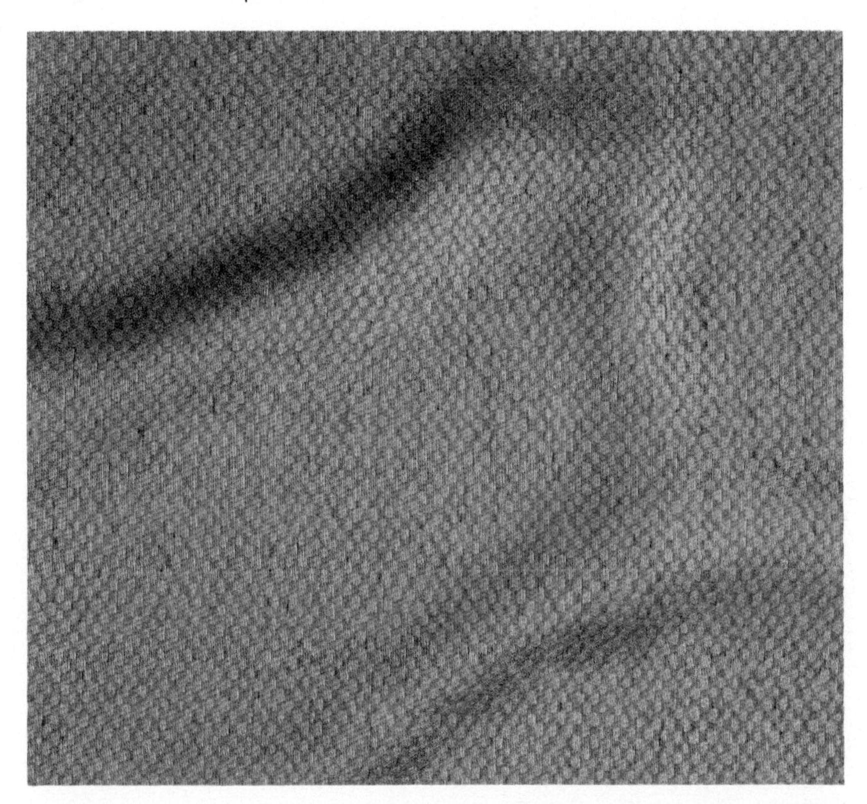

Designer:	Hideo Mori, Japan
Courtesy:	Gallery 91, New York, New York

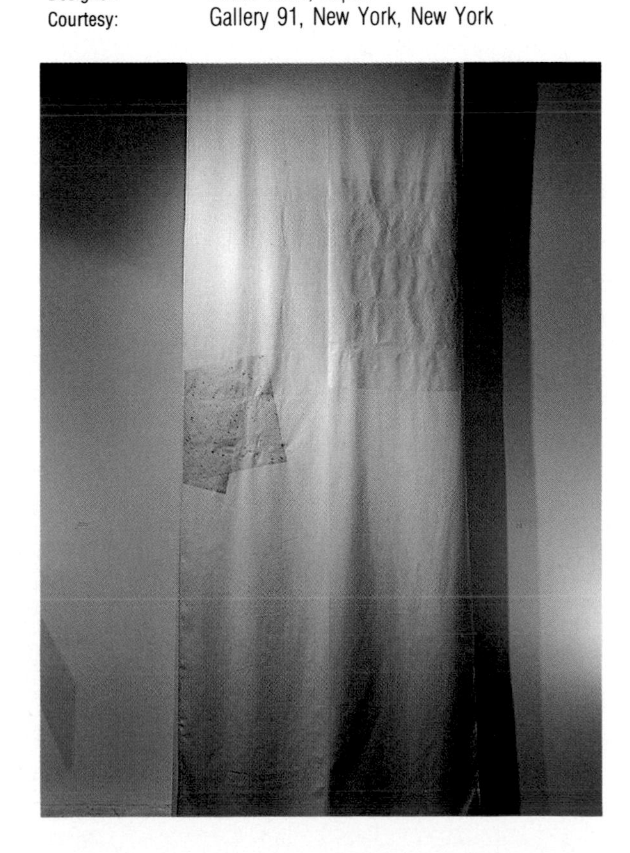

Product: Painted Plains
Designer: Jack Lenor Larsen, New York, New York

Product: Floater
Designer: Carolyn Ray, Yonkers, New York
Design Firm: Carolyn Ray Inc., Yonkers, New York
Materials: 100 percent cotton

Product: BEAMS Collection
Designer: Patricia Green
Client: Groundworks Inc., New York, New York
Materials: Titanium-coated mica chips are mixed with pigment and printed on matte vinyl and Swiss cotton

Product: The Renaissance Collection
Designer: Hazel Siegel
Design Firm: Design Tex Fabrics, Inc.
Awards: ASID International Product Design award

Product: In the Mill
Designer: Carolyn Ray, Yonkers, New York
Design Firm: Carolyn Ray Inc., Yonkers, New York
Awards: 1985 Roscoe Annual Product Design Award: Best Contemporary Printed Fabric
Materials: Cotton poplin and cotton voile

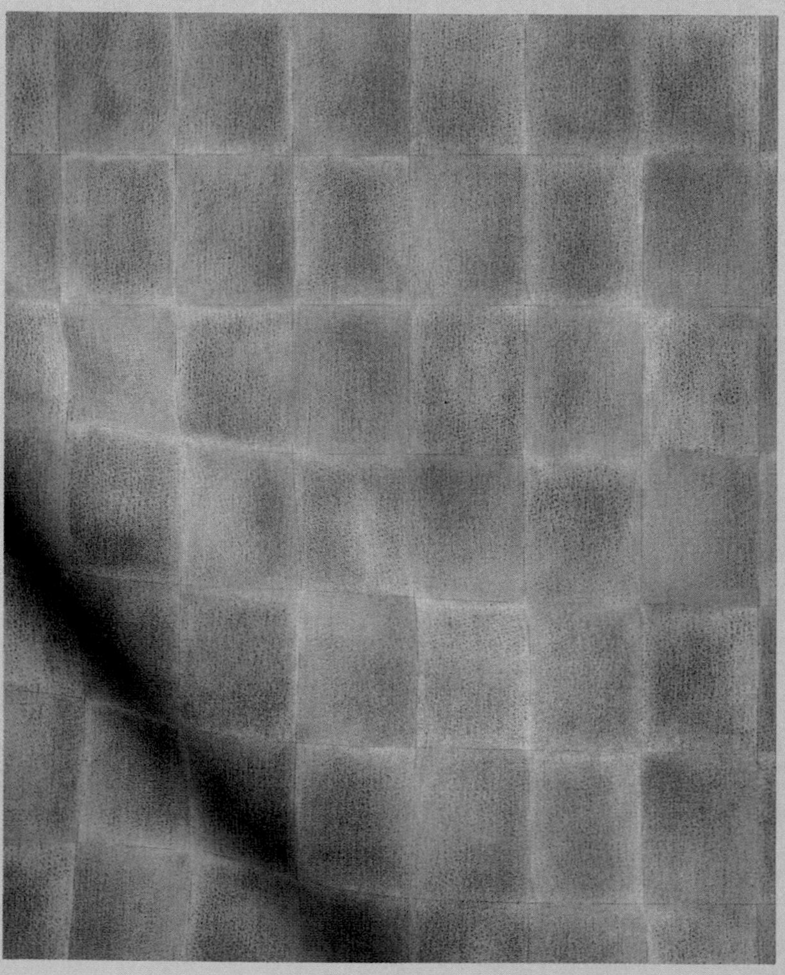

Product: Hover
Designer: Carolyn Ray, Yonkers, New York
Design Firm: Carolyn Ray Inc., Yonkers, New York
Materials: 100 percent cotton

Product: Textured Wave
Designer: Marian Clayden, Los Gatos, California
Design Firm: Marian Clayden Inc., Los Gatos, California
Awards: American Craft Museum Design Award
Materials: Elephant whale cotton corduroy

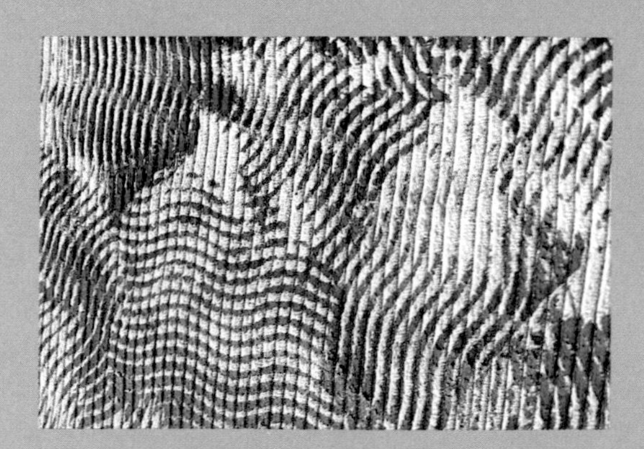

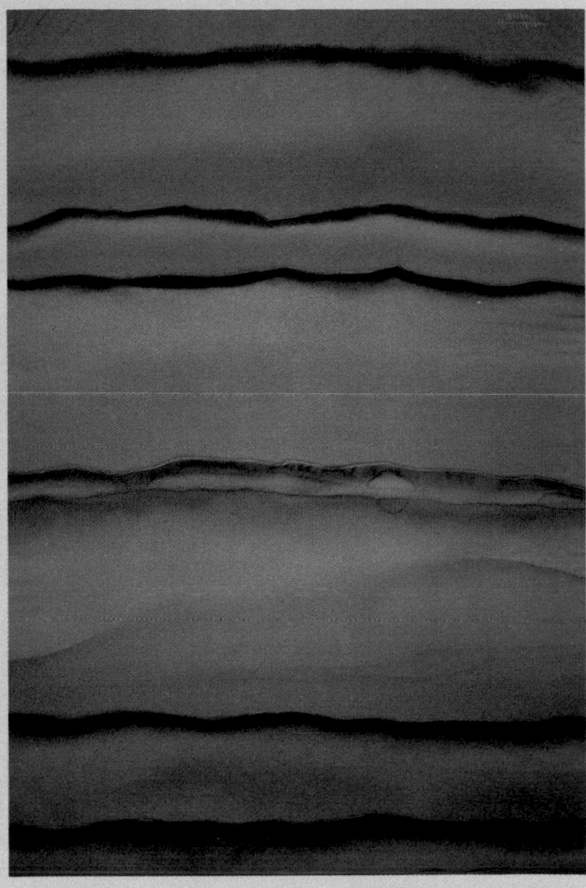

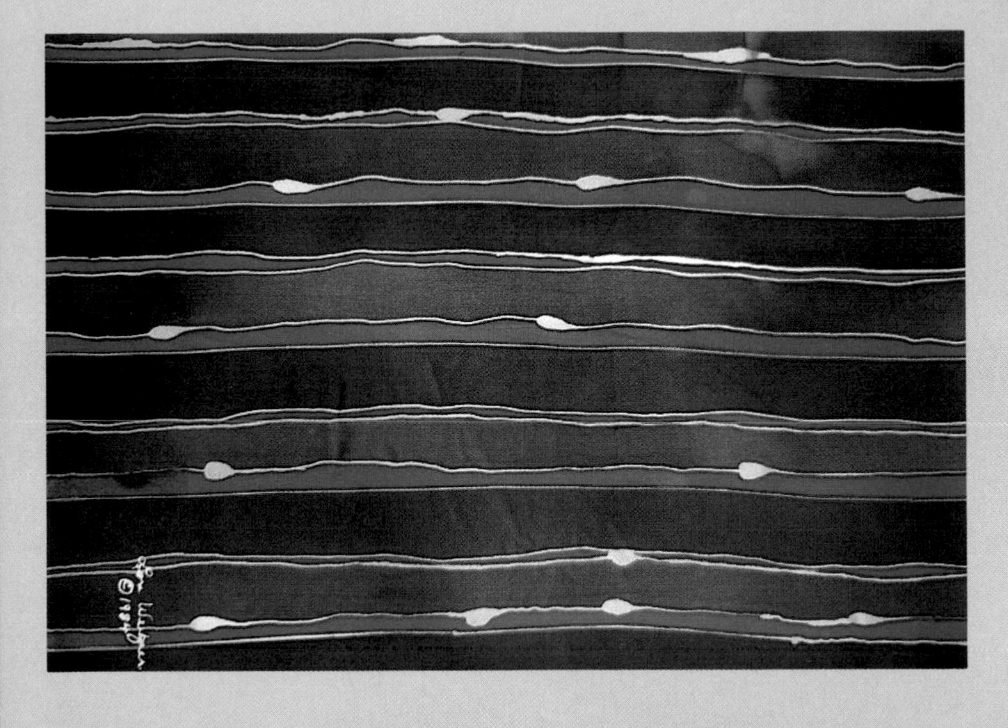

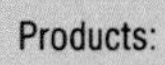

Products: "San;" "Rivulets;" "Passing By;" "Composite Two" (clockwise)
Designer: Lori Weitzner, New York, New York

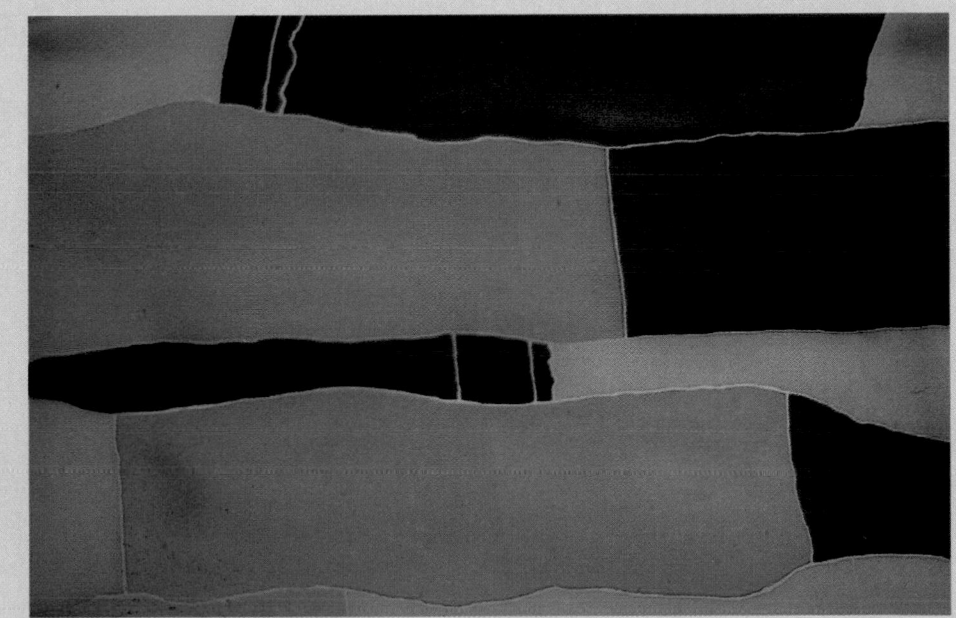

Product: Mardi Gras
Designer: Dorothy Hafner, New York, New York
Materials: 100 percent cotton

Product: Napkins/Tablecloth Collections
Designer: Heleen Heyning, Brooklyn, New York
Photo Credit: Jesse A. Rhines, S. Edwards

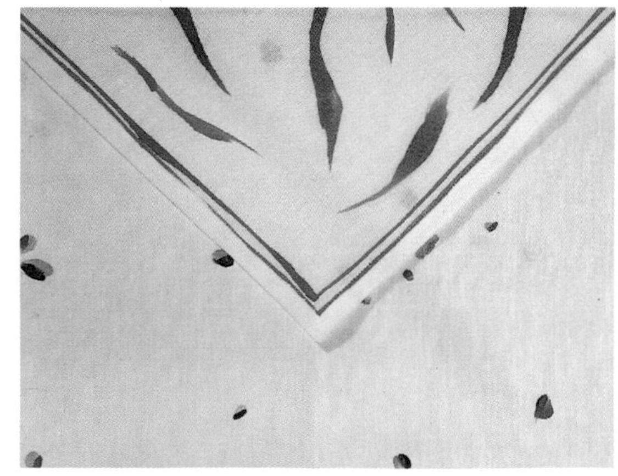

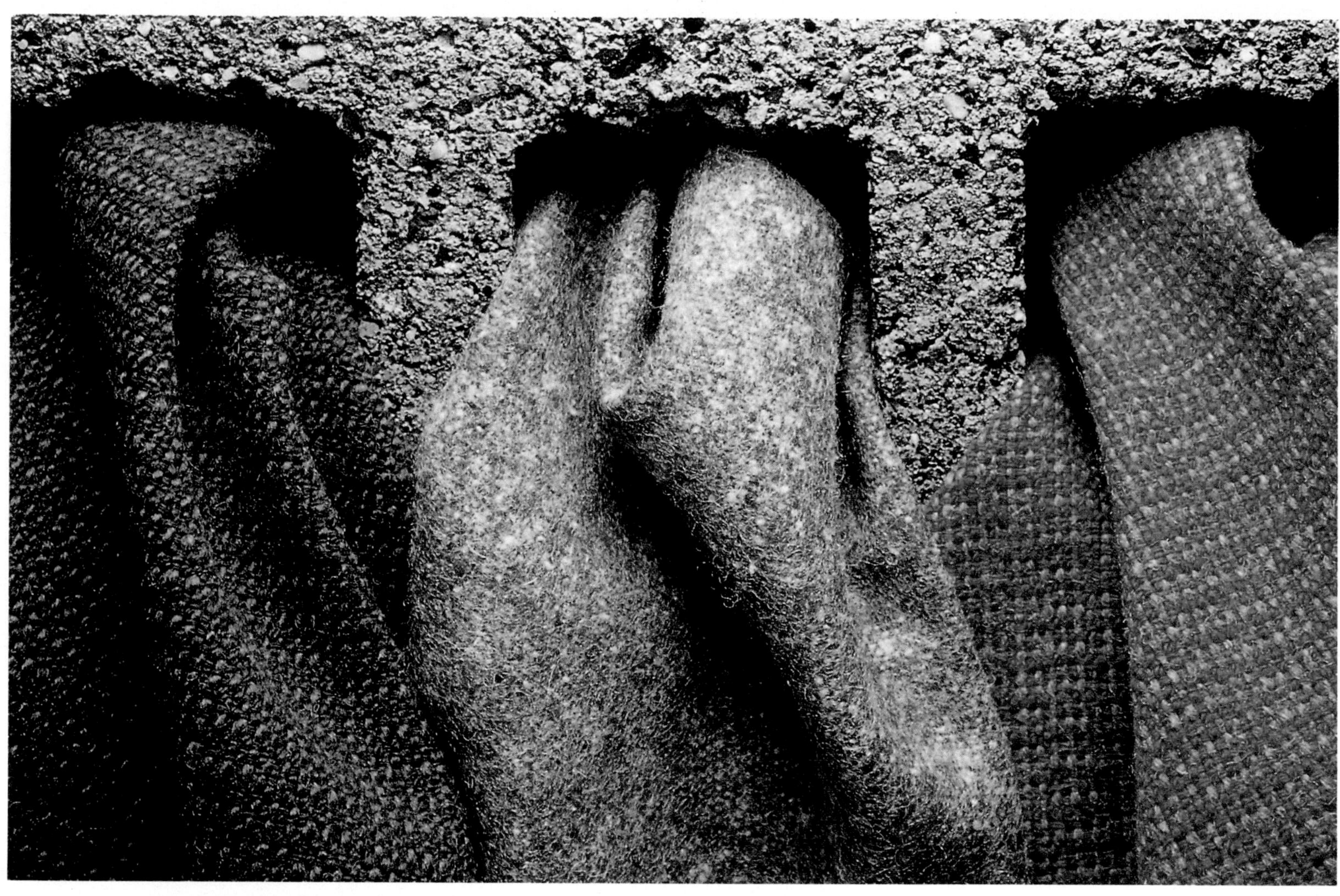

Product: Ragtime Collection: Counterpoint; Bagpipes
Designer: Laura Deubler Mercurio
Manufacturer: Adam James Textiles, Inc. Hauppauge, New York
Materials: Counterpoint, 80 percent nylon and 20 percent wool; Bagpipes, 70 percent wool and 30 percent nylon

Product: Underwater Parade
Designer: Karen Meyerhoff, New York, New York
Courtesy: American Craft Museum
Materials: Hand dyed wool and yarn; handmade felt

Product: Tonga Area Rug
Designer: Jack Lenor Larsen, New York, New York

Product: Anne Beetz Collection
Design Firm: Tissus Anne Beetz, Brussels, Belgium
Materials: 85 percent natural silk, 42 percent wool

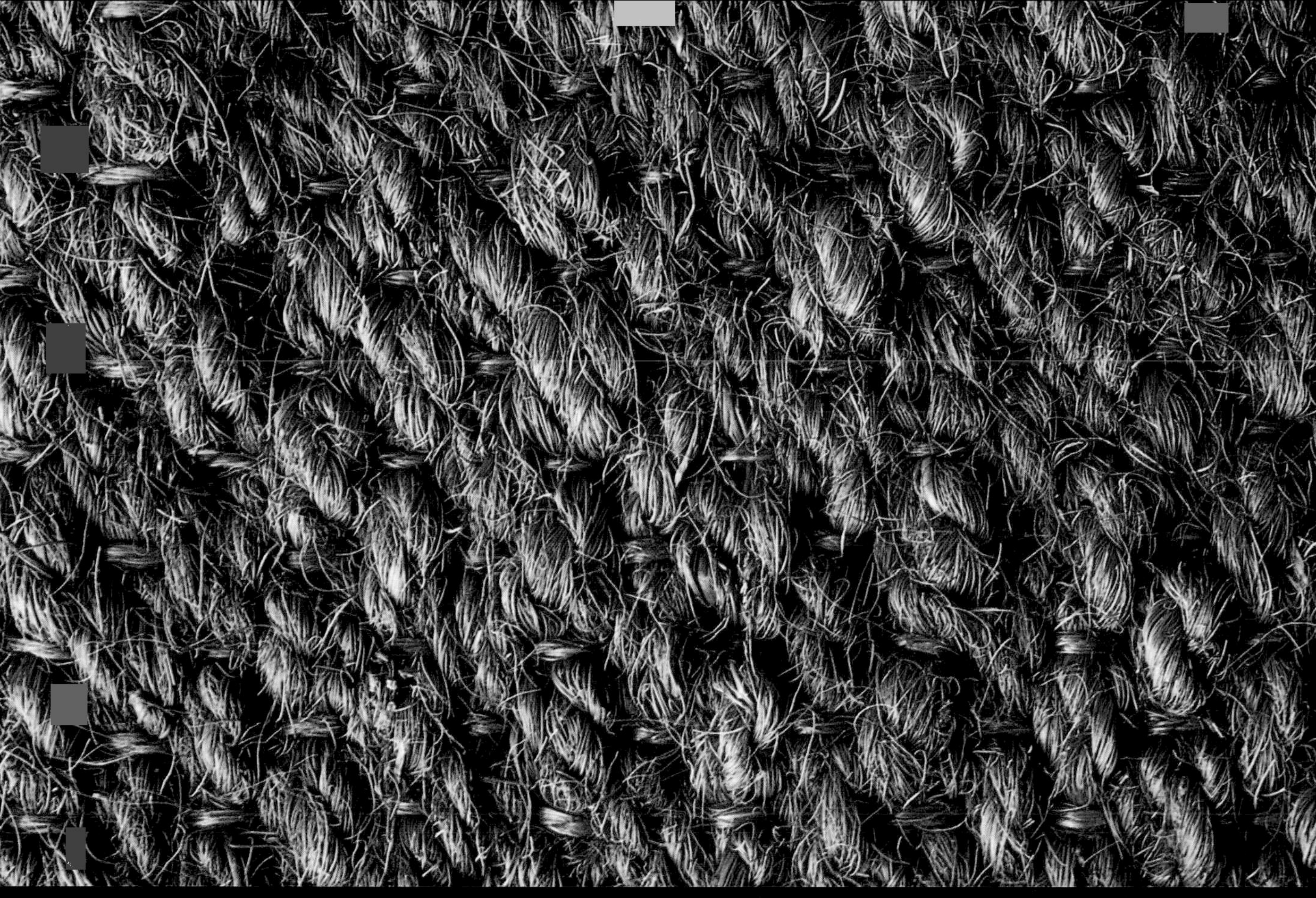

Product: Colombo
Designer: Jack Lenor Larsen, New York, New York

Product: Chevron
Designer: Jack Lenor Larsen, New York, New York

Designer: Tetsuo Kusama, Japan
Courtesy: Gallery 91, New York, New York

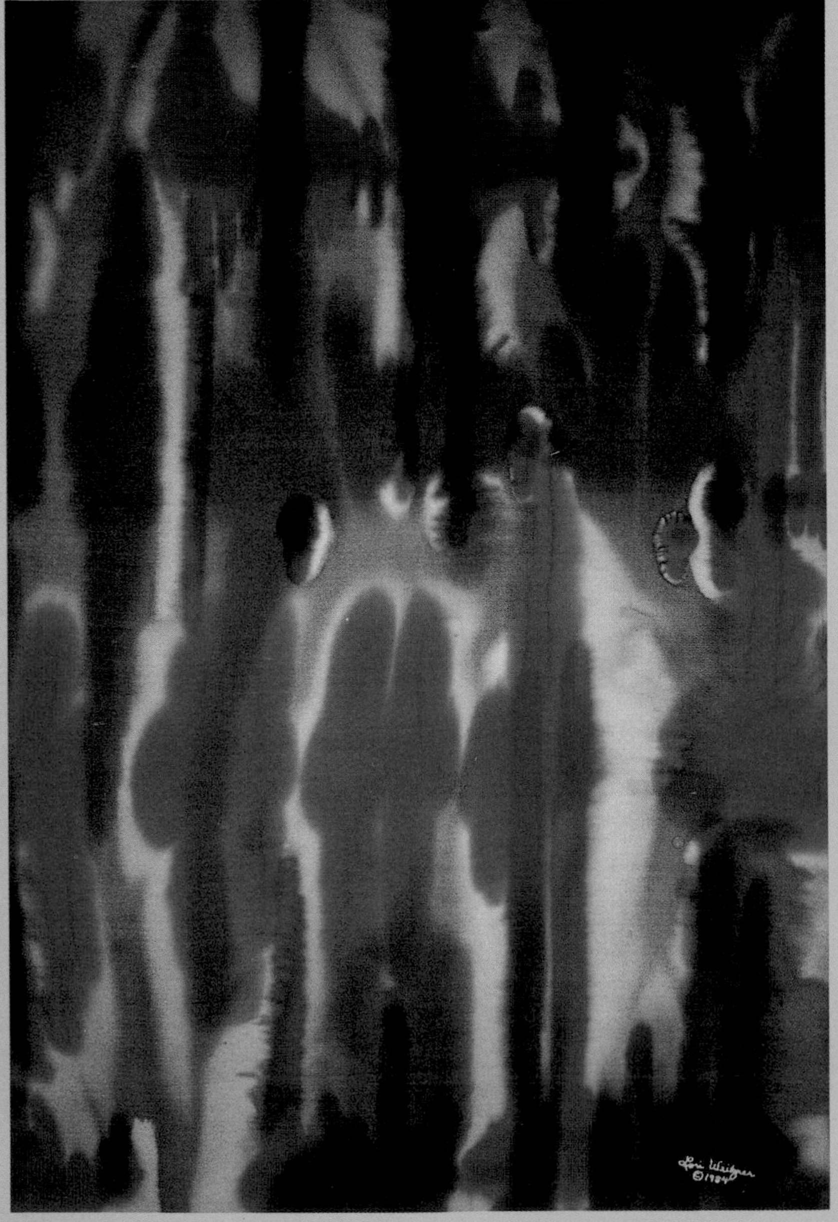

Product: Ellen
Designer: Lori Weitzner, New York, New York
Materials: Silk; handprinted

Product: Grafico IV
Designers: Maurizia Dova, Roger Selden
Client: Manifattura Nai-Oleari S.P.A.
Materials: Harvard, Oxford, and Eqitto

Product:	Six Views Collection
Client:	Collier Campbell Ltd., London, England
Awards:	1984 Design Council Award
Materials:	100 percent cotton

Product:	Premiere Collection: Prelude Group
Designer:	Laura Deubler Mercurio
Client:	Adam James Textiles Inc. Hauppauge, New York
Materials:	100 percent wool

Product: Taco France #6923
Designer: Lori Weitzner, New York, New York
Manufacturer: Taco France

Product: Chamfered Calf
Designer: Jack Lenor Larsen, New York, New York

Product: Taco France #6927
Designer: Lori Weitzner, New York, New York
Manufacturer: Taco France

Product: Maliki
Designer: Lori Weitzner, New York, New York
Manufacturer: Assia S.p.A., Italy

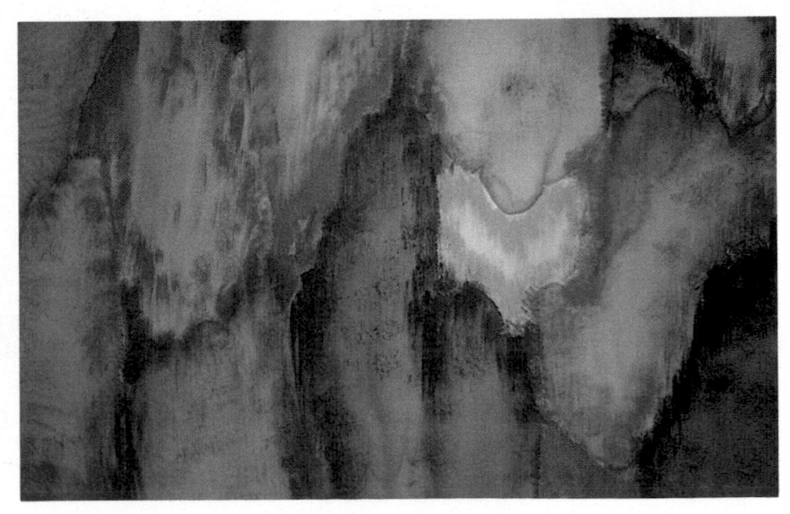

Product: Still Waters; Kilcooney
Manufacturer: Scalamandré, New York, New York
Materials: Still Waters, 89 percent rayon and 11 percent silk; Kilcooney, 70 percent cotton and 30 percent silk

Product: Task System
Designers: Henry Smith-Miller, Laurie Hawkinson
Client: V'Soske, New York, New York
Awards: 1985 *Industrial Design* magazine Design Review selection

CONSUMER ELECTRONICS

CHAPTER

Present day electronics have not only adapted to the way we live, but in taking full advantage of ever-new technologies, have transformed the *way* we entertain ourselves and *where* we choose to do it.

Continued miniaturization is making what looked tiny three years ago seem large and awkward by today's standards. Indeed, what you can now ''take with you'' includes credit-card-sized radios, tape players, television sets, compact disk players, and combination video cameras. The ''home entertainment center'' is home-based no longer.

In the early 1980s, many items in this collection did not exist. Those that did have often moved from luxury item to commonplace commodity. Rapid increases in technological sophistication risk threatening the general consumer. The industry has responded admirably—some might say overcompensated—to this fear with features such as auto-focus (referred to with relief by many grateful, if somewhat technologically-timid users, as ''idiot-proof'').

A recent introduction in the auto-focus category is the camcorder, the 8mm video camera-video cassette recorder combination. Sony's CCD-V8AFU, weighing 5 pounds, exemplifies the trend to combine two or more related-function products into a single, compact unit. Continuing the notion, Sony unveiled the first television set with built-in VCR.

As options rise and prices fall, manufacturers are reaching down to expand their markets. With the second baby boom of this century already in progress, paying attention to this audience is vital. Sharp's radios and Sony's headphones in candyland colors speak to this new wave of electronically literate consumers. And, there is little doubt about the appeal the decoration holds . . . for all the young at heart. Not to be forgotten, the spending potential of today's adolescent is correlated to parental affluence. Attention to this success is evident in bigger-is-better luxury items like the rear-screen projection television sets.

Where next? Flat screen is on its way, but with the door wide open, it is hard to make too many definite predictions. However, if tomorrow's designers are any indication, it is safe to say where we *won't* be visiting. As Hari Nair of the Industrial Design department at University of Cincinnati puts it, ''When my students turn in their design solutions, not *one* is a black box.''

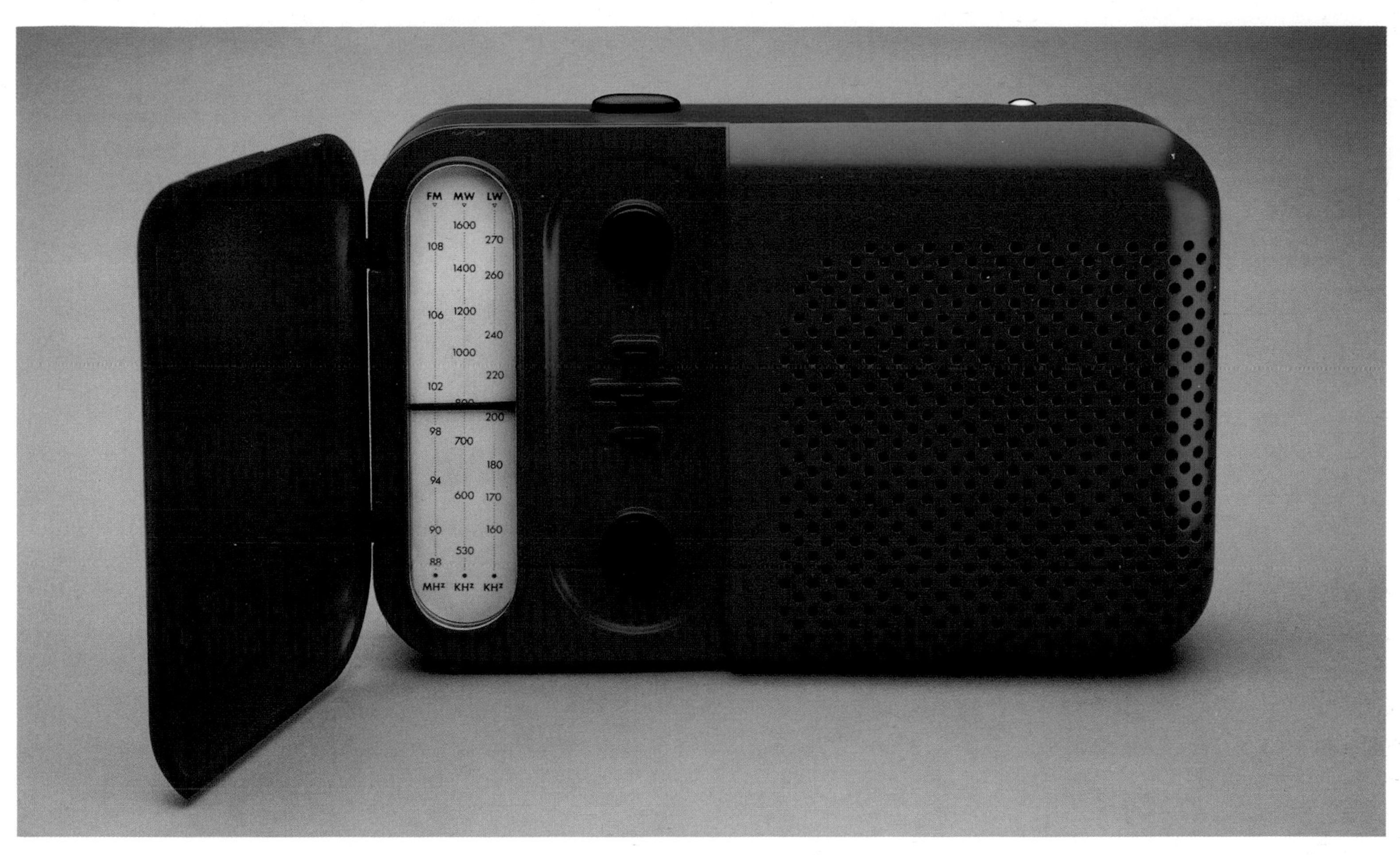

Product: Ross RE-5050 3-Band Portable Radio
Designer: Graham Thomson
Design Firm: Brand New (Product Origination) Limited, London, England
Client: Ross Electronics, London, England
Materials: Printed circuit board, injection molding

Product: NUDE Turbo Sony Headphones
Client: Sony Corporation of America Park Ridge, New Jersey
Manufacturer: Sony Corporation, Tokyo, Japan

Product: Roller Radio
Designer: Consumer Electronics Design Team, Corporate Industrial Design, Nederlandse Philip's Bedrijven
Client: Philips, Netherlands

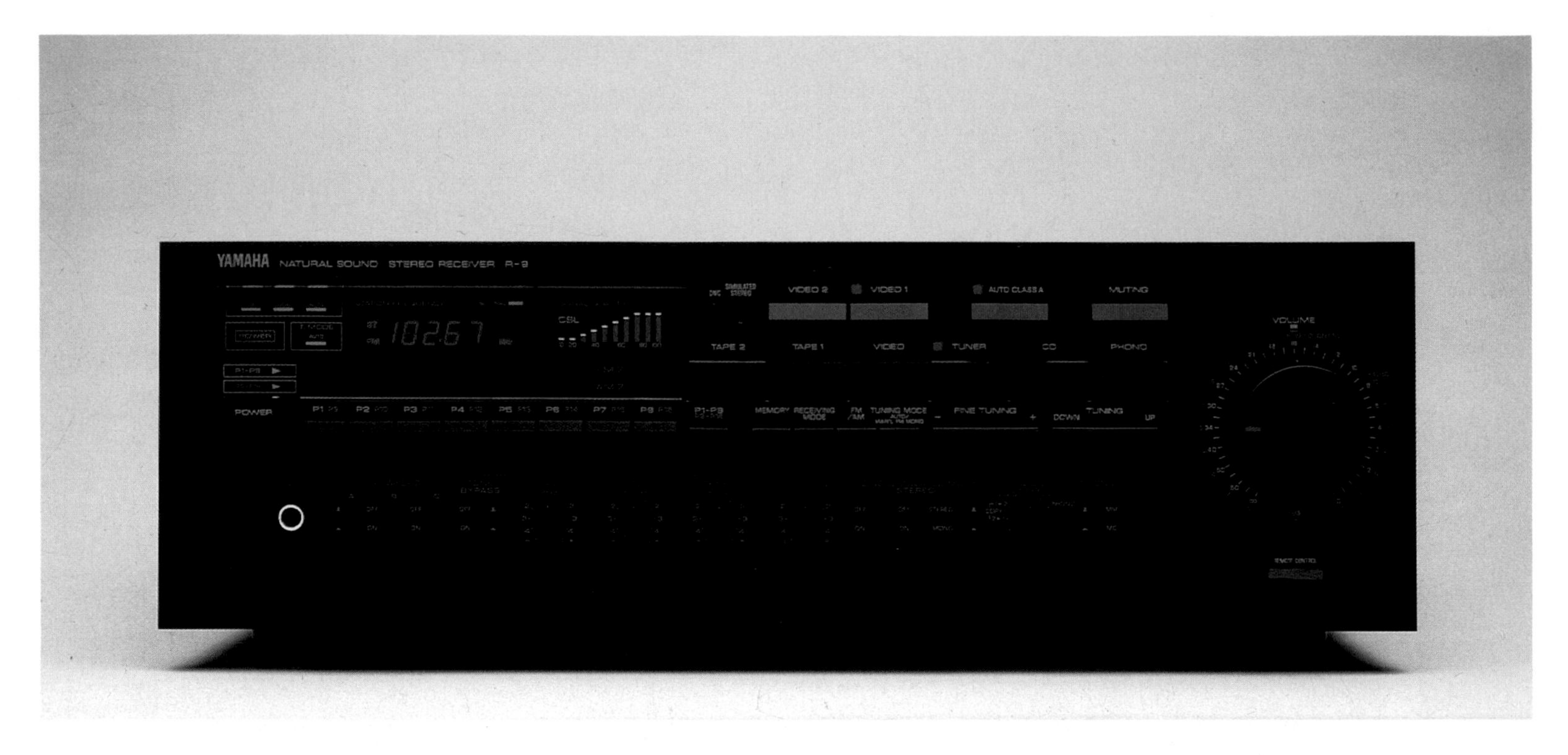

Product:	Natural Sound Stereo Power Amplifier M-80
Manufacturers:	Yamaha Electronics Corporation, USA, Buena Park, California Nippon Gakki Company, Hamamatsu, Japan

Product:	Headphones
Design Firm:	Porsche Design Group
Client:	Yamaha, Electronics Corporation, USA Buena Park, California,

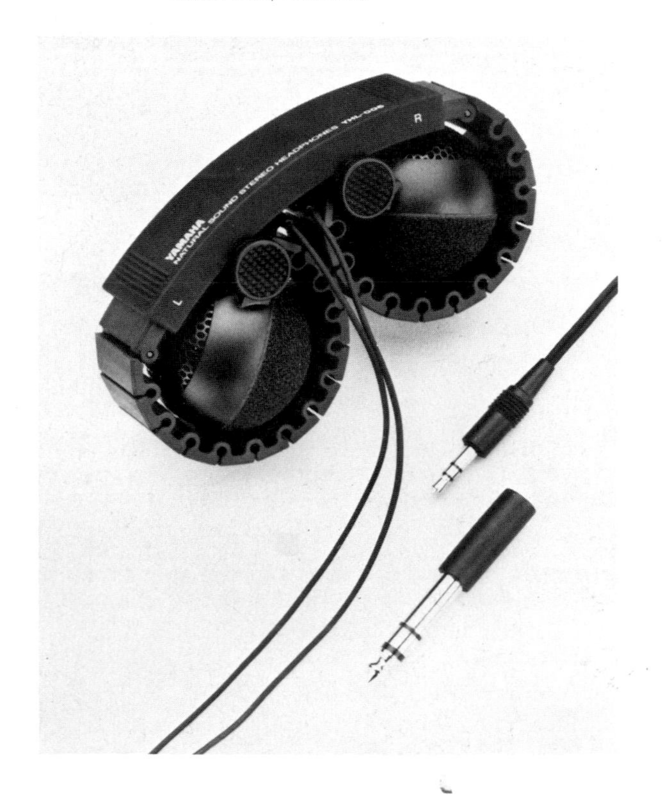

Product:	YHD-1 Head Phones
Designer:	Mario Bellini
Manufacturers:	Yamaha Electronics Corporation, USA, Buena Park, California; Nippon Gakki Company, Hamamatsu, Japan
Materials:	Aluminized mylar, samariam cobalt magnets

Product:	Ross RE-2220/2280 & RE-2330/2360/2390 Designer Range
Designer:	Graham Thomson
Design Firm:	Brand New(Product Origination) Limited,London, England
Client:	Ross Electronics London, England
Materials:	High-velocity drive units; injection molding

Product:	QT 50 Stereo Radio Cassette Recorder
Designers:	Osamu Akiyama, Kiyoshi Sashita
Design Firm:	Sharp Electronics Corporation Mahwah, New Jersey
Manufacturer:	Sharp Corporation, Osaka, Japan
Awards:	International Industrial Design Competition, Osaka, Japan, 1st Prize, 1983; Mainichi Design Competition, 2nd Prize

Product: CD 10 and Battery Pack Compact Disc Player
Design Firm: Corporate Industrial Design Team Netherlands
Client: Philips, Netherlands

Product: Transound 3 Piece AM/FM Stereo Cassette Recorder
Client: Sony Corporation of America Park Ridge, New Jersey
Manufacturer: Sony Corporation, Tokyo, Japan

Product: Sony Discman
Client: Sony Corporation of America Park Ridge, New Jersey
Manufacturer: Sony Corporation, Tokyo, Japan

Product: Beosystem 5000
Designer: Jakob Jensen, Højslev, Denmark
Client: Bang & Olufsen a/s, Denmark
Materials: Injection molded, polyurethene plastic chassis; brushed aluminum; matte black plastic and smoked plastic

Product: KPR-36XBR Rear Projection Television
Client: Sony Corporation of America Park Ridge, New Jersey
Manufacturer: Sony Corporation, Tokyo, Japan

Product: Minimal Television
Design Firm: Brand New (Product Origination) Limited, London, England

Product: KV-2VXR Television with Built-in 8mm VCR
Client: Sony Corporation of America Park Ridge, New Jersey
Manufacturer: Sony Corporation, Tokyo, Japan

Product:	RCA VKP950 Convertible Video Cassette Recorder
Designers:	David Tompkins, Lawrence Mitchell, and Richard Bourgerie
Client:	RCA Consumer Electronics Indianapolis, Indiana
Materials:	Painted sheet steel, injection molded ABS, injection molded acrylic and conductive rubber key pads

Product:	Sony Video 8 Camera
Client:	Sony Corporation of America Park Ridge, New Jersey
Manufacturer:	Sony Corporation, Tokyo, Japan

Product: Radio Television
Designer: Denis Gadbois, Cranbrook Academy of Art Bloomfield Hills, Michigan
Awards: 1985 *Industrial Design* magazine Design Review selection, Concept Category
Materials: 4 LCD screen; touch button; main body in ABS; electro-static speaker; and foam injection molding

Product: FD-2A Watchman Personal TV
Client: Sony Corporation of America Park Ridge, New Jersey
Manufacturer: Sony Corporation, Tokyo, Japan

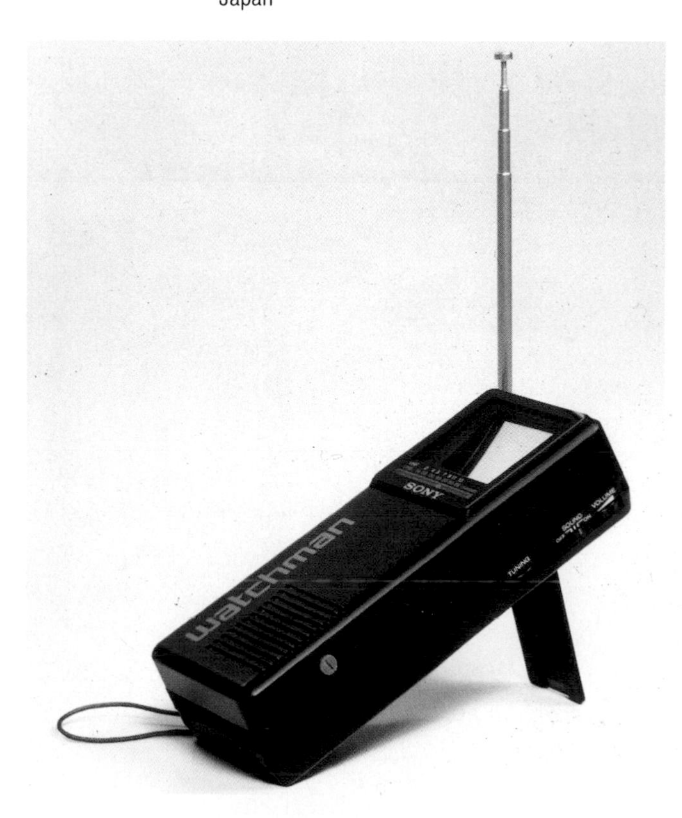

Product: Video Projection Unit
Designer: Winfried Scheuer
Design Firm: ID Two, San Francisco, California

Product: Kurzweil 250 Synthesizer
Designer: Ray Kurzweil
Manufacturer: Kurzweil Music Systems
Waltham, Massachusetts

Product: SDS7 Analog/Digital Electronic Drum Set
Designer: David Simmons, Calabasas, California
Materials: State-of-the-art electronic sound-generation, with a modular design, maintains the range of drumming motions; with the full complement of twelve modules, 1,200 sounds can be user-programmed.

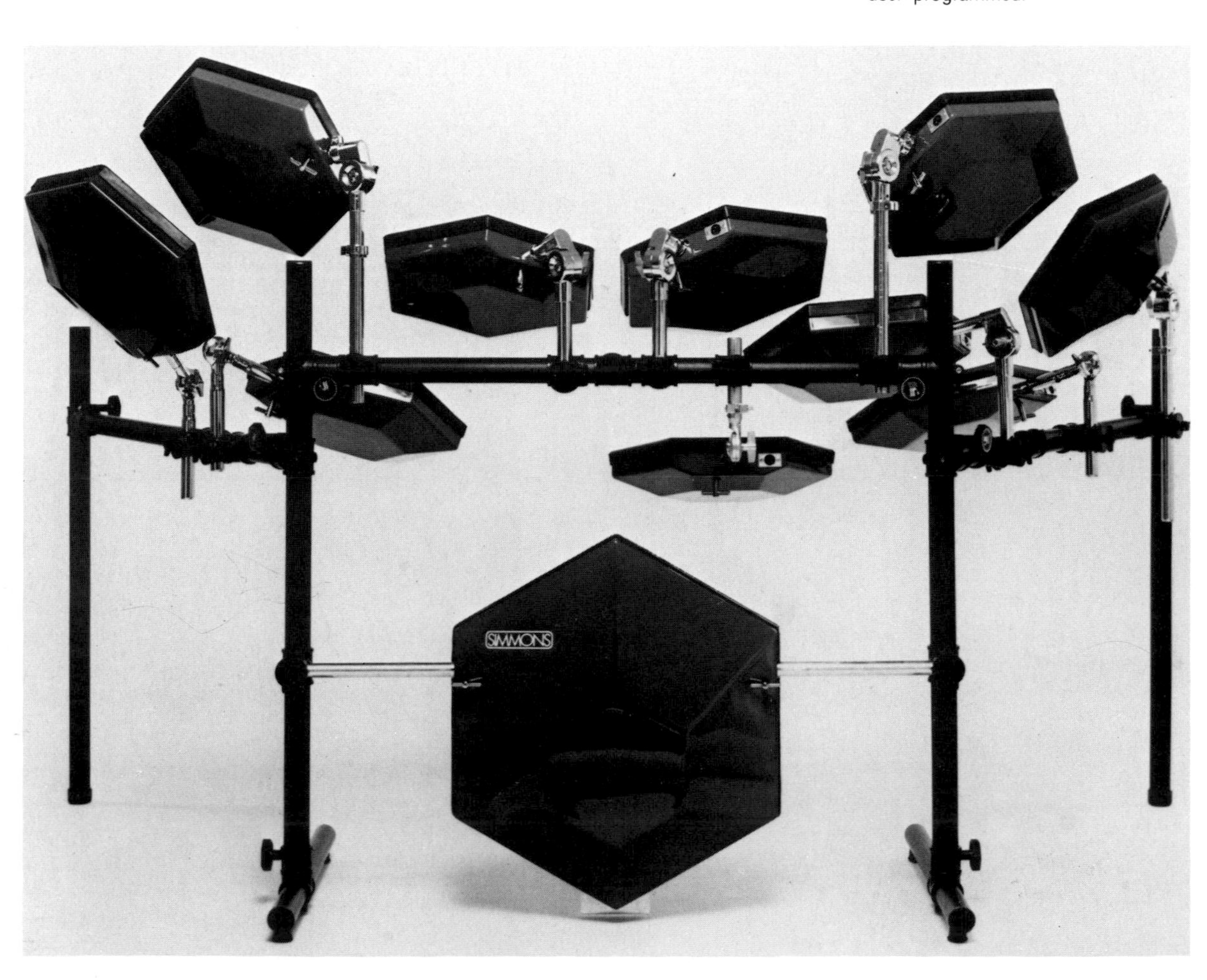

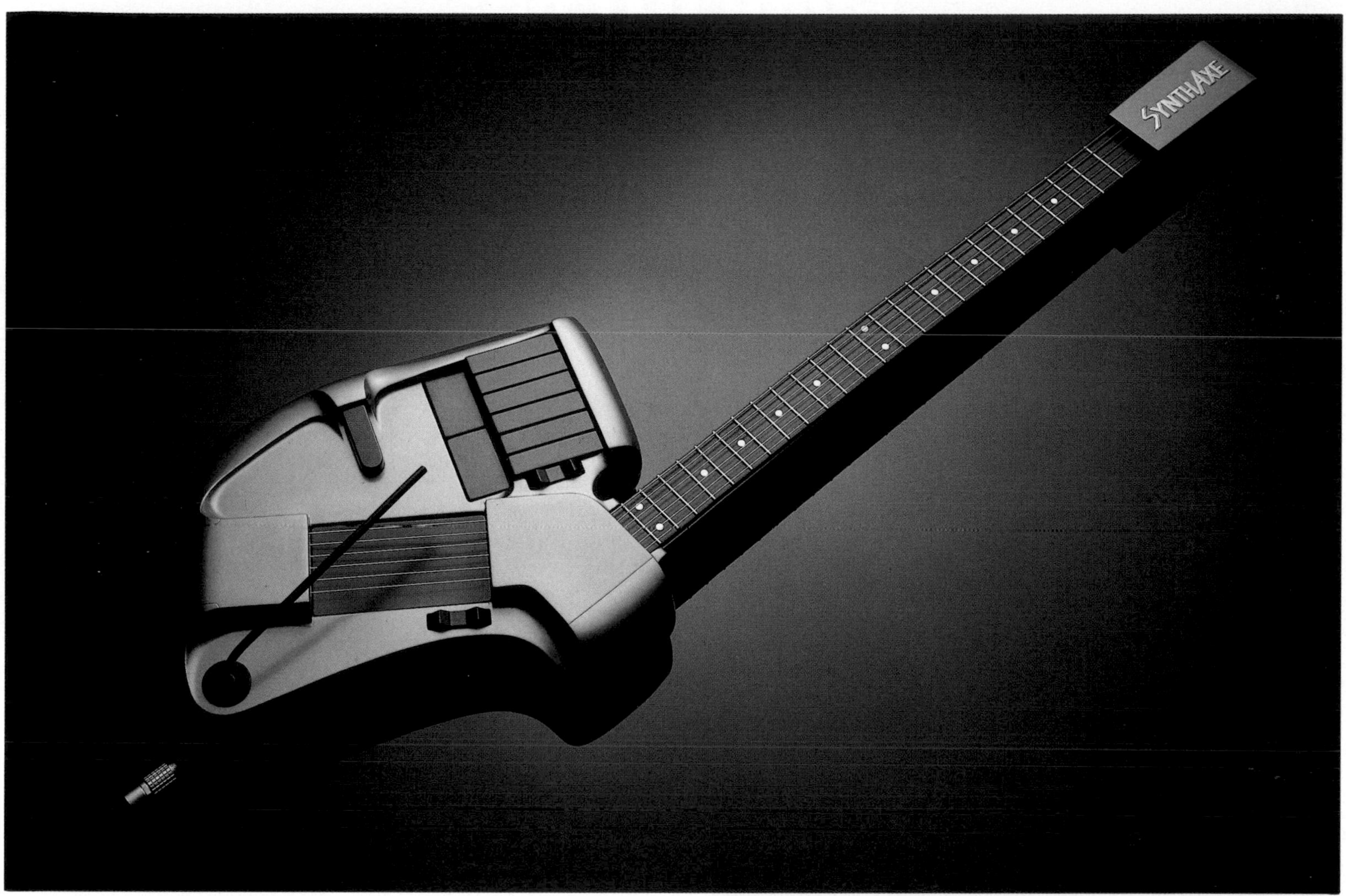

Product: SynthAxe Guitar

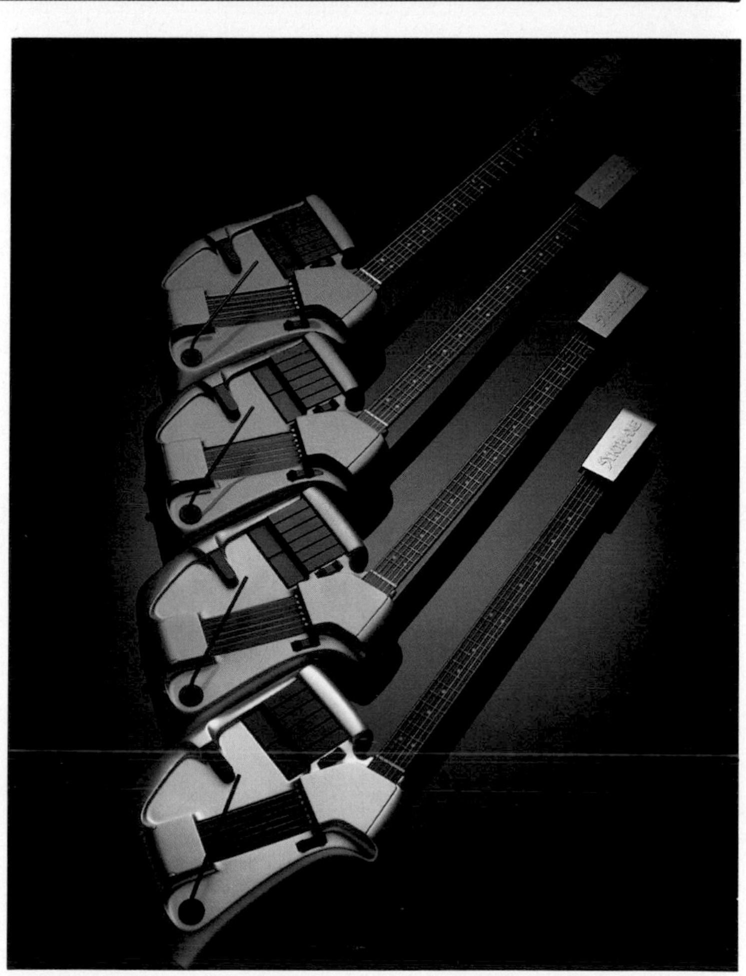

COMPUTERS

CHAPTER

Technophobia is dwindling and with it the distinctions between computers for personal and business use. The personal computer, initially targeted for home-management functions, is now a ubiquitous accessory of the contemporary executive. As miniaturization has advanced the briefcase computer from prototype to reality, it is fast becoming the constant, well-traveled ''associate'' capable of following the business-person's complex agenda.

Whether for personal or business use, however, computer designers and manufacturers have been hard pressed to keep ahead of the consumer's increasing demands to upgrade sophisticated capabilities, expand inter-machine compatibility, and respond to calls to ''humanize'' their use. As Steven Holt author/designer and former editor of *ID* put it, ''Lexicons such as 'user-friendly' used to be technical terms, now they're marketing buzz words.''

Nowhere (with the possible exception of the automobile) has the man/machine interface received such extensive and generalized attention. The health and welfare of terminal users has focused the discourse on such issues as eye and neck fatigue, worker alienation, and safe radiation levels, projecting the role of designers into the limelight like never before.

These machines have dramatically altered the way we do work and the look of where we do it. The computer is unique in the unprecedented early-stage cooperation its development fostered between industrial designers and engineers. Now, further progress is forging new associations between other allied disciplines as placement of the terminal into the workplace presents significant challenges for furnishing, lighting, and architectural designers.

Product: Tandem XL8 Disc Storage Facility

Designers: William A. Monagham, Joerg Ferchau, Victor Trujillo, and James M. Shook

Client: Tandem Computers, Inc. Cupertino, California

Awards: Pradikat if Die gute Industrieform 1985; 1985 *Industrial Design* magazine Design Review selection

Product: Xerox 6085 Professional Systems

Designer: Robin Chu

Design Firm: ID Two, San Francisco, California

Manufacturer: XEROX Corporation, Rochester, New York

Product: Executive Terminal Prototype
Designers: Richard G. Clayton, Tim Stern
Client: Burroughs Corporation
Plymouth, Michigan
Awards: 1985 *Industrial Design* magazine
Design Review selection,
Concept Category
Materials: Die-cast end caps and painted
aluminum extrusions

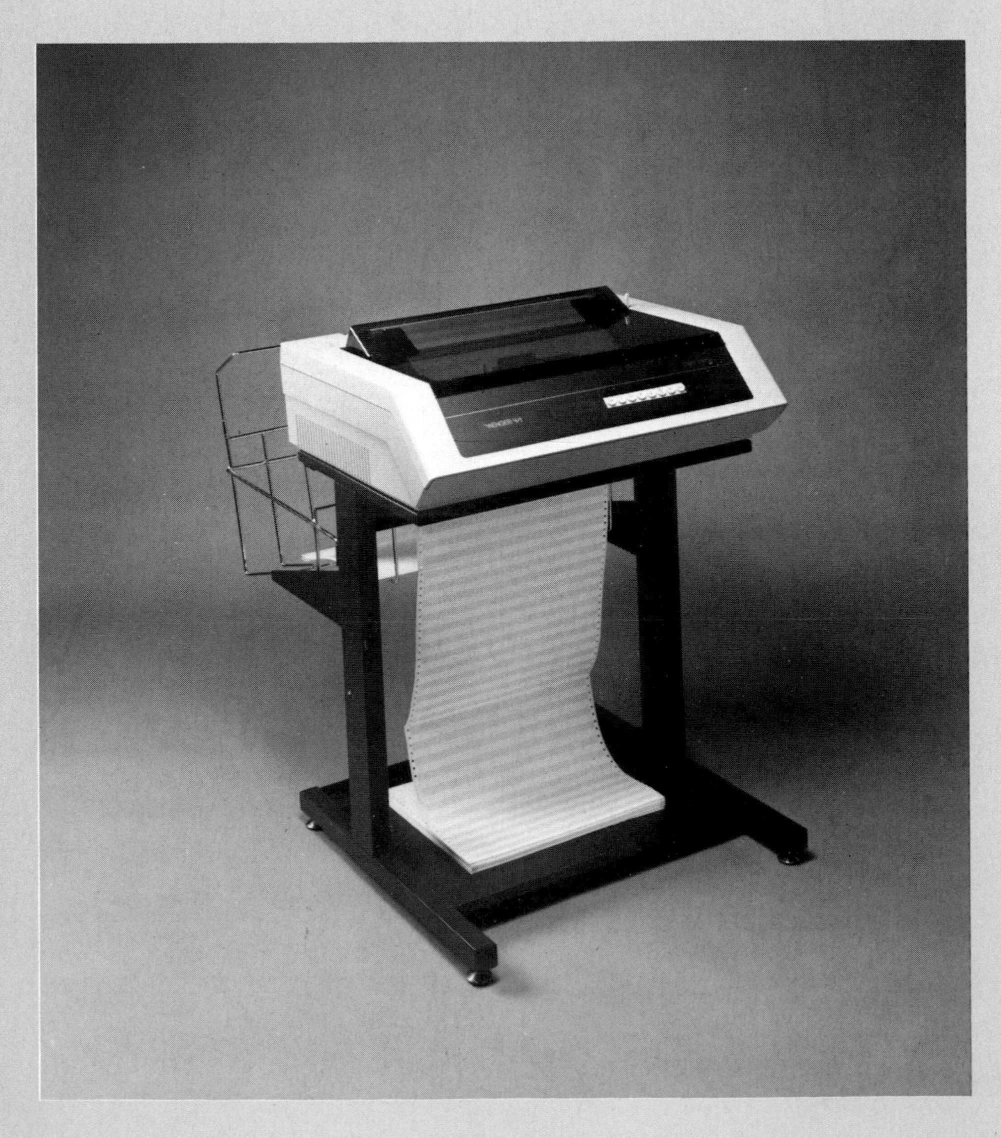

Product: WENGER 4/1
Design Firm: Wenger Datentechnik
Reinach, Switzerland
Awards: Prädikat if Die gute Industrieform
1984

Product: F.R.E.D. Remote Control
Designers: Charlie Patterson, Charles Curbbun, and J. Frank Zinni, Ron Loosen Associates; Joe Lubinski, Jeff Moskin, and Keith Wertz, Androbot, Inc.
Design Firm: Ron Loosen Associates Los Alamito, California
Client: Androbot, Inc., San Jose, California
Awards: 1984 *Industrial Design* magazine Design Review selection
Materials: Injection molded ABS

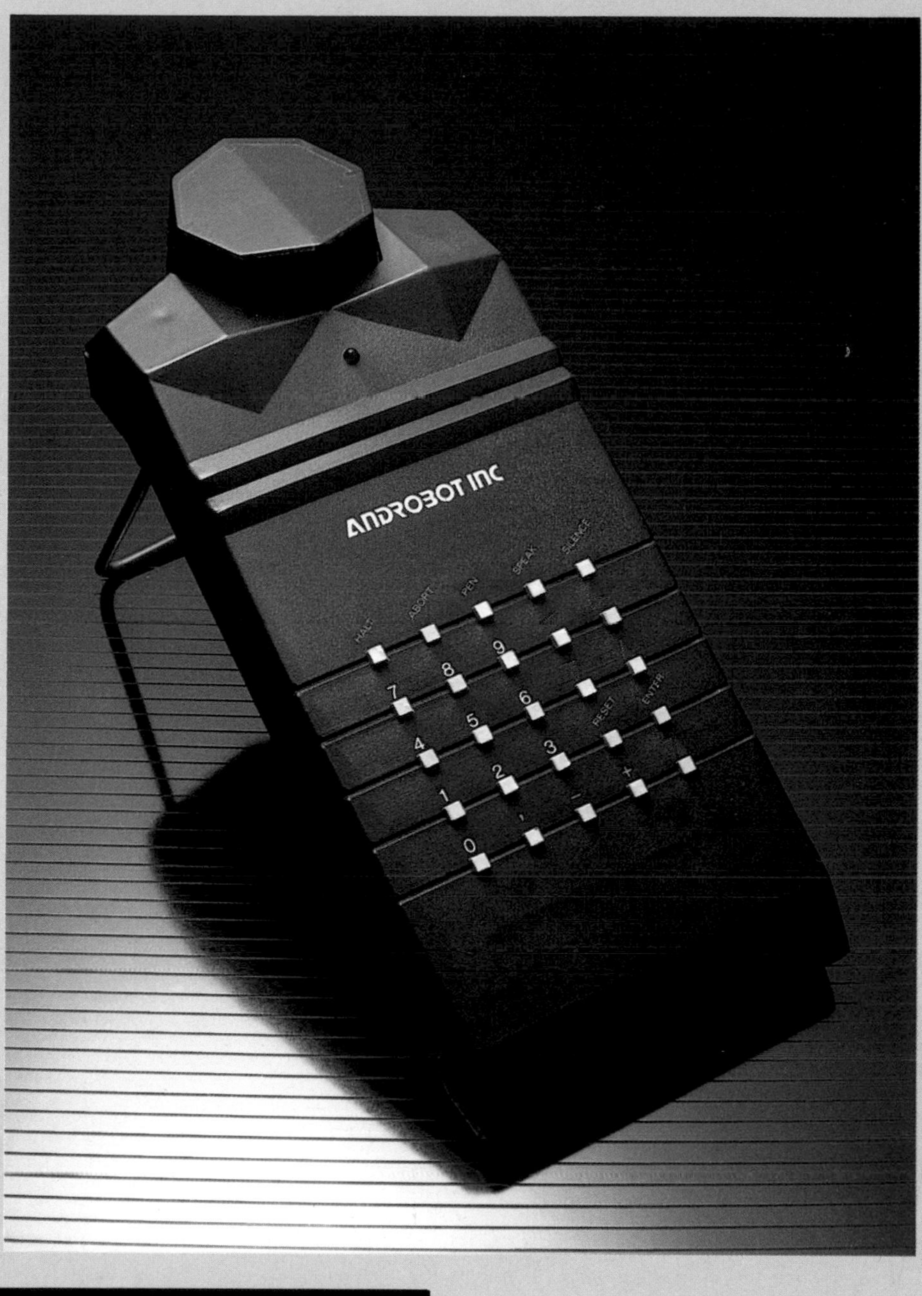

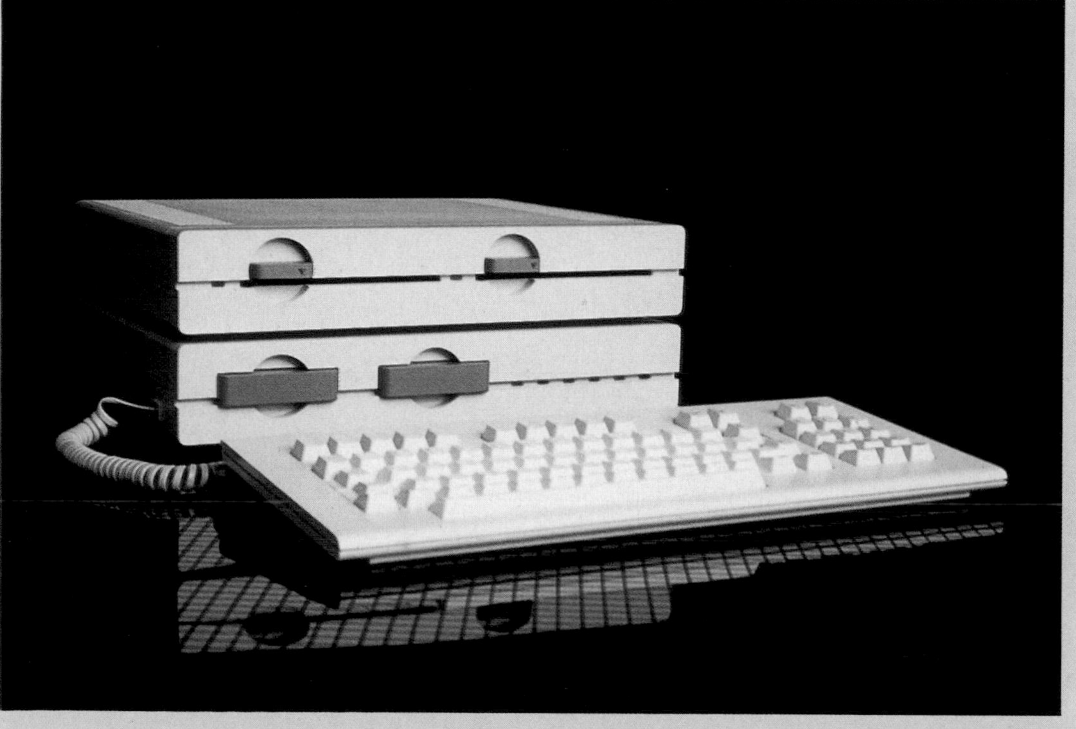

Product: Mindset Personal Computer
Designers: Bob Brunner, Del Coates, John Hoving, and Ben Thomas
Design Firm: GVO Inc., Palo Alto, California
Client: Mindset, Sunnyvale, California
Awards: 1984 IDSA Industrial Design Excellence Award

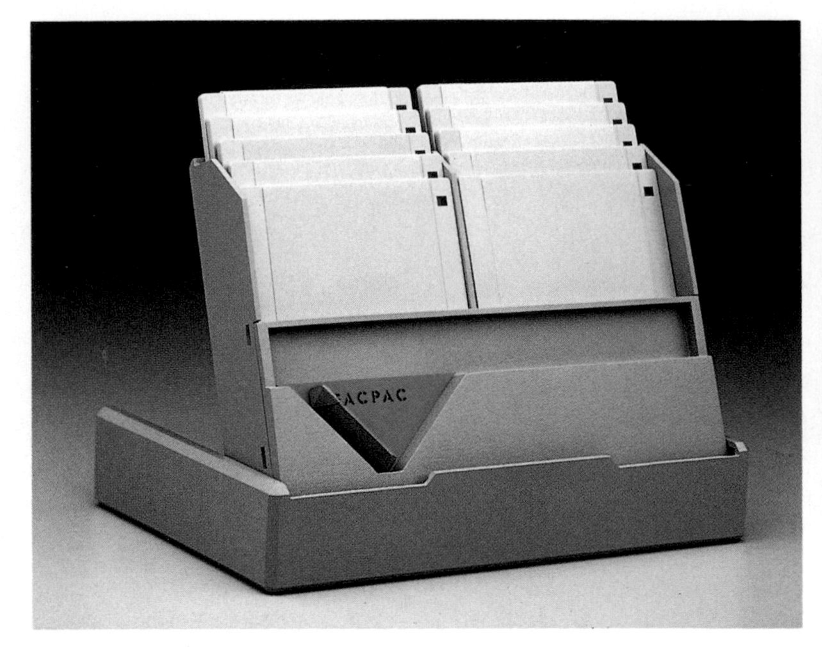

Product: FACPAC Media Storage
Designers: W. Robert Worrell, James B. Libby, Royce Rumsey, and Gordy Rosenlund
Design Firm: Worrell Design Inc. Minneapolis, Minnesota
Client: Norwesco, Minneapolis, Minnesota
Awards: 1985 *Industrial Design* magazine Design Review selection
Materials: Injection molded in high impact styrene and finished with a Rawal RE6622 texture

Product: PCW 1 Word Processor

Consultant Design: Bill Moggridge, ID Two, San Francisco, California, Rickson Sun, Dave Kelley Design, Palo Alto, California

Staff Design: M. Konishi, M. Yoshida, T. Nishimura, and V. Carlson, Carlisle Systems, Burlington, Massachusetts

Client: Minolta, Osaka, Japan and Ramsey, New Jersey

Awards: 1985 *Industrial Design* magazine Design Review selection

Materials: ABS enclosures using snap assembly features, injection molded

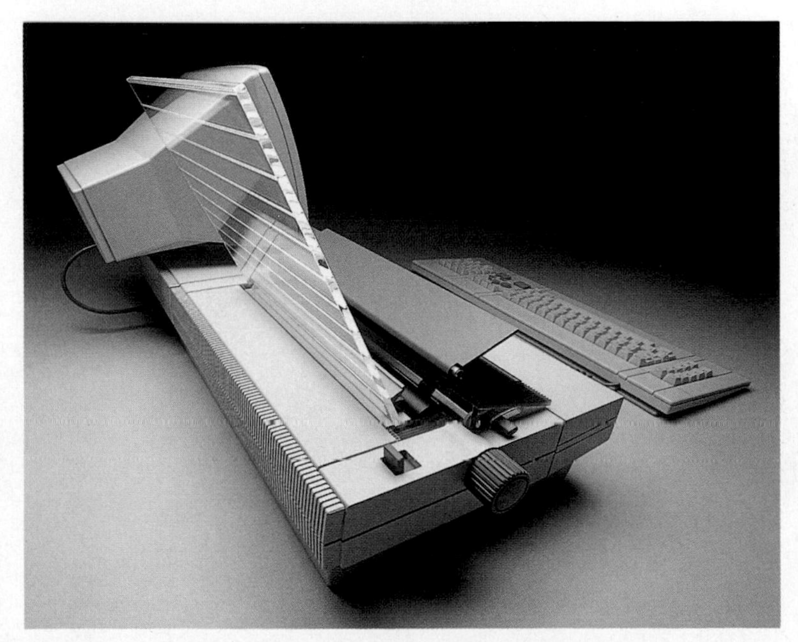

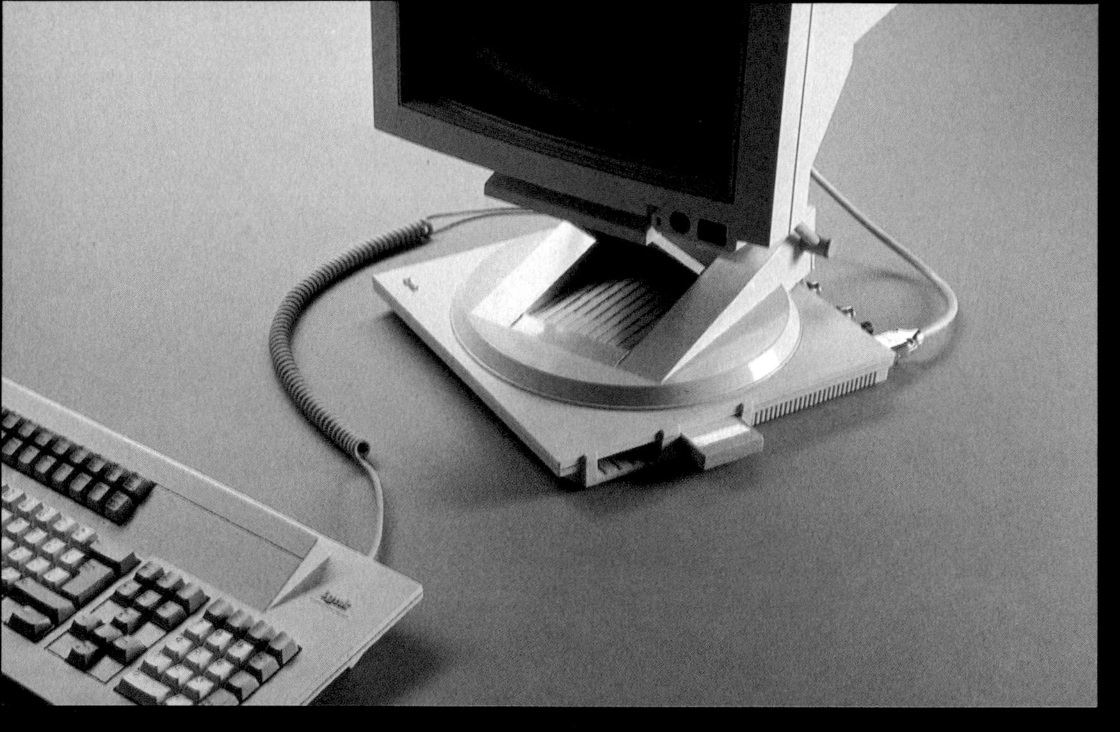

Product:	Lynk Computer
Designer:	Win ied Scheuer
Design Firm:	ID Two, San Francisco, California
Client:	Lynk Computer
Photo Credit:	Don Fogg

Product:	Metaphor Workstation
Design Firm:	Matrix Product Design, David Kelley Design Palo Alto, California
Client:	Metaphor, Mountain View, California
Awards:	1985 IDSA Industrial Design Excellence Award; 1985 Industrial Design magazine Design Review, Best of Category

XEROX 6065 Personal Computer
XEROX Corporation, Rochester, New York

Product:	T1100 Portable Personal Computer
Manufacturer:	Toshiba Corporation of Tokyo, Japan
Available:	Toshiba America Inc., Information Systems Division, Tustin, California

Product: HICOM Multiterminal 3510 Voice Activated Computer
Design Firm: Siemens Design Center
Iselin, New Jersey
Client: Siemens, Muenchen & Berlin, West Germany
Materials: Keyboard, display, CPU, and handset base: noryl structural foam; handset ABS

Product: PC D
Design Firm: Siemens Design Center
Iselin, New Jersey
Client: Siemens, Muenchen & Berlin, West Germany
Materials: Keyboard, display, and CPU housing: noryl structural form

Product:	Laser CRT Terminal Prototype
Designers:	Michael H. Tooke, James D. Trickle, and John Frost
Design Firm:	Tooke Associates Westlake Village, California
Awards:	1985 *Industrial Design* magazine Design Review selection, Concept Category

Product:	Apple 11C
Design:	Apple Computer, Inc. Cupertino, California; frogdesign, Campbell, California
Client:	Apple Computer, Inc. Cupertino, California
Awards:	1984 IDSA Industrial Design Excellence Award; *Time Magazine* Design of the Year; 1985 *Industrial Design* magazine Design Review, Best of Category

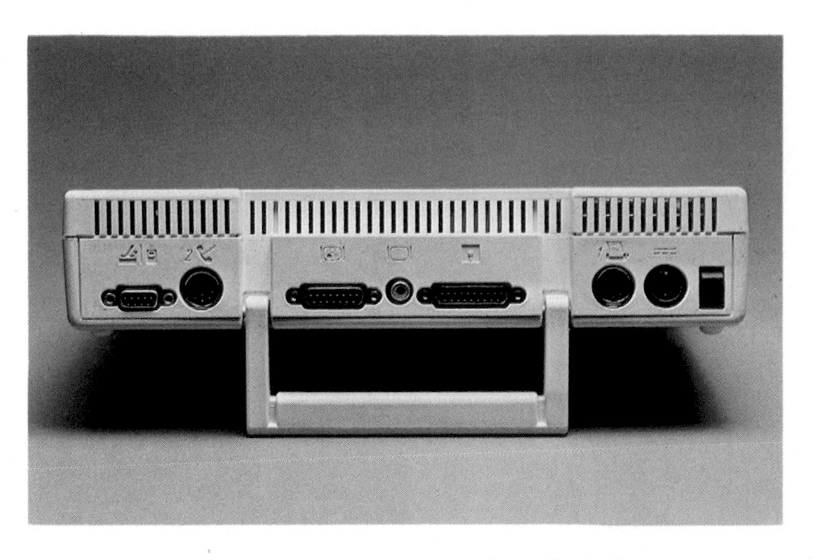

Product:	Apple Scribe Printer
Designers:	Steven Peart, Harmut Esslinger
Design Firm:	frogdesign, Campbell, California
Staff Design:	Bill MacKenzie, Mark Pruitt
Client:	Apple Computer, Inc. Cupertino, California

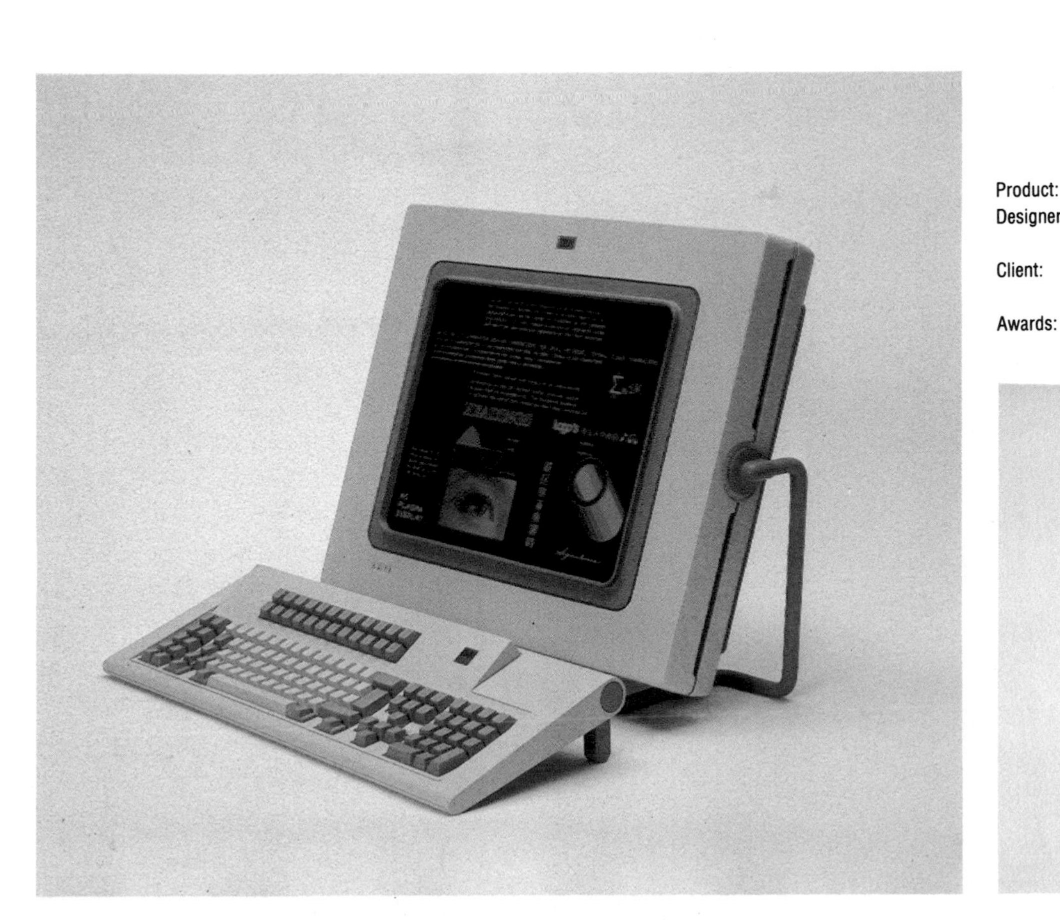

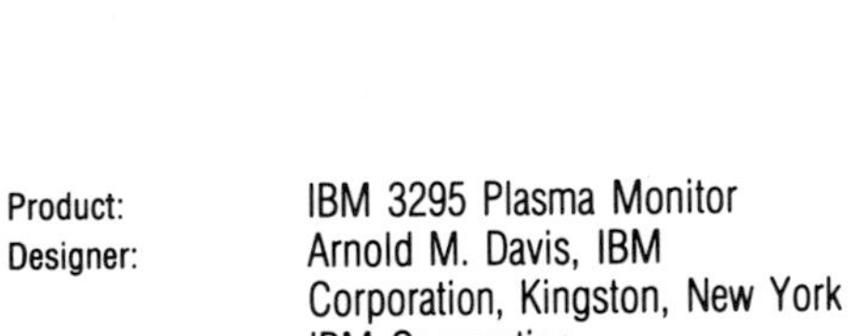

Product:	IBM 3295 Plasma Monitor
Designer:	Arnold M. Davis, IBM Corporation, Kingston, New York
Client:	IBM Corporation Kingston, New York
Awards:	1985 *Industrial Design* magazine Design Review selection

Product: Hewlett-Packard 7978 Streaming Tape Drive

Designers: James Dow, Mo Khovaylo, Doug Domel, John Dong, Dave Jarrett, and Dave Jones

Client: Hewlett-Packard
Greeley, Colorado

Materials: Permanent mold aluminum casting unit base, precision-machined; glass-filled Lexan foam cover door, injection molded, with sheet Lexan window with SAR coating; ABS head and panel covers, injection molded; glass-filled polycarbonate reel hubs and roller caps, injection molded.

Product: Apricot Portable

Manufacturer: Applied Computer Techniques, Inc., England

Distributor: Apricot, Inc., Santa Clara, California

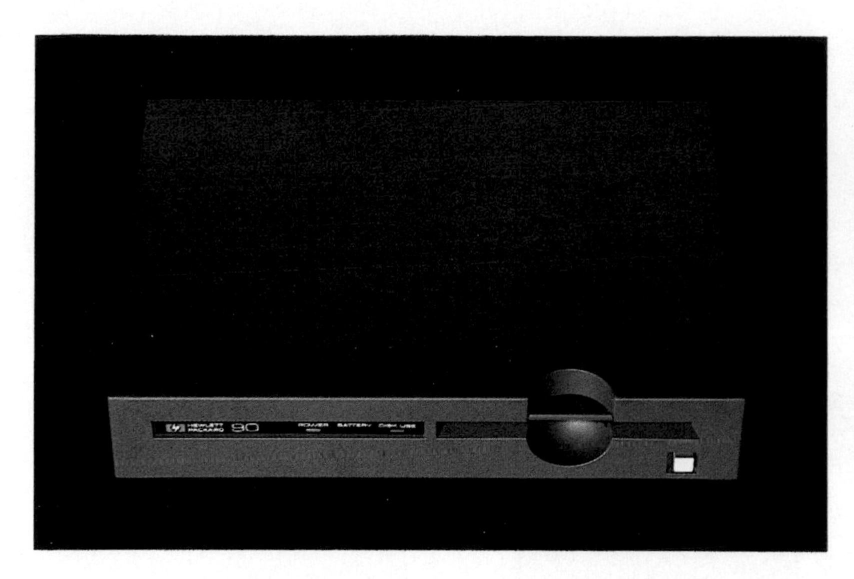

Product: Micro Flexible Disc Drive
Designers: Mo Khovaylo, Steve Anderson, Jim Dow, John Christiansen, Ben Kimbell, Wes Smith, and Jesse Gerard
Client: Hewlett-Packard
Greeley, Colorado
Materials: Molded in polycarbonate

Product: M 21 Personal Computer
Client: Olivetti, Italy
Awards: 1984 SMAU Industrial Design Award

Product: NCR Design Strategy
Design Firm: Richardson/Smith, Worthington, Ohio
Client: NCR Corporation, Dayton, Ohio
Awards: 1984 IDSA Industrial Design Excellence Award

Product: Archtech 310 Design System
Manufacturer: Skok Systems Incorporated
Cambridge, Massachusetts

Product: OT 700 Printer
Consultant Design: Loyd Moore, Nick Barker, Dick Liu, and David Niereschire, Technology Design, Bellevue, Washington
Staff Design: Nate Searle
Client: Output Technology, Bellevue, Washington
Awards: 1985 *Industrial Design* magazine Design Review selection

Product: DDE Supermax Computer-Serien/Series
Designers: Christian Bjorn, Per Boelskifte, and Michael Lindeburg
Client: Dansk Dataelectronik A/S, Denmark
Awards: The ID Prize, Denmark

Product: Modular Desktop Computer
Design Firm: Matrix Product Design
Palo Alto, California
Client: Convergent Technologies
San Jose, California
Awards: 1985 IDEA award, Recognition of Design Achievement

Product: NCR 7770 Proof and Encode Workstation
Designers: Harry Mahler, Thom Tedham, and Vern Tarbutt
Design Firm: NCR Waterloo Design Staff
Waterloo, Ontario, Canada
Materials: Painted styrene structural foam; internally flame-sprayed with zinc oxide for conductivity; formed or welded sheet metal panels; molded-in-color polycarbonate; molded-in-color PPO; keyboard keycaps: double injection molded ABS with a clear window for customer replaceable key legends; CRT housing is a die cast part to control emissions; armrest: eurethane foam with a slush-molded PVC cover

BUSINESS EQUIPMENT

CHAPTER

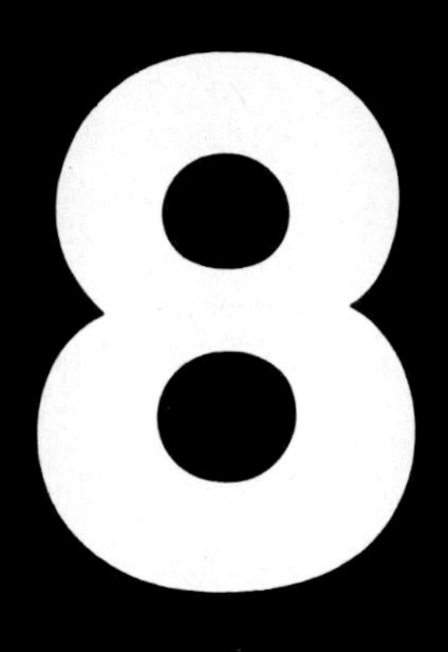

After the introduction in the 1920s of Raymond Loewy's design for a duplicating machine, the technical categories have been something of a design vacuum. That is changing. After the functional phase, styling begins. Enter the ''facelift'' age.

''Manufacturers are desperate for a new style,'' stated Gary Grossman, vice-president of Innovations and Development, Inc., in summarizing the importance of a vertical-styling design trend that surfaced in the review of submissions to the *1986 ID Annual Design Review.* Mid-decade designs give witness to a new level of experimentation in both form and color (particularly accent colors) that offer promise to this emerging concept and to the possibility of satisfying market needs. Admittedly, design departures in business equipment are decidedly safer than in other product design areas. However, when the relative youthfulness of these products is considered (plates and chairs, after all, have been around quite a bit longer), design advances have been remarkably rapid.

Accelerating this change has been the workforce shift from laborer to information processor/manager. Now that time has provided some feedback on this high-performance equipment, the needs of the human operator are refining the shapes of office technology. Researchers have determined that design factors, including color, materials, and patterns of use, have potent effects on worker satisfaction and productivity. Manufacturers may merely be addressing a product development area companies can no longer afford to ignore.

Adrian Forty in this book, *Objects of Desire,* (New York: Pantheon Books, 1986) offers another explanation for the entrance of the post-modern aesthetic into the workplace:

> *Design has the capacity to cast myths into an enduring, solid, tangible form. . . take as an example the common assumption that modern office work is more friendly, more fun, more varied, and generally better than office work in ''the old days''. . . the myth is given daily sustenance and credibility by modern equipment in bright colors and slightly humorous shapes, designs that help make the office match up to the myth.*

Whatever the reason, it is undeniable that outfitting the workplace to accommodate the equipment of the information age has revamped the office landscape.

Product: Xerox 1090 Copier
Designers: Clint Farnsworth, Binns C. Hardy, Susan Miller, and Nicholas Mastrodonato
Client: Xerox Reprographic Business Group, Stamford, Connecticut
Awards: 1985 *Industrial Design* magazine Design Review selection
Materials: Painted structural foam and I.J. covers and bezels; fabricated steel frame and honeycomb base support; graphics are silkscreened, pad printed, and applied labels allowing customization to multinational requirements

Product: 928 Graphics Plotter
Design: Howard M. C. Tanner
Salt Late City, Utah
Client: Optical Computer Inc., Boulder, Colorado
Materials: Investment cast aluminum base supports; extruded aluminum legs; formed mild steel sheet tie bars
Awards: 1985 *Industrial Design* magazine Design Review selection

Product: Gevafax X-23
Manufacturer: Agfa-Gevaert AG, Leverkusen, West Germany

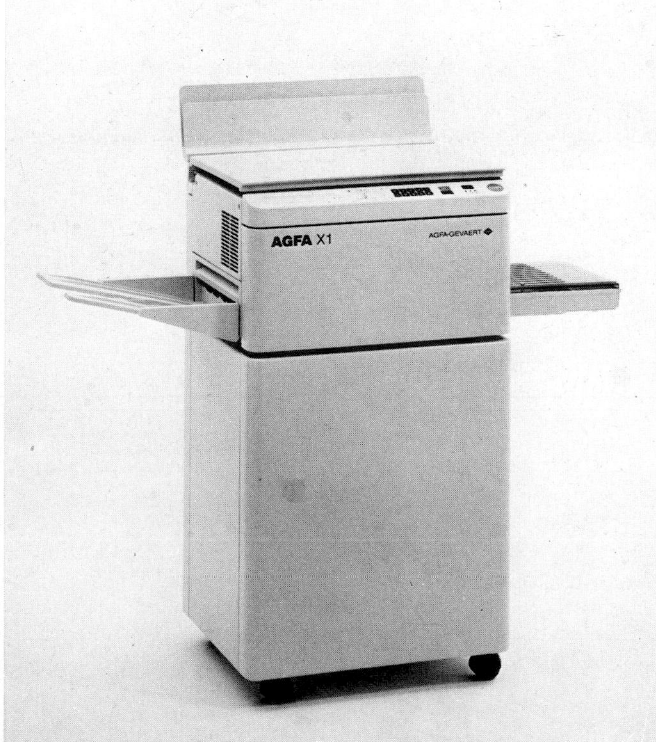

Product: Orbital Colour Print Processor & Power Drive
Designer: Eric Taylor
Client: Paterson Product Ltd., England
Awards: 1984 Design Council Award

Product: McCarthy Presentation Unit
Designer: Rory McCarthy, Tucson, Arizona
Client: IBM Corporation, General Products Division, Tucson, Arizona
Materials: Steel; Perforated steel sheeting; lightweight expanded styrene panels with plastic laminate surface; rubber sheeting, acrylic enamel paint

Product: Hertz Driving Directions
Designers: Michael Young, Hiroaki Kozu, Flushing, New York
Client: The Hertz Corporation, New York, New York
Manufacturer: MKB Group Inc., New York, New York
Materials: Fabricated wood cabinet with steel support

Products:	Movable Platforms, Pushcart, Stocking Carts
Designers:	Bruce Burdick, Susan Kosakowsky, Larry Mayers, and Marco Pignatelli
Design Firm:	The Burdick Group San Francisco, California
Client:	Esprit de Corp, Inc. San Francisco, California
Materials:	Steel tubing shaped, extruded aluminum rods; vinyl matting; perforated steel

Product: NCR 5080 Automated Teller Machine
Design Firm: NCR (Manufacturing) Ltd., Dundee, England
Client: NCR Corporation, Dayton, Ohio
Awards: 1985 Design Council Award

Product: 4430 Magnetic Strip Reader (MSR)
Design: Jim Pagella, Don Forsythe
NCR Corporation, Cambridge, Ohio
Client: NCR Corporation, Dayton, Ohio

Product: Chemical Bank's Automated Banking Center (ABC)
Designers: Samuel Lebowitz, Jay Chalson, and Gloria Rabino
Design Firm: Lebowitz/Gould Design, New York, New York
Client: Chemical Bank, New York, New York
Materials: Columns: 3⁄16 in. aluminum sheet, formed, fine brushed, and natural anodized; roof and floor slab: welded square and rectangular aluminum tubing, sheathed on exterior with 3⁄16 in. black ABS; customer activated terminals: formed and welded sheet metal chassis with integral bosses and brackets for mounting electronic components; exterior housing: 1⁄4 in. thermo-formed ABS; louvers: assembled from a custom extruded aluminum element; sign facia: 1⁄4 in. gray tinted plexiglas; desk surface: black ABS reinforced with aluminum sheet tubular framing members

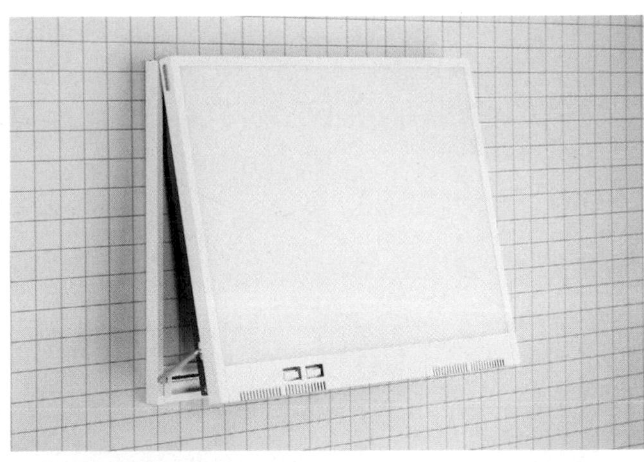

Product:	Portable Lighboxes with Standard and Color-Corrected Illumination
Designers:	Bernard Morcheles, George Ramer
Client:	Stacor Corporation, New Jersey
Materials:	Lamp tray: 040 aluminum; frame: 22 gauge steel; handle/stand: 5⁄16 in. round rod, chrome plated; diffuser/working surface: ¼ in. acrylic; paint: high-solid, semi-gloss baking enamel

Product:	Mobile Storage/Filing System
Manufacturer:	Spacesaver Corporation Fort Atkinson, Wisconsin

Product: Xerox 645 Memorywriter
Manufacturer: Xerox Corporation Rochester, New York

Product: Modu Plus 6000 Desk Accessories
Manufacturer: Smokador, Roselle, New Jersey
Awards: 1984 *Industrial Design* magazine Design Review selection
Materials: Plastic

Product: IBM Typewriter and Printer Ribbon Cartridges
Designer: James Wang
Client: IBM Corporation, Lexington, Kentucky
Awards: 1985 *Industrial Design* magazine Design Review selection
Materials: High impact polystyrene; injection model; raven black cartridges; color coded knobs; satin texture and high gloss finishes

Product: Kroy Adjustable Tape Trimmer
Designers: Casey Carson, W. Robert Worrell
Design Firm: Worrell Design Inc.
Minneapolis, Minnesota
Staff Design: Dennis Bauman, Mike Paque,
Kroy Inc.
Client: Kroy Inc., Scottsdale, Arizona

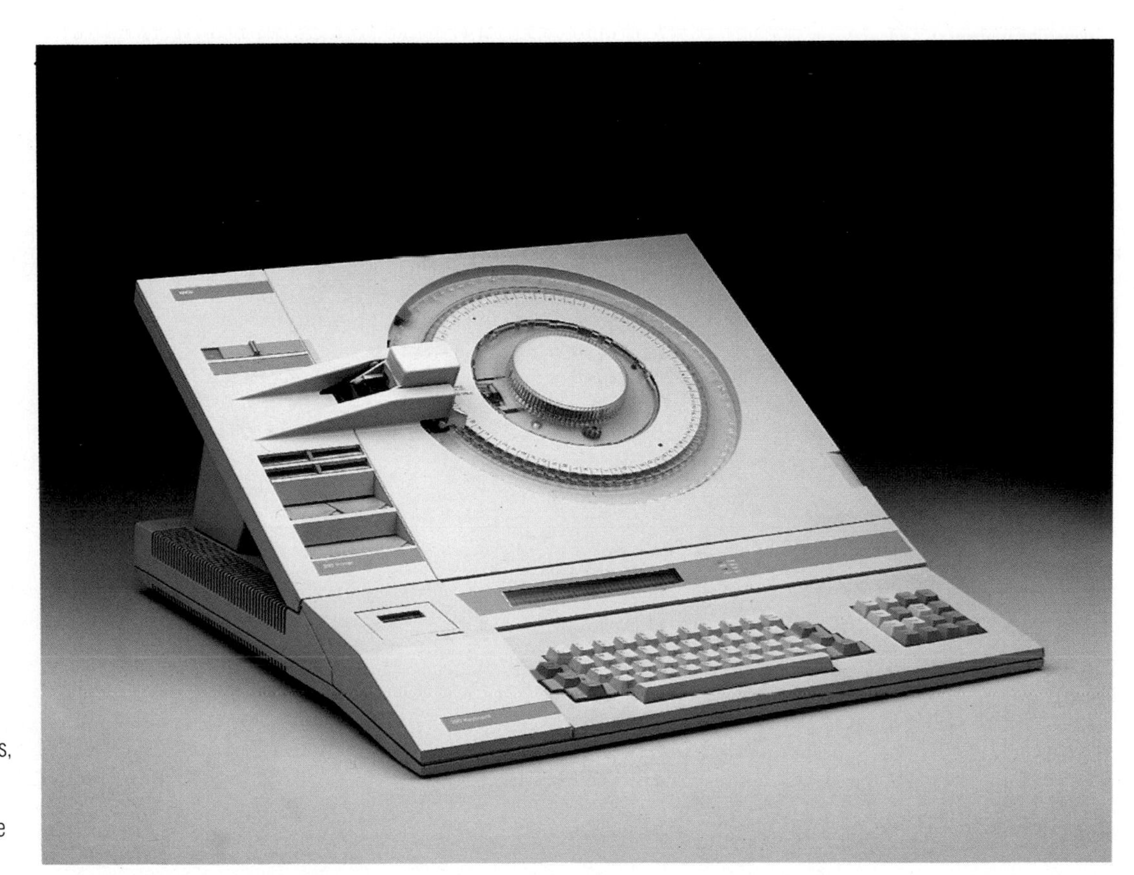

Product: Kroy 290K Lettering System
Designer: W. Robert Worrell
Design Firm: Worrell Design Inc., Minneapolis,
Minnesota
Client: Kroy Inc., Scottsdale, Arizona
Awards: 1984 *Industrial Design* magazine
Design Review selection

Product: ITTE — European Telephone
Designer: Hedda Beese
Design Firm: ID Two, San Francisco, California
Client: ITTE
Awards: Museum of Modern Art Selection, New York, New York

Product: Telephone/Telephone Answering Machine, IT-A600
Client: Sony Corporation of America Park Ridge, New Jersey
Manufacturer: Sony Corporation, Tokyo, Japan

Product: STC Executel
Design Firm: Cross Almond & Partners, England
Designer: Robert Cross
Client: STC Telecommunications Ltd., England
Awards: 1984 Design Council Award

Product: Telenova Telephone Systems
Designers: Bill Moggridge, ID Two; Rickson Sun, David Kelley, Hovey-Kelley
Design Firms: ID Two, San Francisco, California; Hovey-Kelley, Palo Alto, California
Client: Telenova, Inc., Los Gatos, California
Awards: 1984 *Industrial Design* magazine Design Review selection
Materials: Injection molded ABS

Product: STC Radio Pager
Designer: Hedda Beese
Design Firm: ID Two, San Francisco, California
Client: STC, London, England

Product: Kodak IM 40 Copier
Manufacturer: Canon, Inc., Tokyo, Japan
Distributor: Eastman Kodak, Rochester, New York

Product: RICOH M5 Copier
Client: RICOH DEUTSCHLAND GMBIT, Eschborn, West Germany

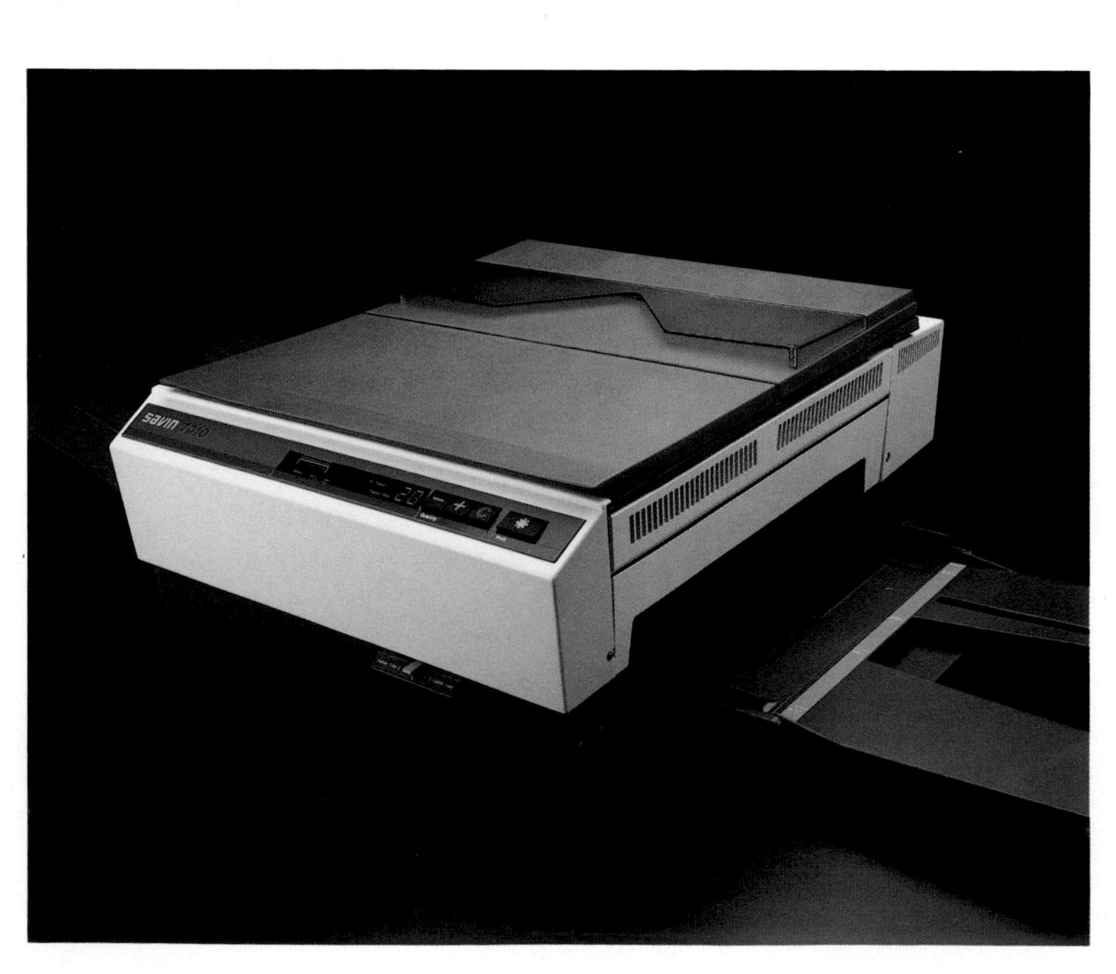

Product: Savin 7010 Photocopier
Designer: Andrew T. Serbinski
Design Firm: Plumb Design Group, Inc. New York, New York
Staff Design: M. Umino
Client: Ricoh Company Ltd., Tokyo, Japan
Awards: 1985 *Industrial Design* magazine Design Review selection
Materials: Base: noryl structural foam; covers: injection molded noryl

Product: Eskofot Daylight Camera 8200
Designer: Jan Trägårdh, MAA IDD
Client: Eskofot A/S, Ballerup, West Germany
Awards: The ID Prize 1985, Danish Design Council

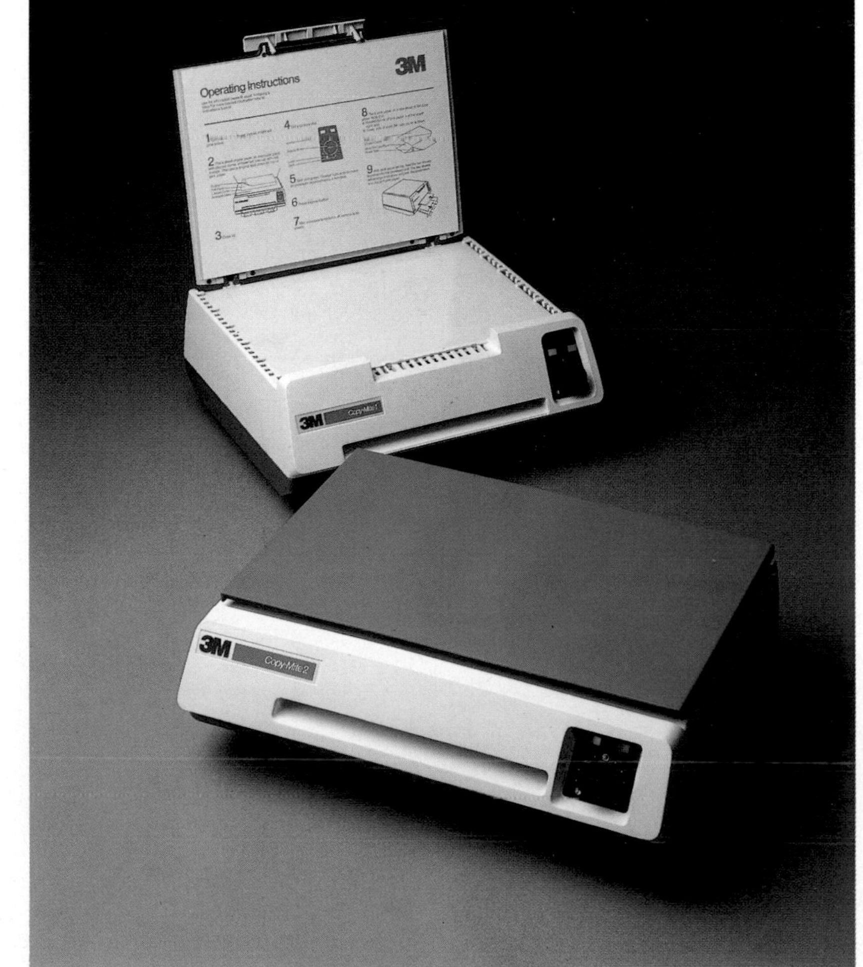

Product: 3M Copy-Mite 1 and 2
Designers: David Miller, Robert Dawson, and Thomas Pendleton
Design Firm: King-Casey, Inc. New Canaan, Connecticut
Client: 3M Corporation St. Paul, Minnesota
Materials: Polycarbonate, ABS and low carbon steel

MEDICAL EQUIPMENT

CHAPTER

An old client of George Nelson's once remarked, ''Designers are the only people who ever give a moment's thought to the people who will be using these products.'' According to Nelson, this is true not because designers are especially nice people, but because you cannot design for human use without thinking about the human user.

That posture is creating a noticeable improvement in the development of medical equipment because industrial designers have joined the formerly exclusive domain of engineers and scientists, bringing with them a professional obsession with human factors. Whereas an engineer's interest lies in *machine* activity, a designer deals with *human* activity. That is, the designer plays the role of the user, examining not only how equipment works and is built, but evaluating its social and physical impact. Formerly grotesque machines have been softened with elegant forms and appealing colors; cold metals are replaced by the new plastics. All this has significant social and financial implications.

The silver lining in the current health care crisis in the U.S. may prove to be the recognition that design can be a major marketing tool in an increasingly competitive industry. In a field where ''imaging wellness'' has become a rallying cry—signalling the shift in consumer attitude and delivery of service—an institution's ability to project that image may not only affect their patient's survival, but it may also affect their own.

Expounding on the ''we care'' message, designer James Falick, Falick/Klein Partnership, Houston, said in a report to *Interiors* magazine, ''Let's face it . . . patients and staff choose the most attractive and comfortable hospital. Successful design must include fulfilling humanistic needs.''

Product: Prior Fibre Optic Microscope
Designers: John Stoddard, Martin Derbyshire
London, England
Design Firm: Moggridge Associates, a division of Design Development, Ltd.
London, England
Client: Prior, London, England

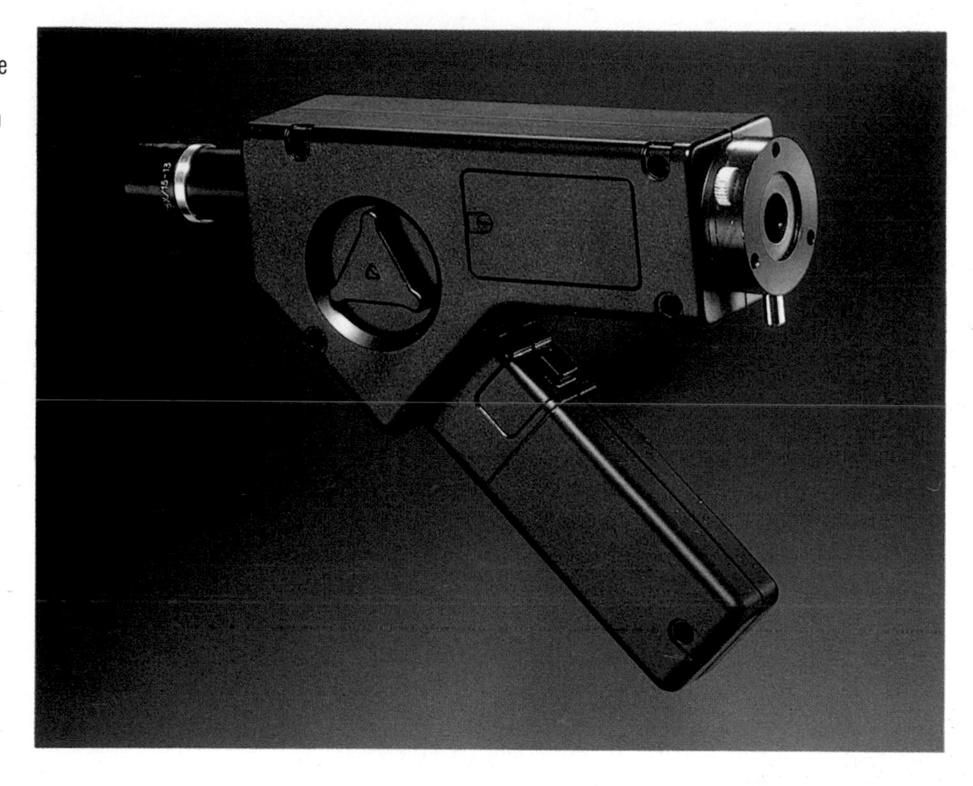

Product: Spate 860 Stress Pattern Analysis
Design Firm: Roberts Weaver, London, England

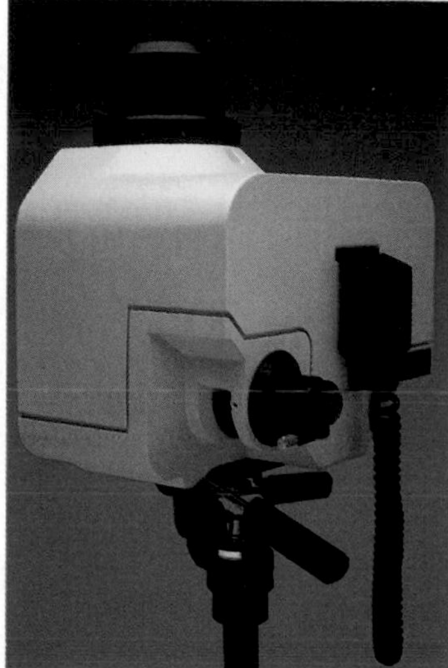

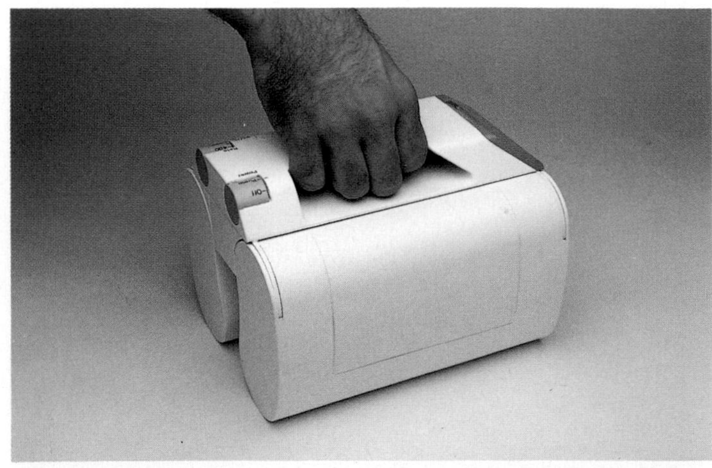

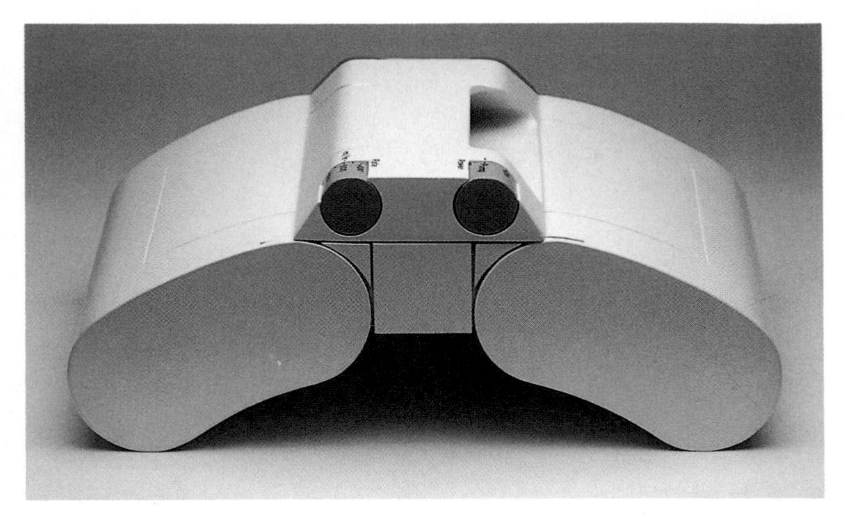

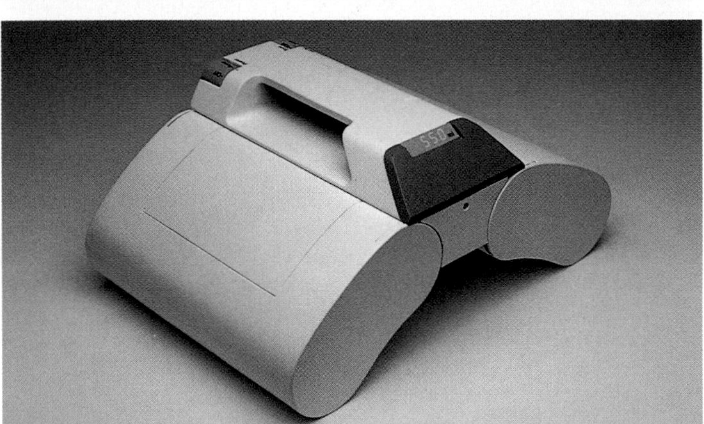

Product: Emergency Intravenous Infusion Pump
Designer: James B. Libby, Minneapolis, Minnesota, University of Wisconsin
Awards: 1984 *Industrial Design* magazine Design Review selection; 1984 IDSA Industrial Design Excellence Award
Materials: Injection molded ABS; parastalic pump; stepper motor; ni-cad battery cluster

Product: Companion Dialysis Machine
Designer: Alexander Gajowskyj, along with the Manchester Royal Infirmary Hospital's Technical & Clinical Staff, Manchester, England
Client: Manchester Royal Infirmary Hospital, Manchester, England

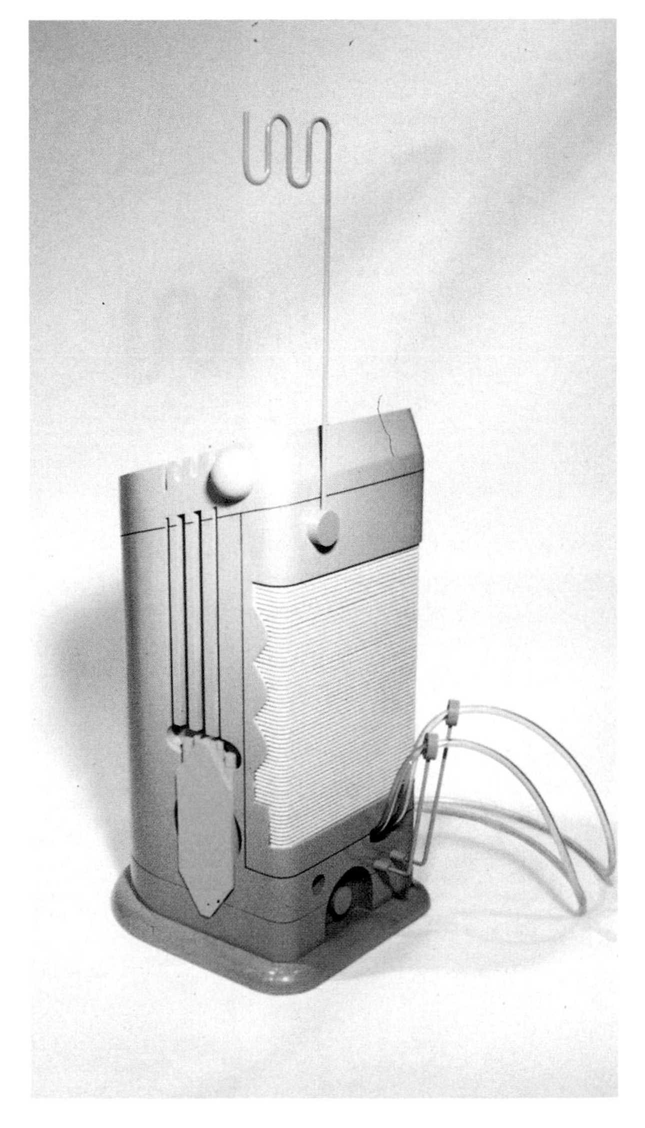

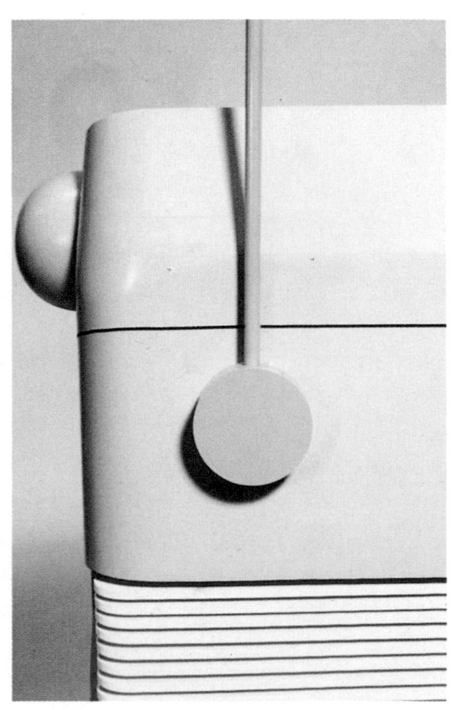

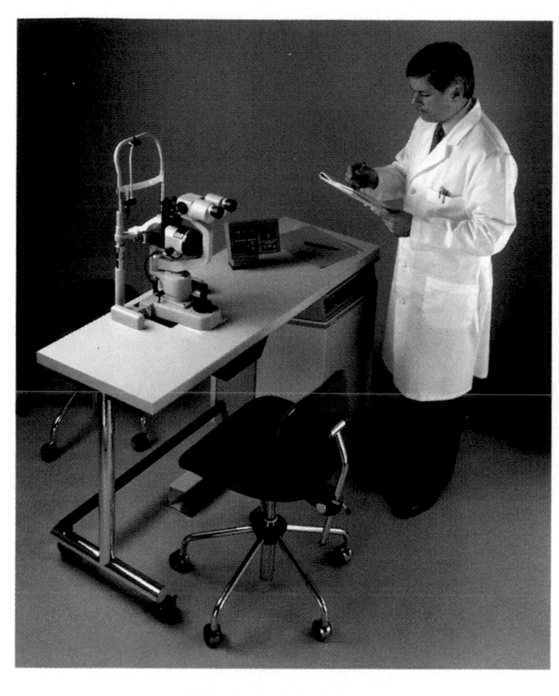

Product: YAG Opthalmic Laser
Design Firm: Human Factors/Industrial Design, Inc., New York, New York
Client: Lasers for Medicine

Product: MEDICOR MS 325, X-ray Generator Control Console
Designers: John Stram, Kevin Greer, and Paul Reeder
Design Firm: Dave Ellies Industrial Design, Inc. Columbus, Ohio
Client: Medicor USA Ltd., Columbus, Ohio
Materials: Sheet metal housing; fiberglass back component cover

Product: Hybritech Photon-Immunossay Analyzer
Designer: Alvaro Corzo, La Jolla, California
Design Firm: Corzo & von Kalinowski, La Jolla, California
Client: Hybritech Inc., San Diego, California
Manufacturer: Ocean Scientific, Anaheim, California
Materials: Enclosure: ABS pressure formed; lens: acrylic; keyboard: lexan pressure formed; front and rear panel: perforated sheet metal, aluminum

Product: INTREX Dental X-ray System
Designer: Carl Yurdin
Design Firm: Carl Yurdin Industrial Design, Inc. Port Washington, New York
Client: The SS White Company, Holmdel, New Jersey
Materials: Arm cover, control box, and support covers: painted, plastercast aluminum; graphics panel: duralith multi-layer mylar

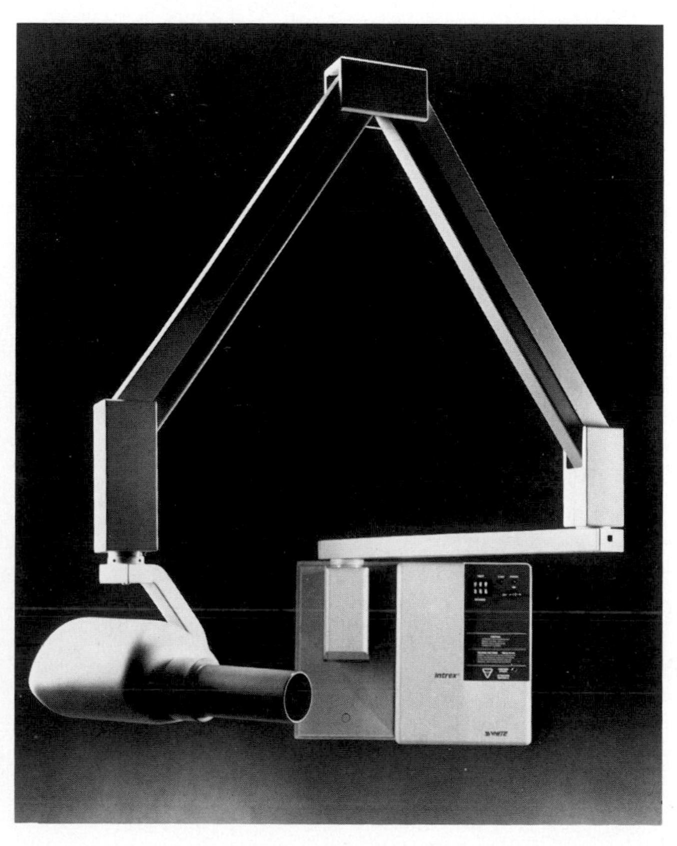

Product:: MEDILOG 9000, EEG monitor
Designer: John Wickham, Bell Wickham Associates
Design Firm: Oxford Medical Systems Ltd. Abingdon, Oxfordshire, England
Awards: 1985 Design Council Award
Materials: A unique ambulatory system for EEG (electroencephalogram) monitoring

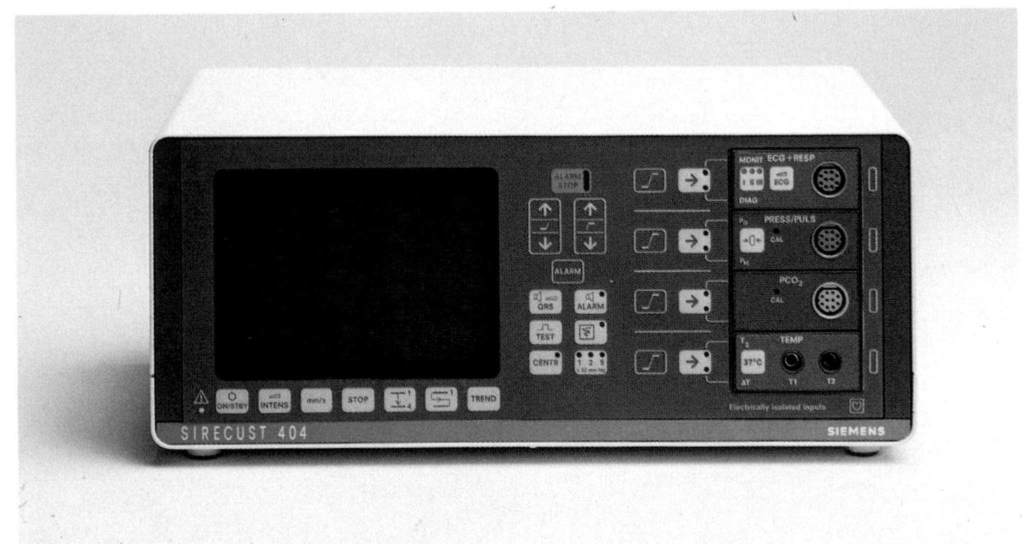

Product: SIRECUST System 400
Design Firm: Siemens Design Center, Muenchen & Berlin, West Germany
Client: Siemens Medical, Erlangen, West Germany
Materials: Metal housing; sensor-front panel; electronic components

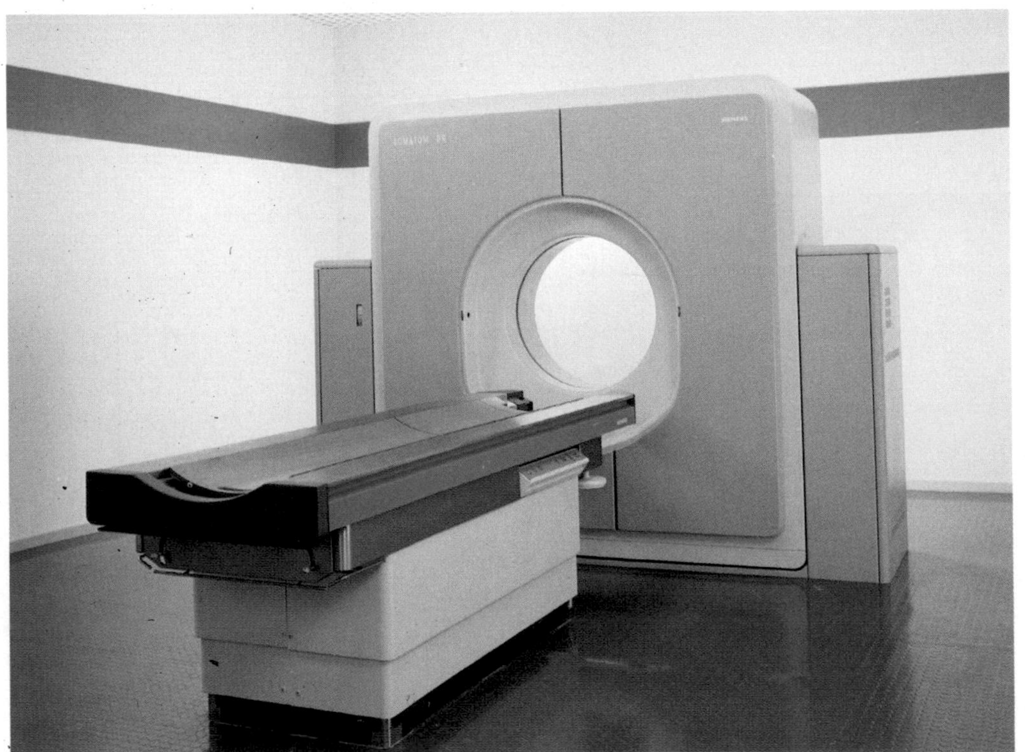

Product: SOMATOM DR, computer tomography unit
Design Firm: Siemens Design Center, Muenchen & Berlin, West Germany
Client: Siemens Medical, Erlangen, West Germany
Materials: X-ray units, plastic and metal covers, electronic and mechanic components

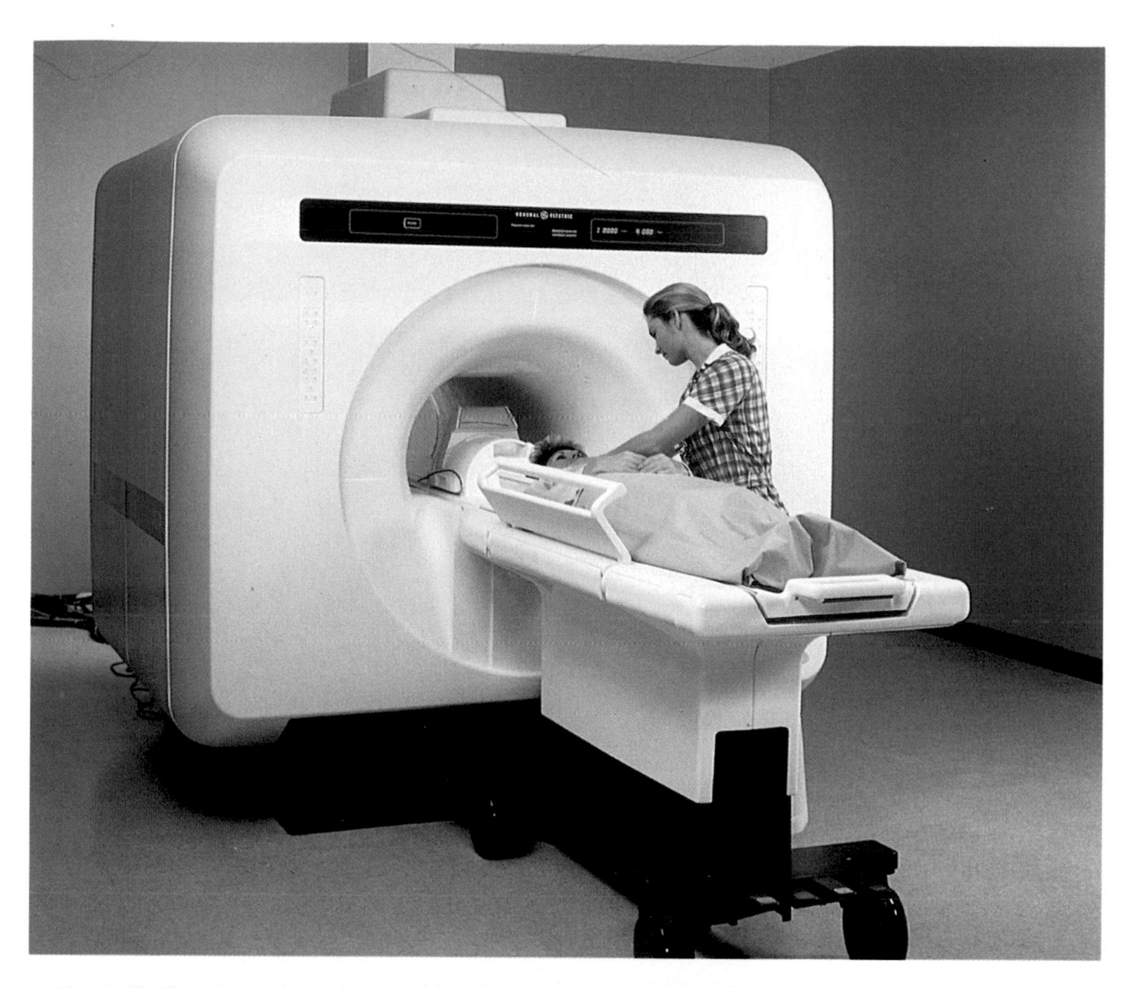

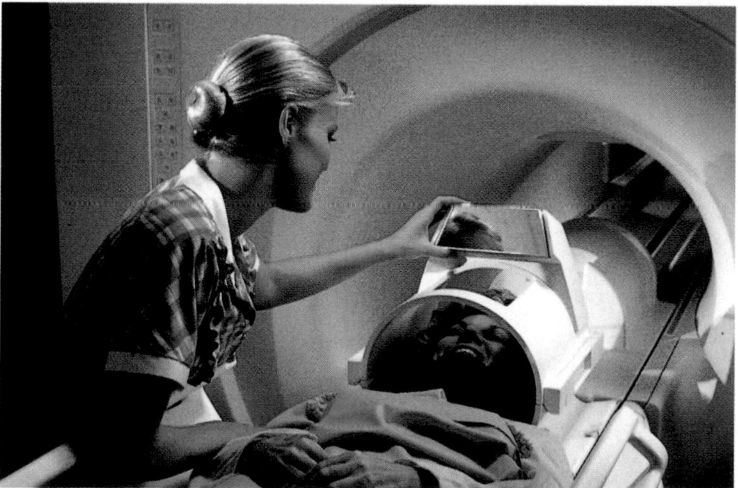

Product:	SIGNA Magnetic Resonance System
Designer:	Seth R. Banks, Christine Fletcher, Edward P. Stevens, and Herb F. Velazquez, Industrial Design & Human Factors Unit
Client:	General Electrlc Company, Medical Systems Group, Milwaukee, Wisconsin
Awards:	1984 IDEA Award
Materials:	Fiberglass housings for the magnet enclosure; fiberglass and aluminum side panels for the mobile patient table; RIM for operator's console screen cover and keyboard housing; fiberglass for base covers

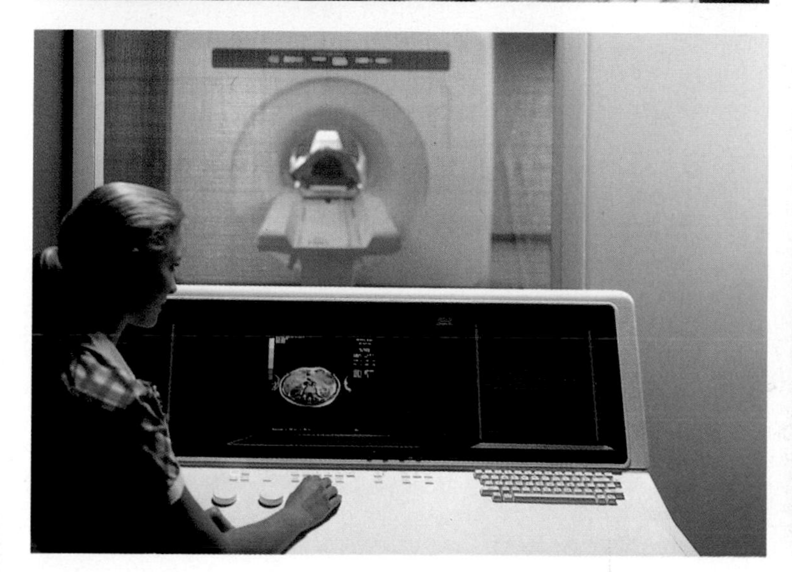

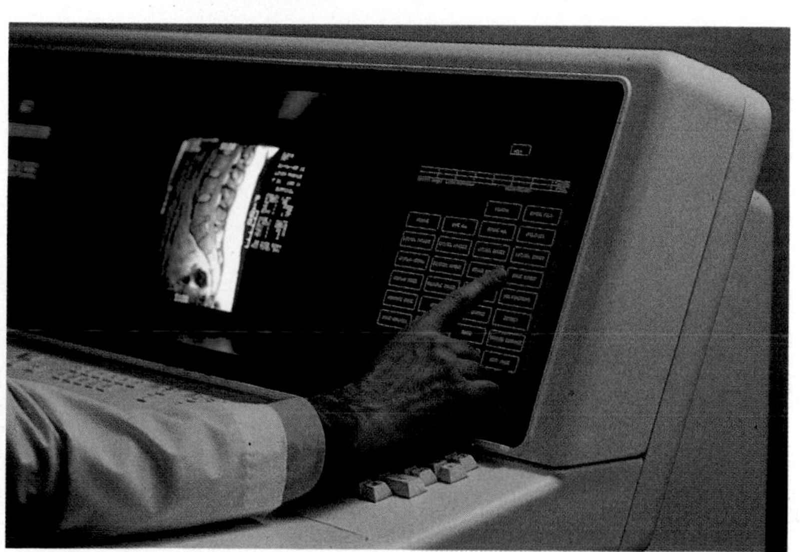

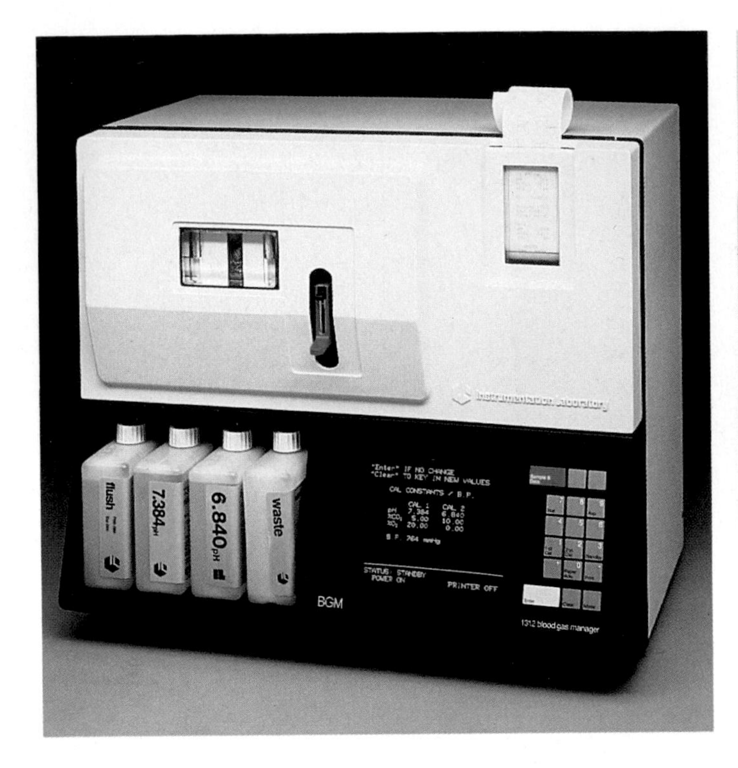

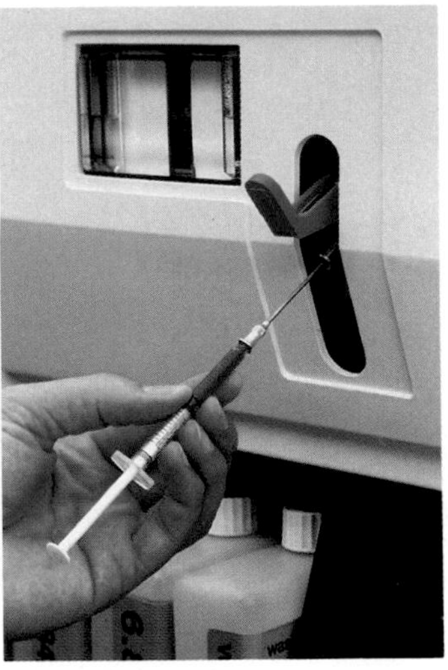

Product: BGM Blood Gas Analyzer
Designers: Gianfranco Zaccai, IDSA, Richard Holtz, Susan Kielty, and Gianmario Longoni
Client: Instrumentation Laboratory, SpA
Awards: 1985 IDSA Industrial Design Excellence Award

Product: Cryogenic Refrigerators and Dewars
Designers: M. Baldwin, J.C. Kaufman, H.R. Roudebush, L.R. Miller, S.L. Mitchell, and W.R. Abraham
Design Firm: Industrial Design Associates, Inc., Indianapolis, Indiana
Staff Design: R.H. Raft, L.G. Svelter, R.H. Crane, R. Zevnick, and J. Young
Client: Union Carbide Corporation Indianapolis, Indiana
Awards: 1984 *Industrial Design* magazine Design Review selection
Materials: Aluminum, plastic

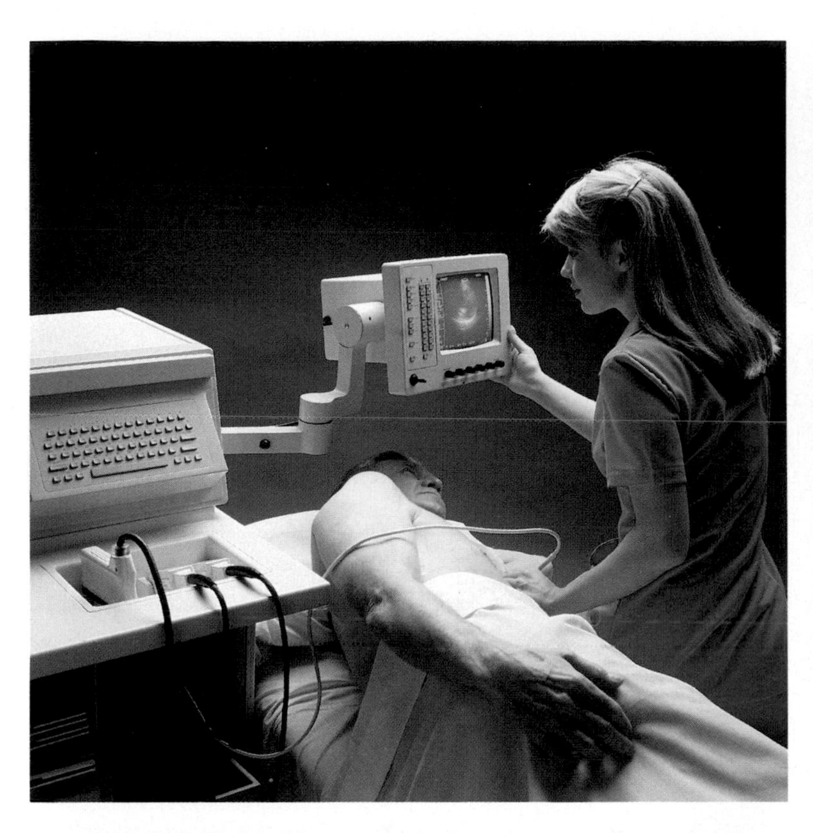

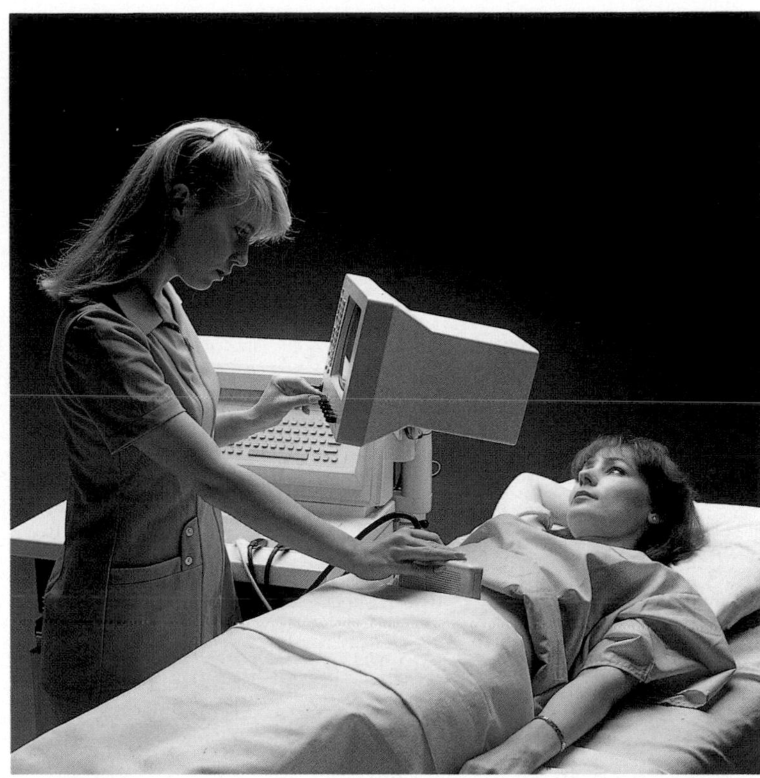

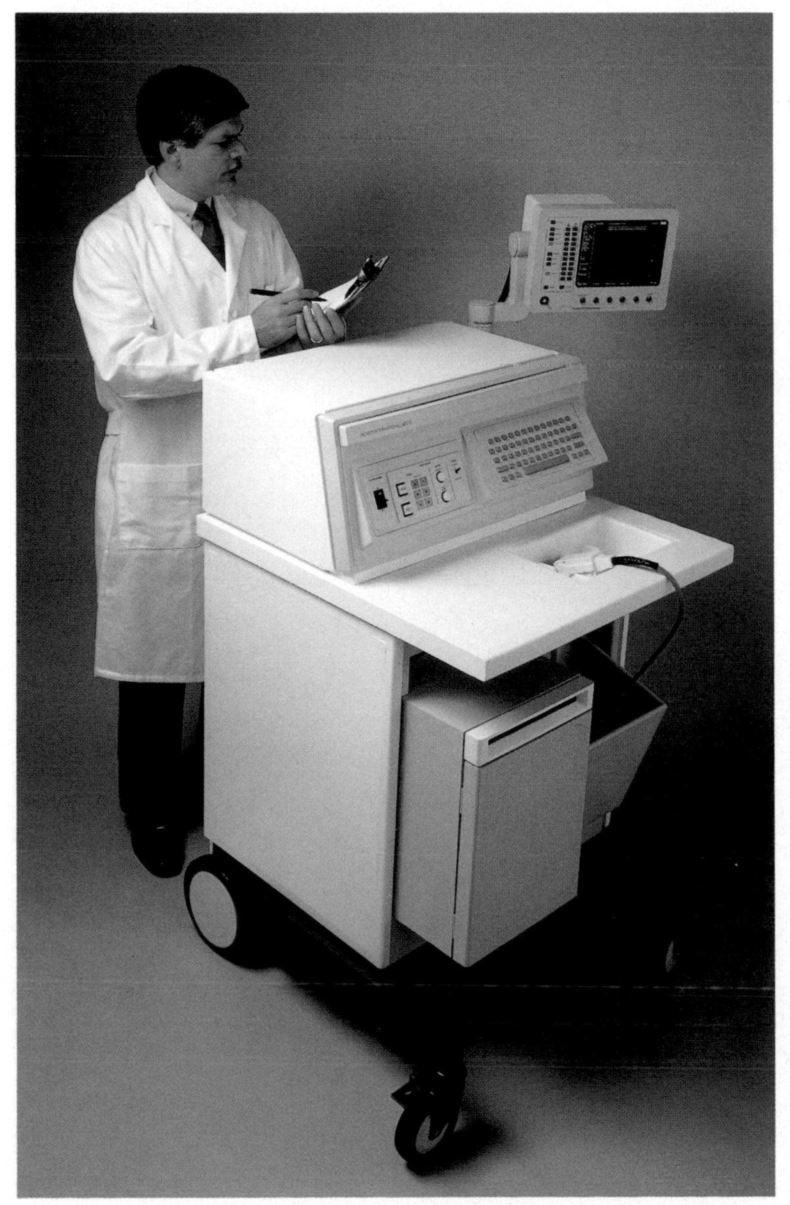

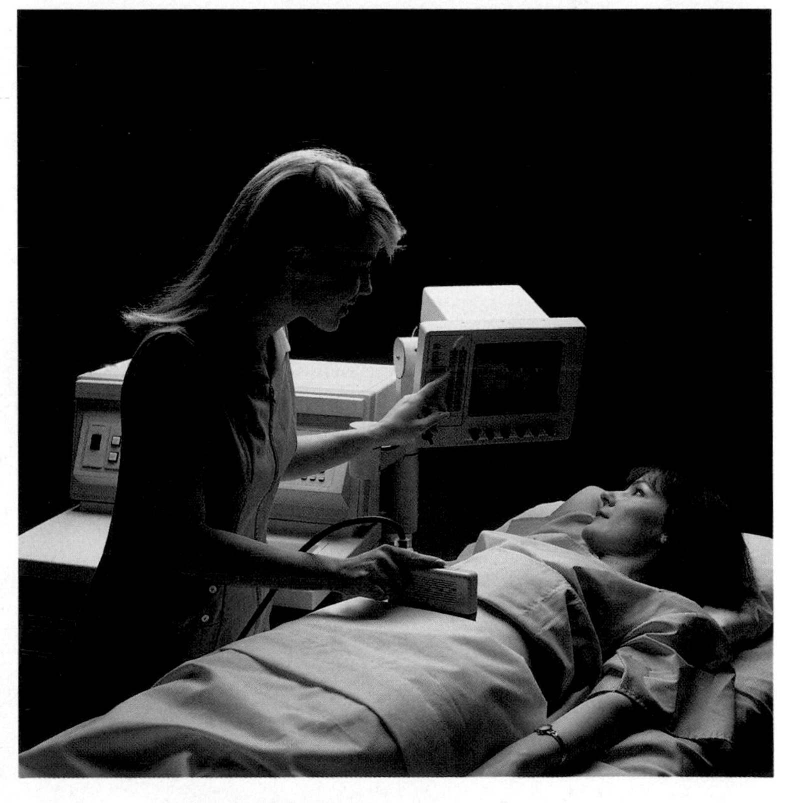

Product:	ARTIS Multi-Modality Ultrasound Imaging System
Design Firm:	Human Factors/Industrial Design, Inc., New York, New York
Client:	Picker International, Northford, Connecticut

Product:	STAAR Micro Surgical System
Designers:	Doug Patton, Matt Duncan, and Rick Jung
Design Firm:	Patton Design Enterprises Irvine California
Staff Design:	Tom Waggoner, Bev Barnes, and Bruce Cuthberthson
Client:	STAAR Surgical Company Monrovia, California
Manufacturer:	Surgical Technologies, Monrovia, California
Awards:	1985 *Industrial Design* magazine Design Review selection

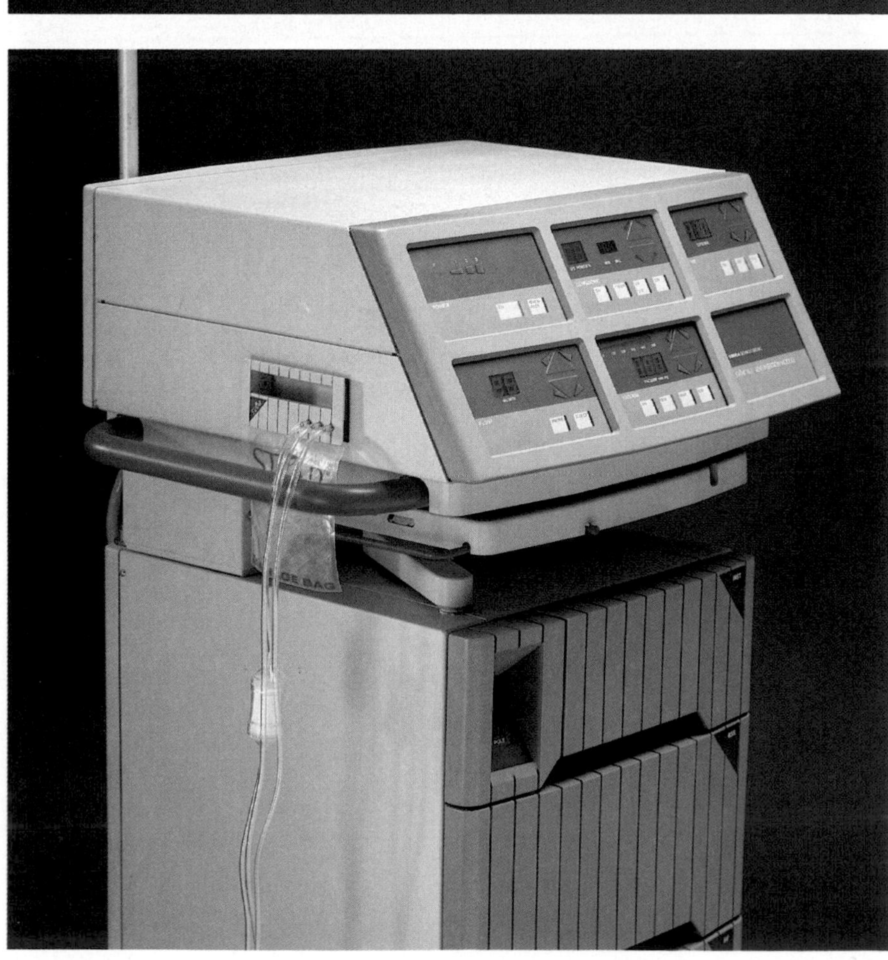

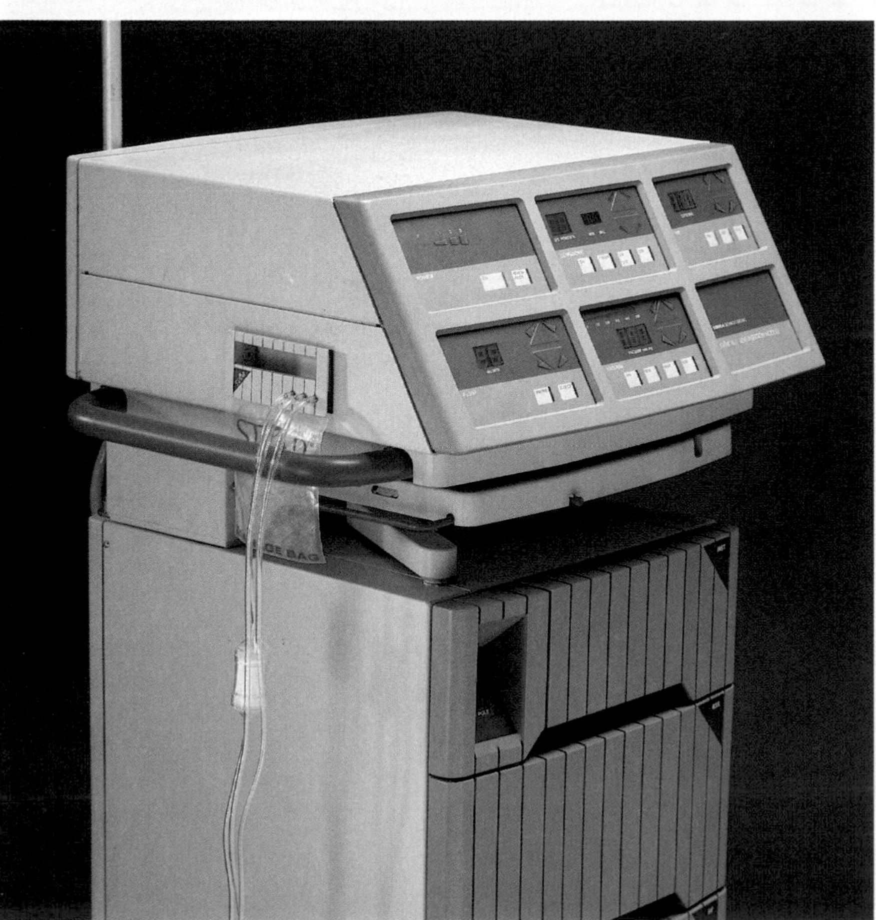

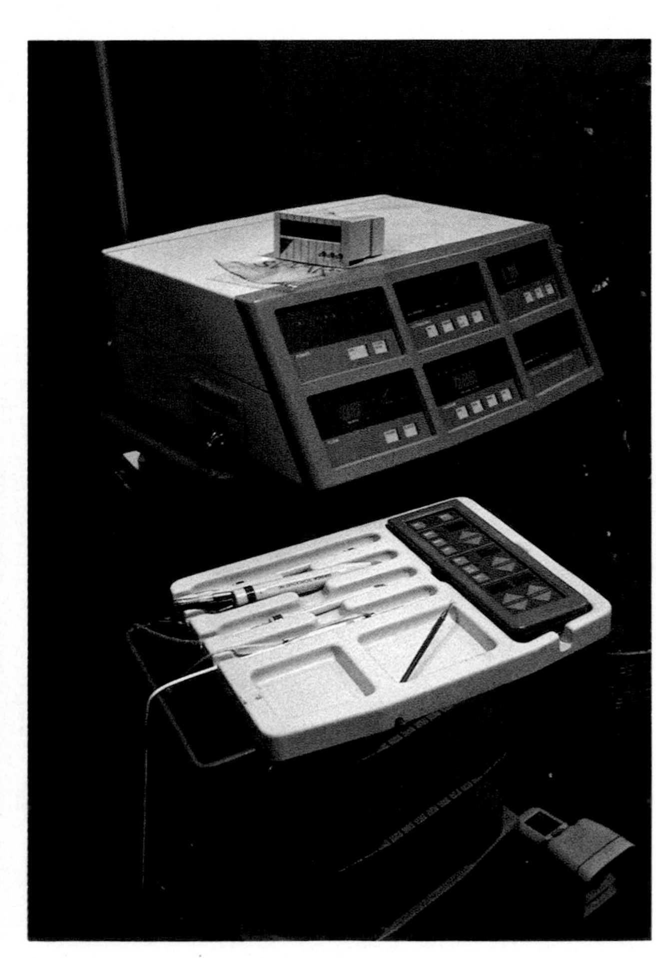

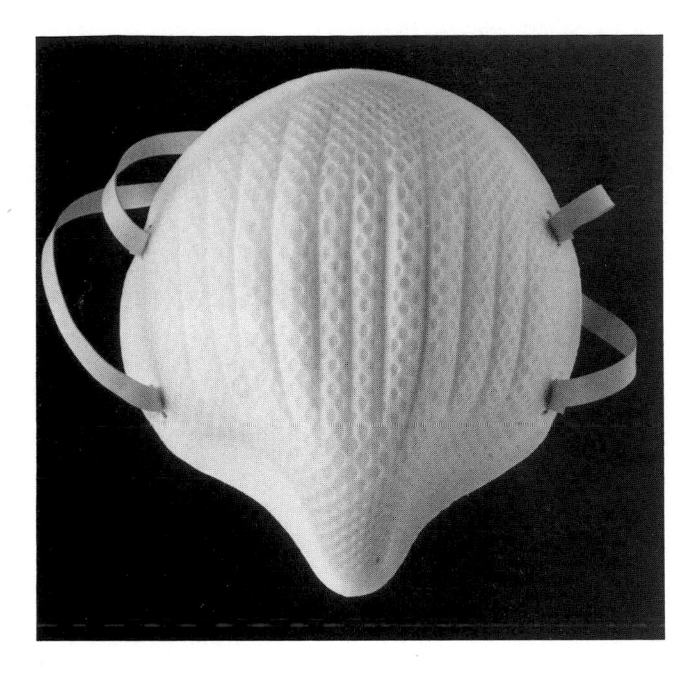

Product: 2200 Respirator
Designers: Mark Magidson, Otto Huber
Design Firm: Moldex Metric, Inc., Culver City, California
Client: Moldex Metric, Inc., Culver City, California
Materials: Polyester, polypropylene, vinyl plastic mesh

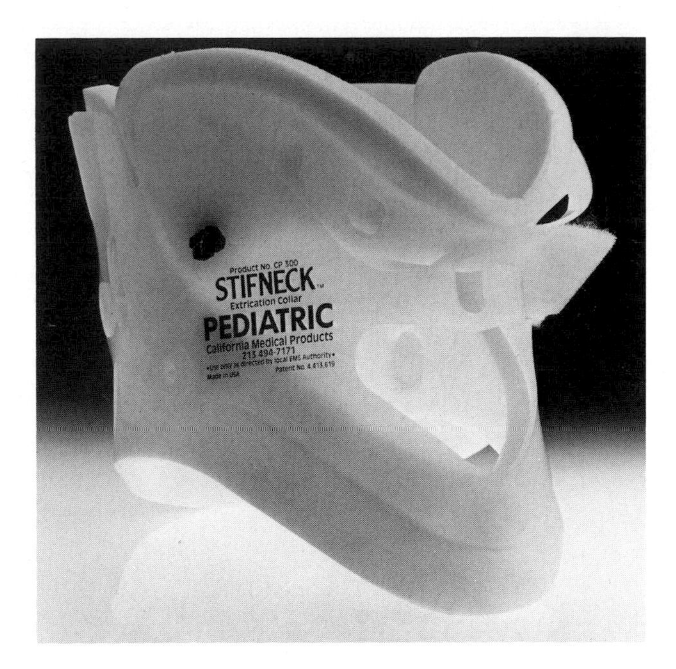

Product: STIF-NECK Pediatric Extrication Collar
Designers: Geoffrey C. Garth, Charlie Patterson
Design Firm: Garth & Associates Long Beach, California
Client: California Medical Products Long Beach, California
Materials: High density polyethylene; ¼-in. Volara foam; Velcro® closure system; Fastex fasteners

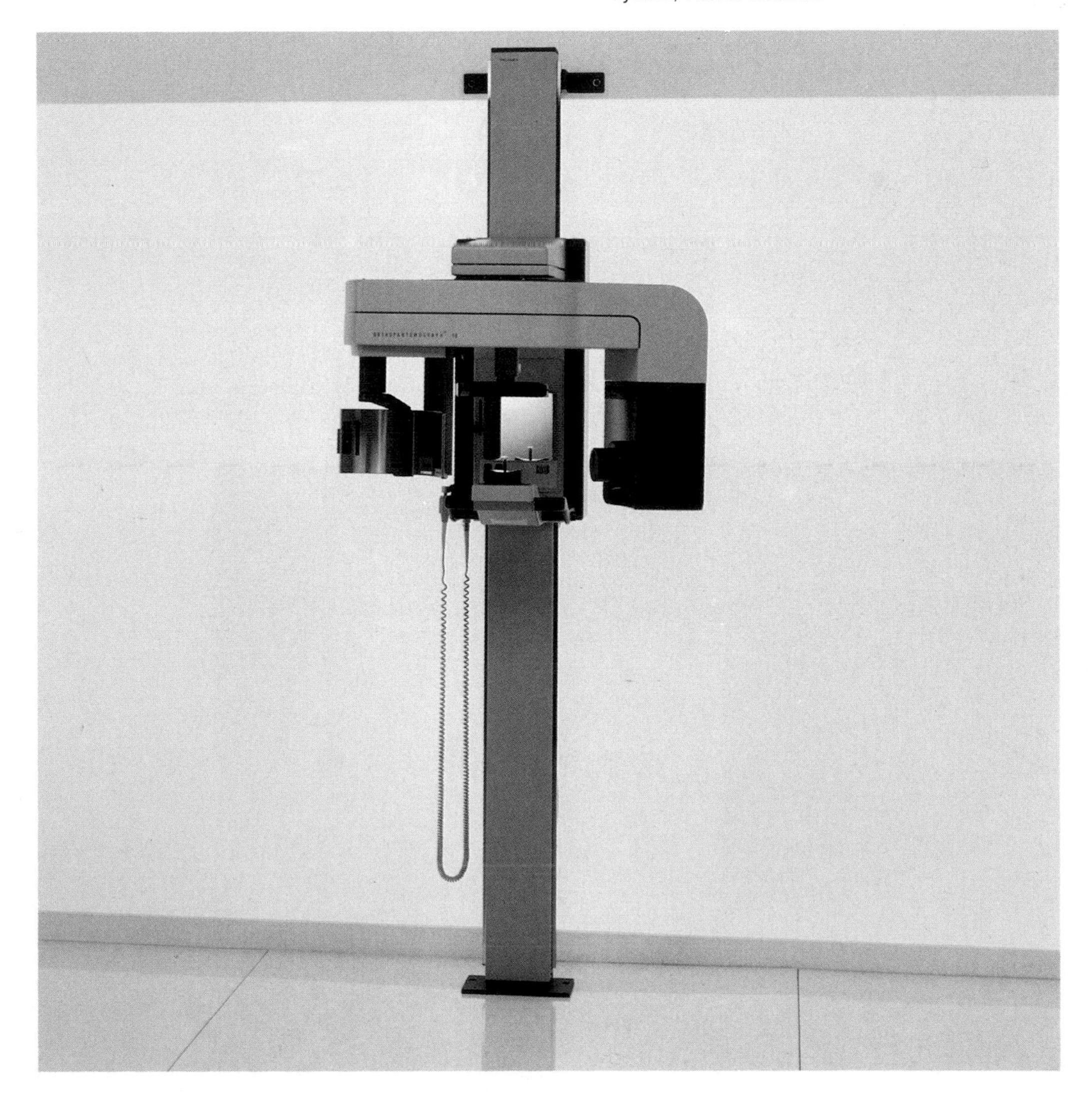

Product: Orthopantomograph, panoramic X-ray unit
Design Firm: Siemens Design Center, Munich & Berlin, West Germany
Client: Siemens Medical, Erlangen, West Germany
Materials: Injection plastic mold, sheet metal, and metal profile

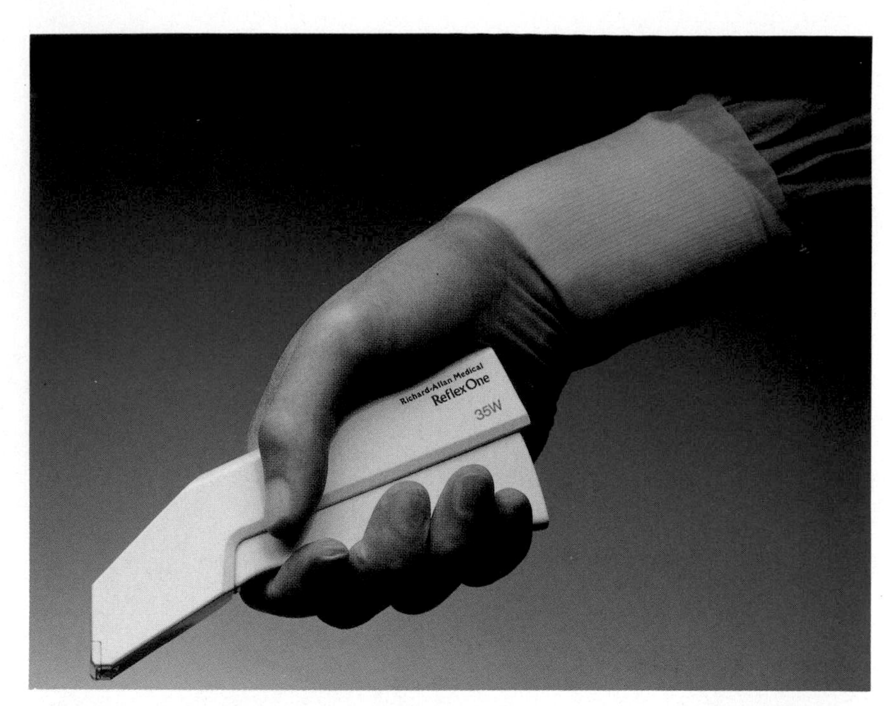

Product: Disposable Skin Stapler
Design Firm: Human Factors/Industrial Design, Inc., New York, New York
Client: Richard-Allan Medical, Kalamazoo, Michigan
Materials: Polycarbonate, ABS, 300 series stainless steel, 400 series stainless steel

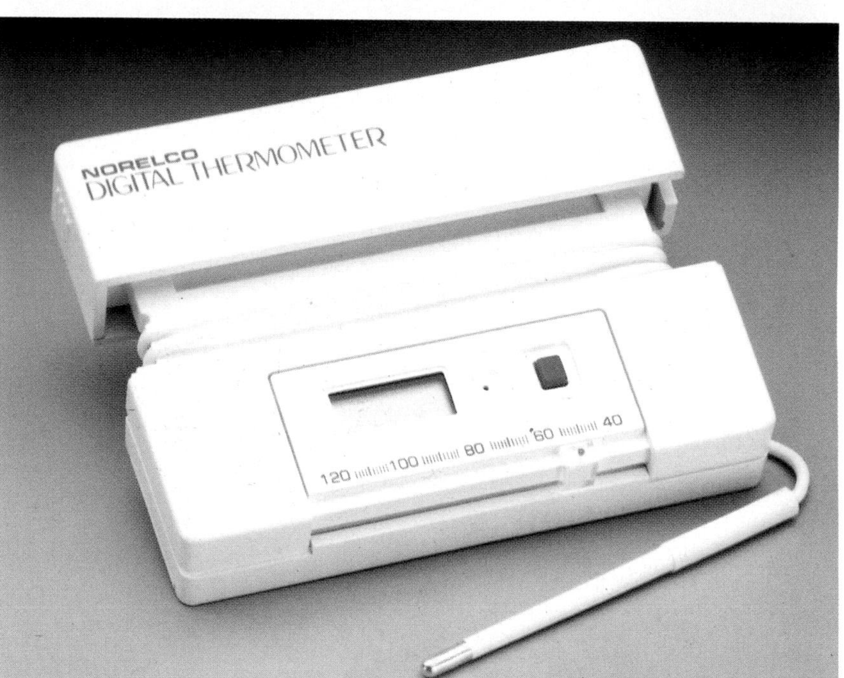

Product: Digital Thermometer HT-987
Client: NORELCO Consumer Products Division, North American Philips Corporation, Stamford, Connecticut

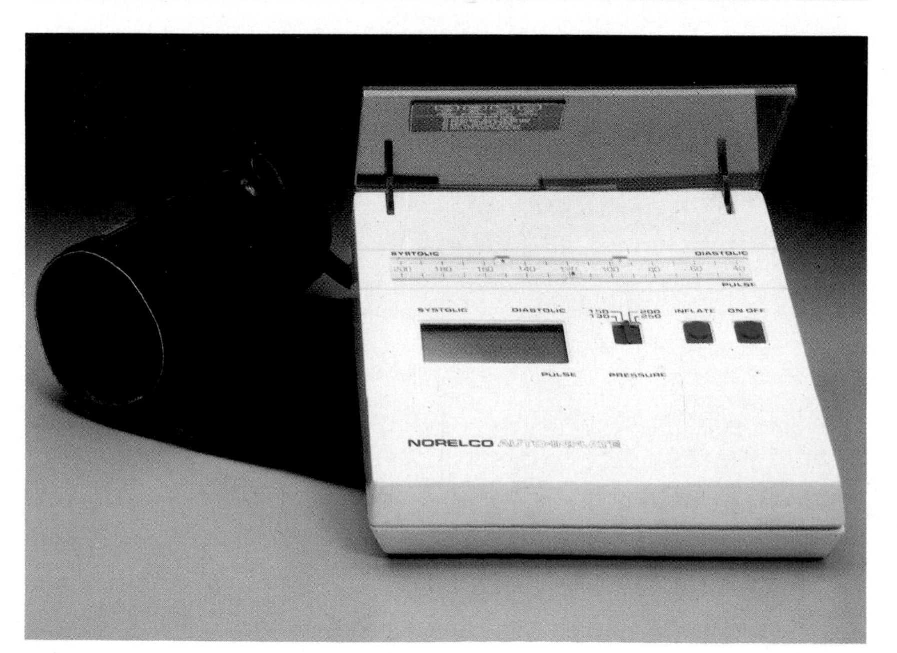

Product: Digital Blood Pressure Meter
Client: NORELCO Consumer Products Division, North American Philips Corporation, Stamford, Connecticut

Product: Micro Hook
Designers: Kazuna Tanaka, Jeffrey Kapec
Design Firm: Tanaka Kapec Design Group, Inc. South Norwalk, Connecticut
Client: Ethicon, Inc., Somerville, New Jersey
Awards: 1985 *Industrial Design* magazine Design Review selection

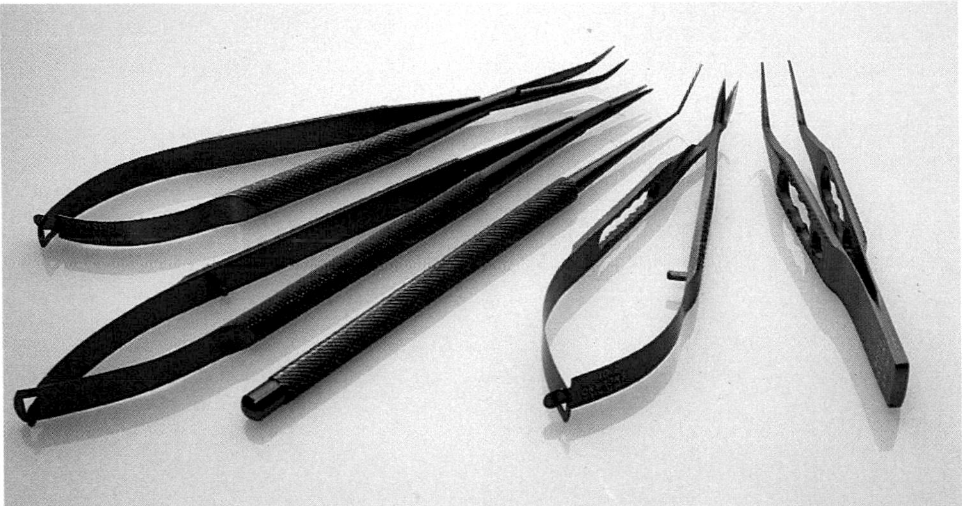

Product: Titanium Instruments for Ophthalmology
Design Firm: Microsurgical Administrative Services, Ltd., Luton, Bedfordshire, England
Awards: 1985 Design Council Award
Materials: Titanium; tungsten carbide coating

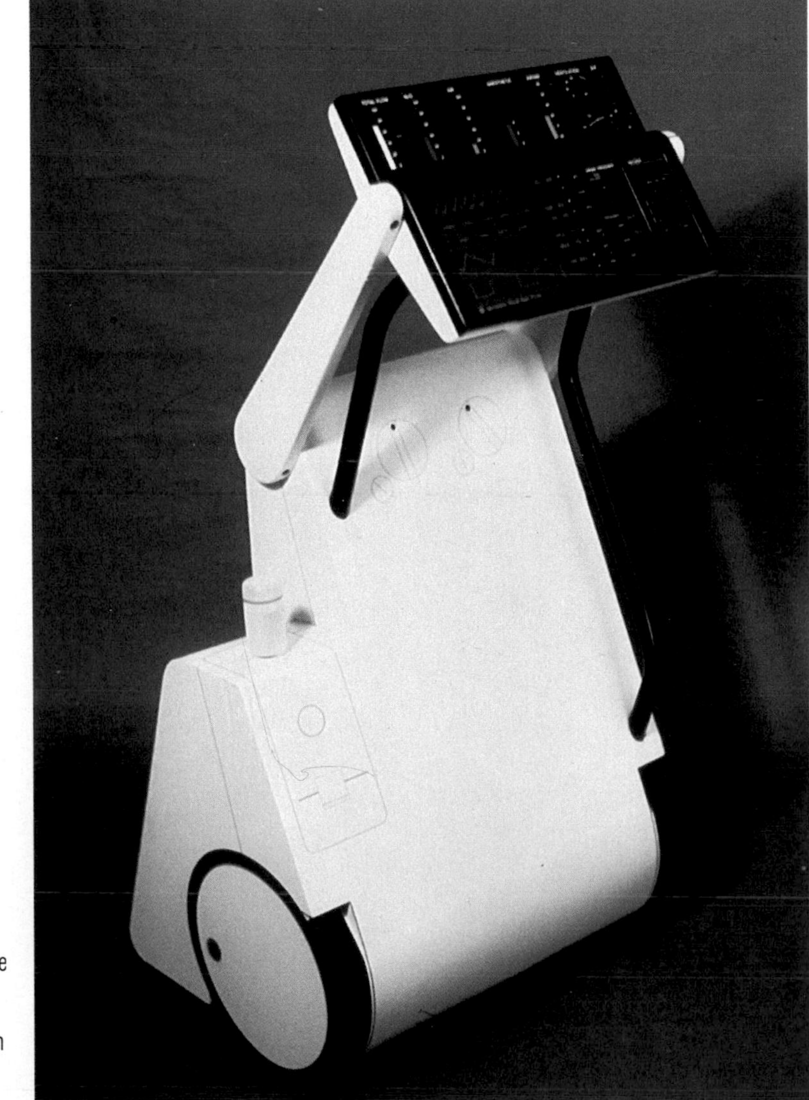

Product: Anesthetic Gas Delivery & Patient Monitoring System
Designer: George Simons, Jr. Minneapolis, Minnesota
Design Firm: Simons Design, Minneapolis, Minnesota
Awards: 1985 *Industrail Design* magazine Design Review selection, Concept Category
Materials: Injection molded structural foam with metal internal component supports

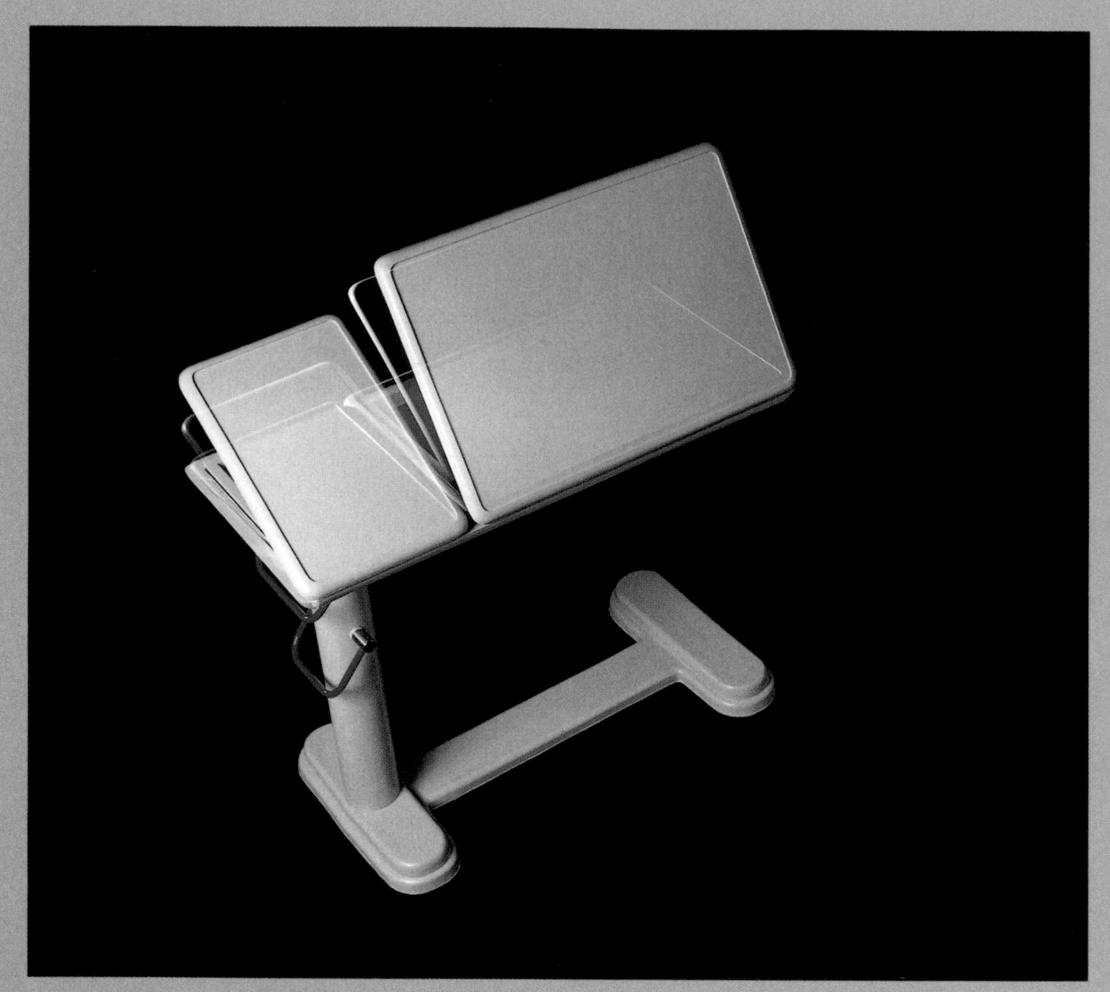

Product:	Baycrest Overbed Table
Designers:	Keith Muller, Anne Carlyle
Design Firm:	Keith Muller Limited, Toronto, Canada
Client:	Baycrest Hospital, Toronto, Canada
Manufacturer:	GLOBALcare
Photo Credit:	David Allen

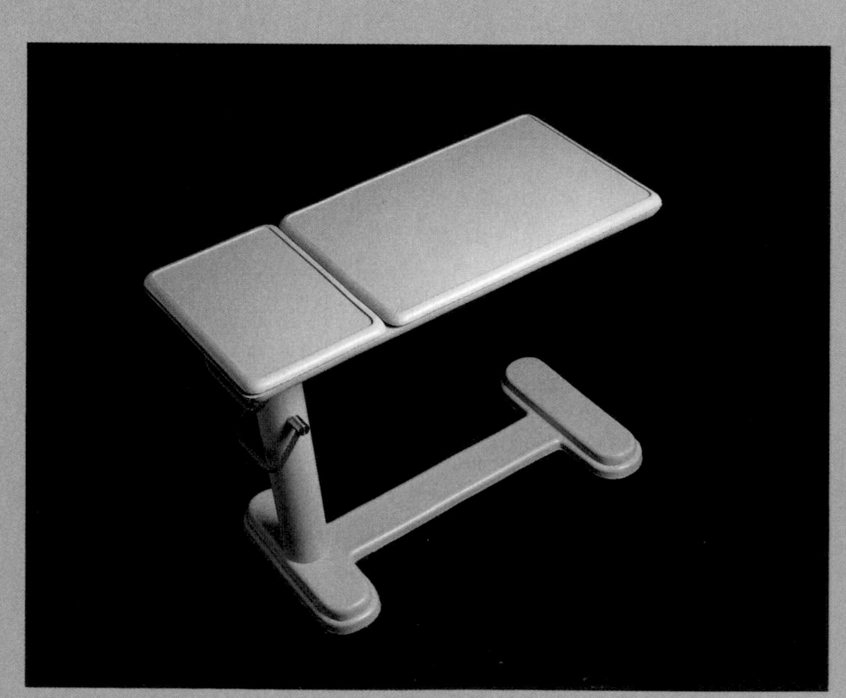

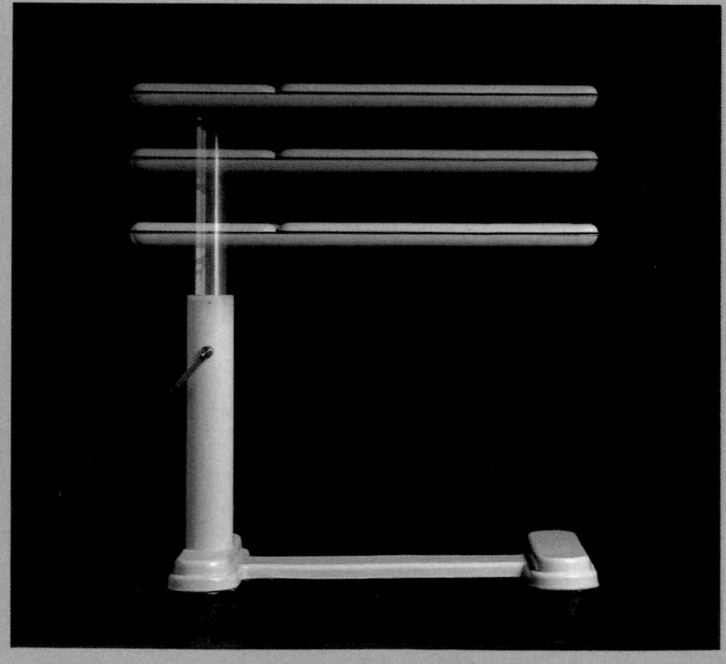

Product: Portable Nursing Unit Terminal
Designers: Eugene Helmetsie, David McAlpine, Brad Roark, Steven O'Connell, Keith Kenyon, Richard Quaif, Avinash Thukral, and Kenneth Schory
Design Firm: NCR Corporation, Dayton, Ohio
Client: NCR Corporation, Dayton, Ohio

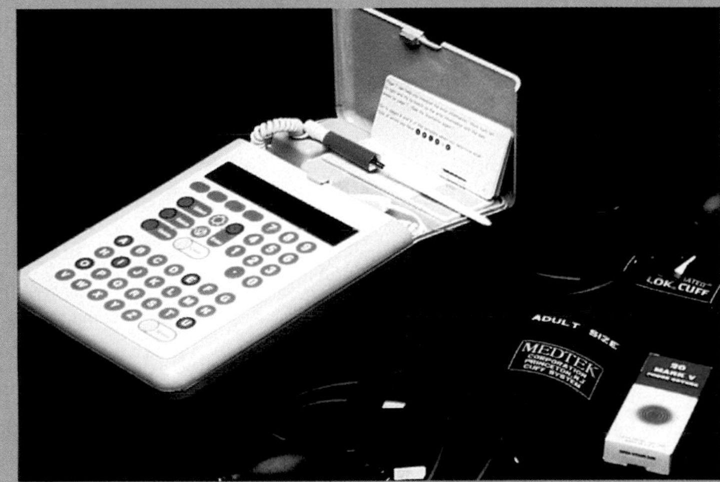

Product: Universal Crutch
Designer: Vladimir Pezdirc
Design Firm: Studio Kvadrat, Ljubljana, Yugoslavia
Client: ZRI Rehabilitation Center Ljubljana, Yugoslavia
Awards: 10th International Biennial of Industrial Design in Ljubljana gold medal winner

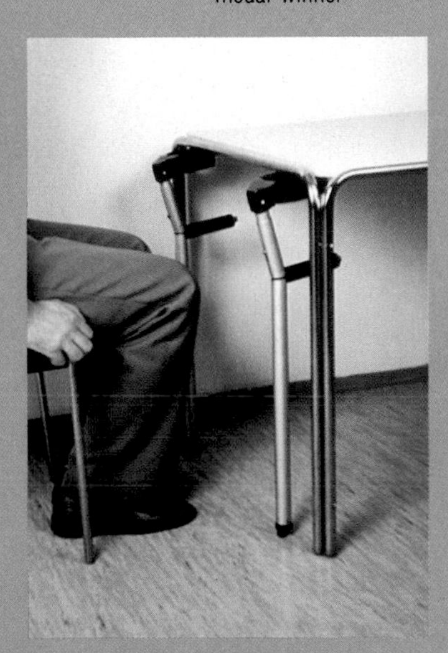

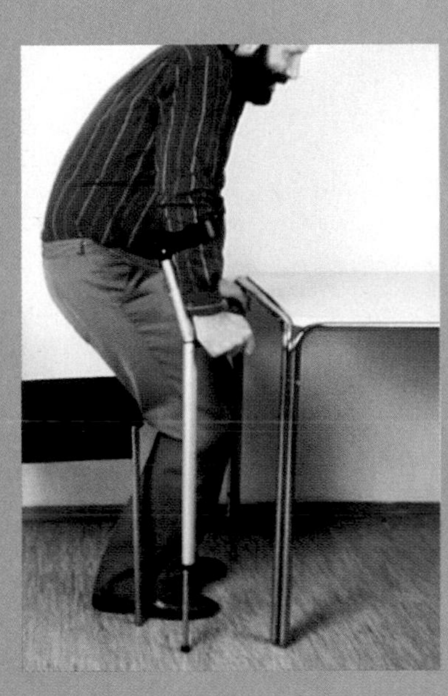

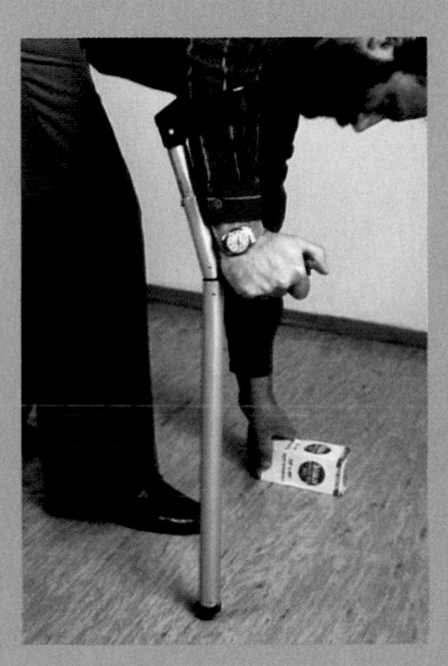

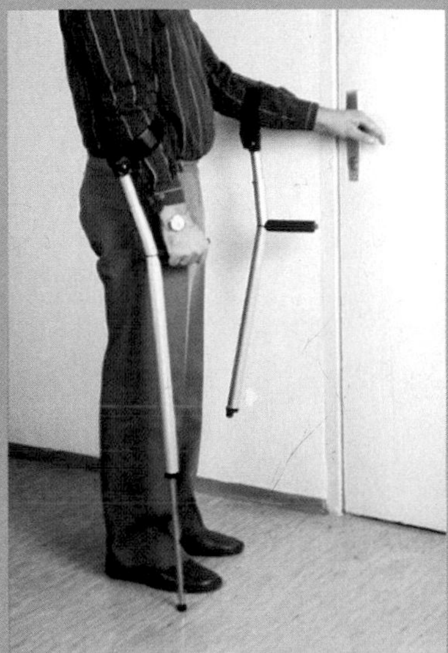

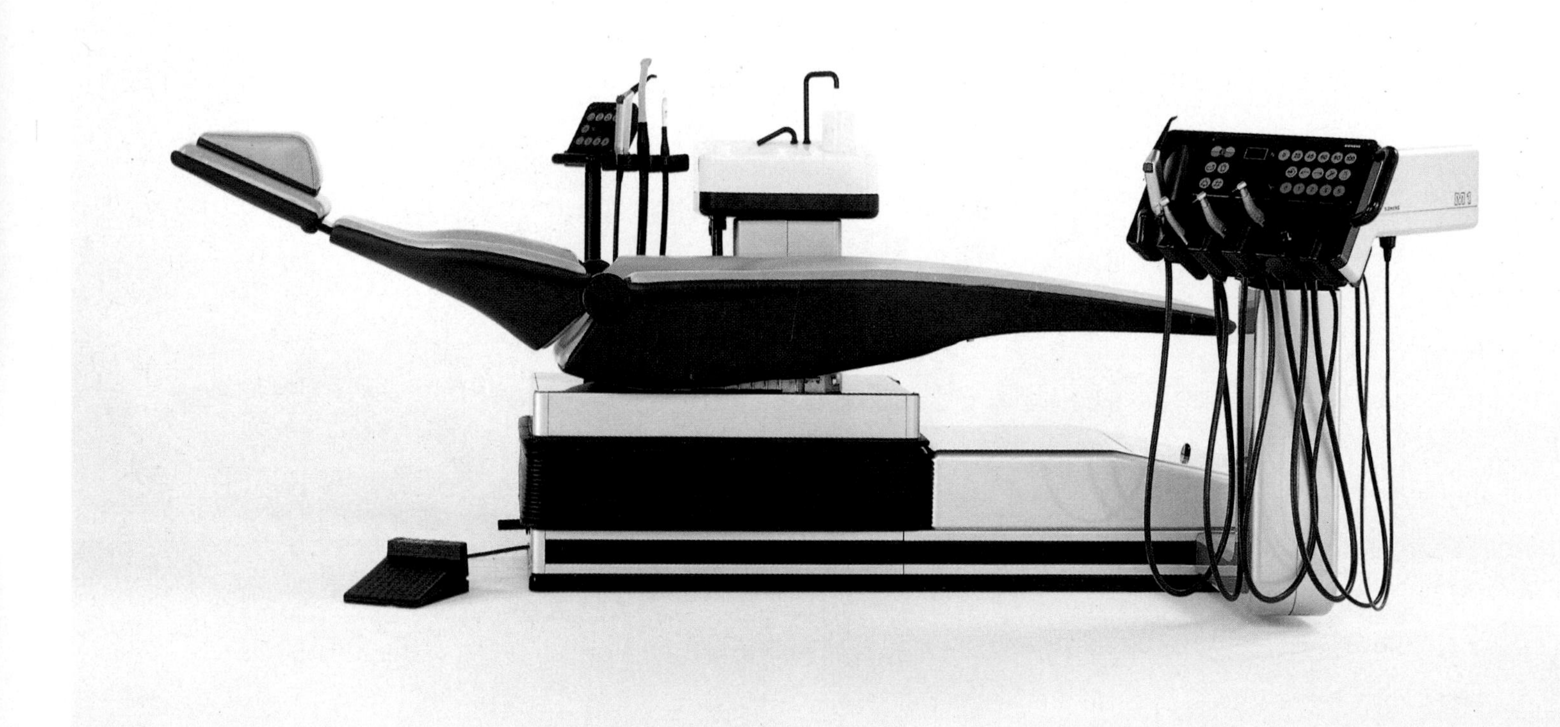

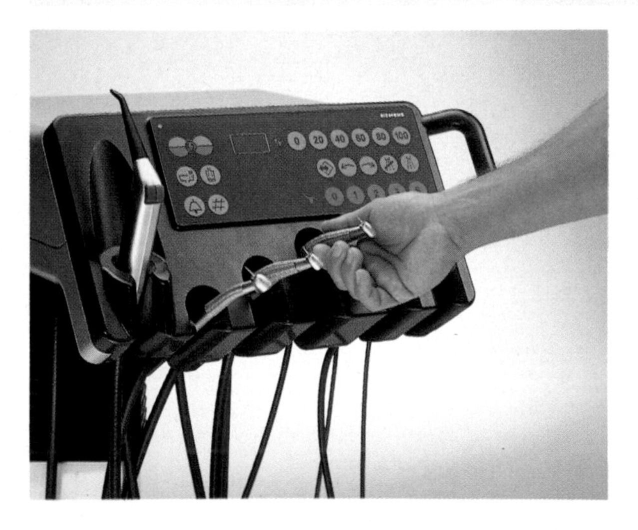

Product: SIRONA M 1, dental unit
Design Firm: Siemens Design Center, Munich & Berlin, West Germany
Client: Siemens Medical, Erlangen, West Germany
Awards: 1985 *Industrial Design* magazine Design Review selection
Materials: Injection plastic mold; plastic foam and upholstery

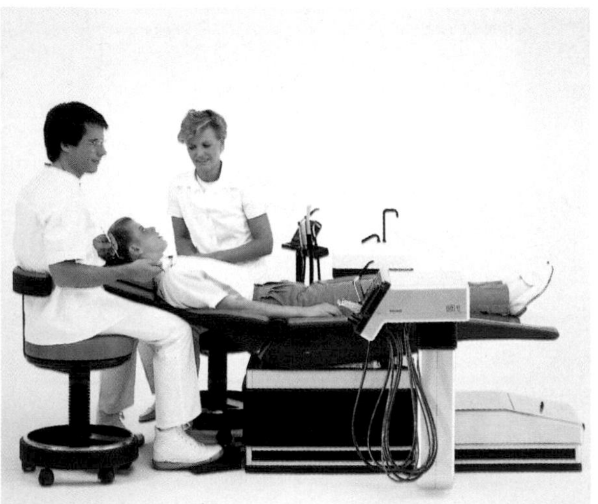

Product: SIRONA System 4000
Design Firm: Siemens Design Center Muenchen & Berlin, West Germany
Client: Siemens Medical, Erlangen, West Germany
Materials: Metal-casting and lathering-milling surface

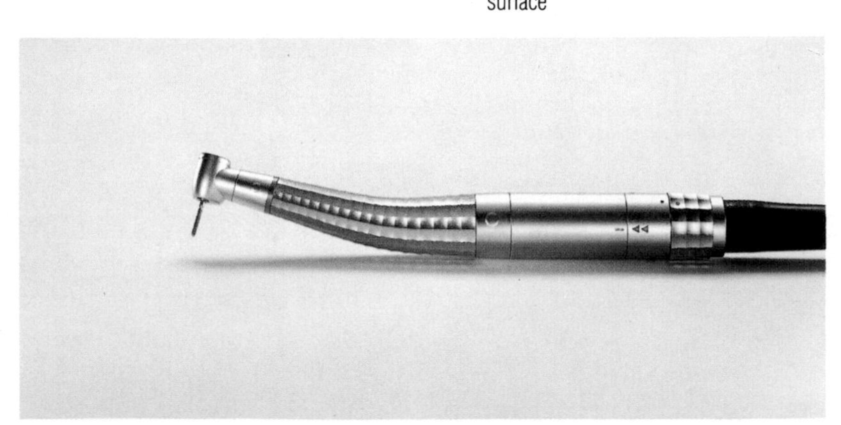

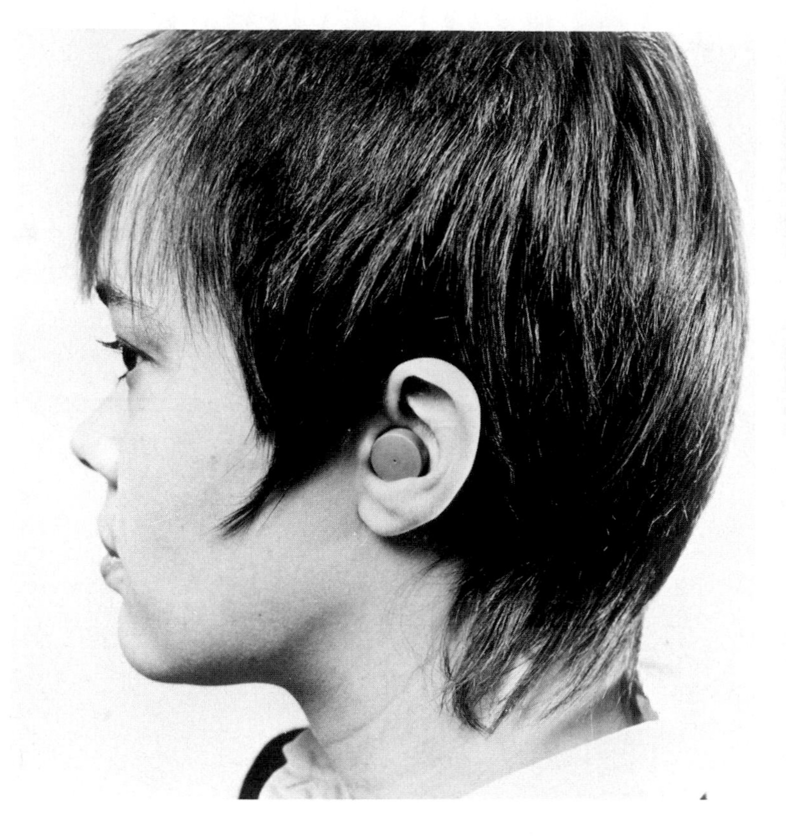

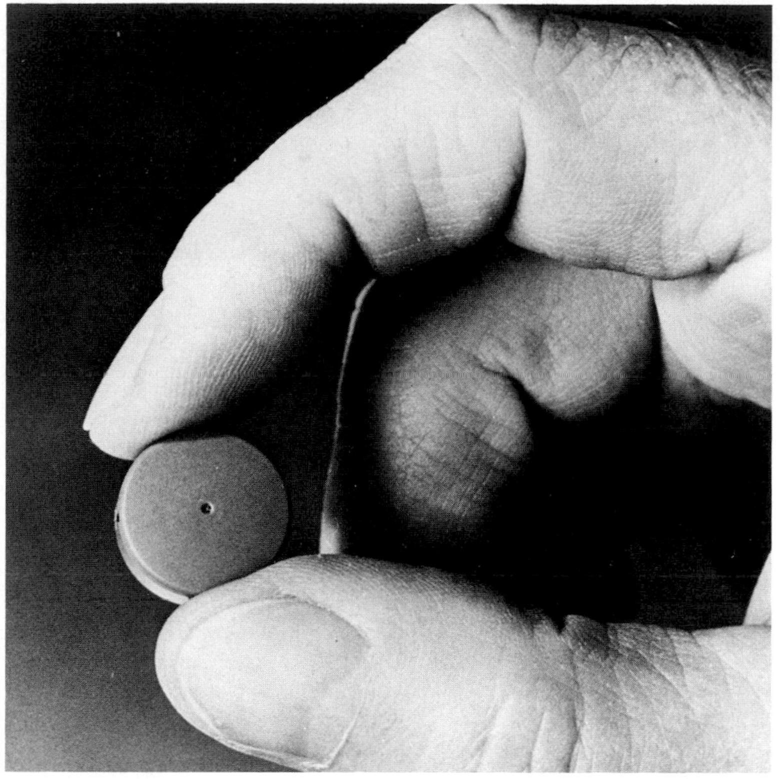

Product: WIDEX Audilens Hearing Aid
Designer: Christian Tøpholm, Denmark
Client: Tøpholm & Westerman, Ballerup, Denmark
Awards: The ID Prize 1985, Denmark

Product: KaVo REGIE 1050
Design Firm: frogdesign, Campbell, California
Client: KaVo Werk, Riss, West Germany
Awards: Stuttgart Design Centre Award

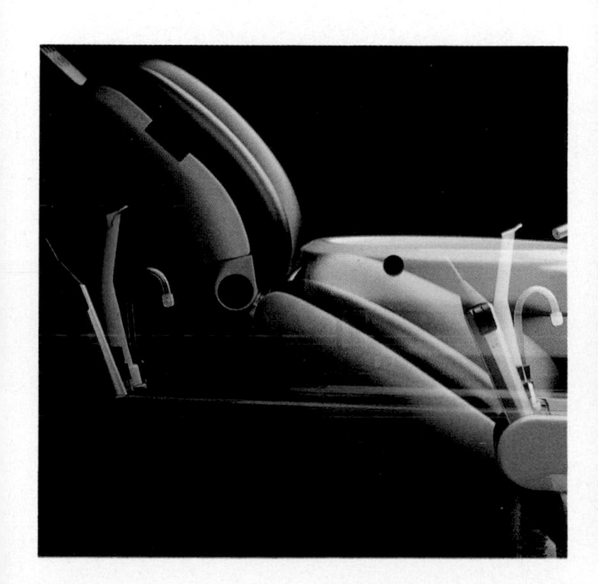

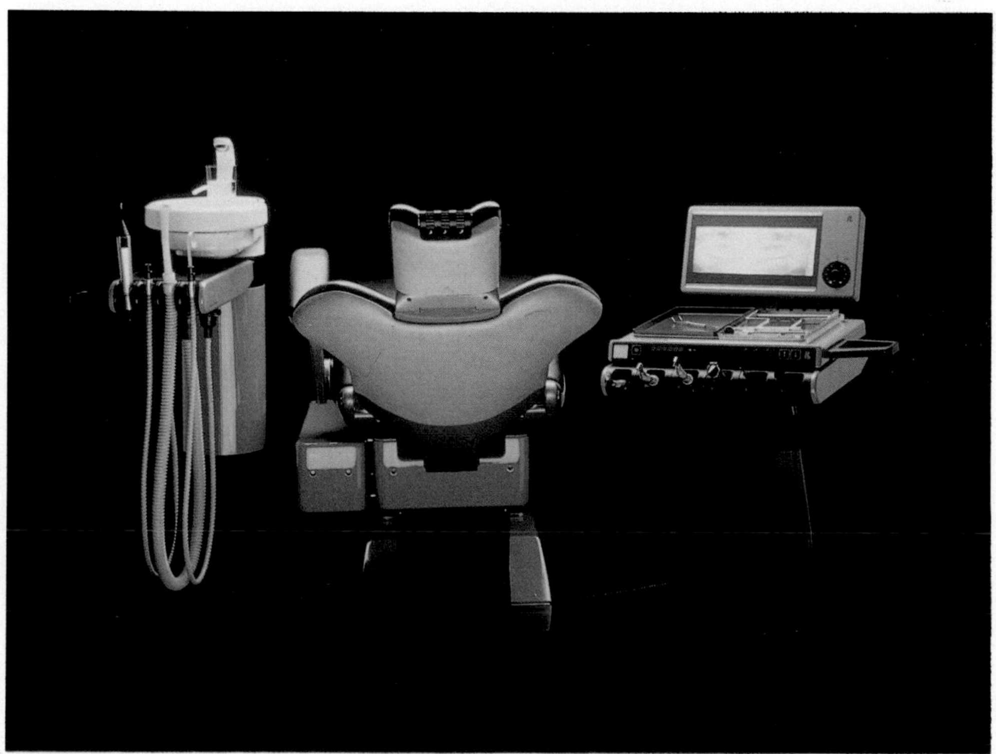

INDUSTRIAL EQUIPMENT

CHAPTER

In defining a career decision to focus heavily on the design of industrial equipment, Alexander Bally said, ''I enjoy the challenge of satisfying these demanding, tightly hemmed-in design limitations.'' Demanding they are. These must be designs that *work.* (As the saying goes, these are the designs that ''move America''—quite literally in some cases.)

It used to be that you could tell if a product belonged in the industrial equipment category by how big or ugly it was. No longer. Aesthetics, sacrificed for so long to functional or economic concerns, are making a comeback. These designs hold their own against any in other product categories. Like the selections in the '85 *ID Annual,* ''these products not only contained state of the art technology, but embraced it in their styling.''

While graphics still suffer from substandard applications in many instances, user comfort has reached an all-time high in this equipment, with attention to safety features, quieter operating conditions, and better handle and control level designs.

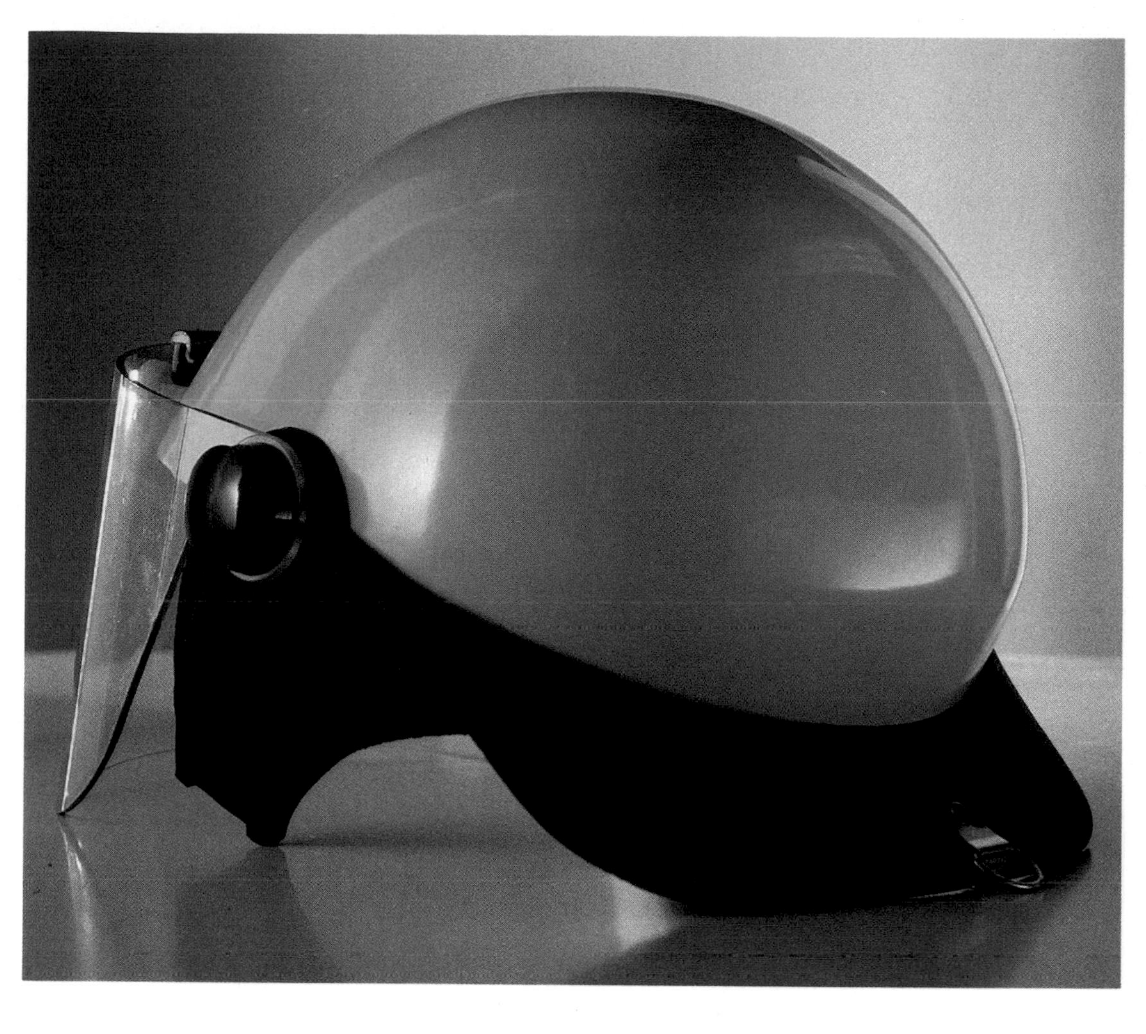

Product: Brigade Firefighter Helmut
Designers: M. Baldwin, J. C. Kaufman, H. R. Roudebush, L. R. Miller, S. L., Mitchell, and William R. Abraham
Design Firm: Industrial Design Association Indianapolis, Indiana
Staff Design: R. H. Raft, L. G. Svelter, R. H. Crane, R. Zevnick, and J. Young
Client: Union Carbide Corporation, Engineering Product Division, Indianapolis, Indiana
Awards: 1985 *Industrial Design* magazine Design Review, Best of Category

Product: Bench Top Fume Cupboard
Design Firm: ninaber/peters/krouwel, industrial design, Netherlands
Client: S+B, Rotterdam, Netherlands
Materials Plywood with hard plastic, safety glass, plastic extrusion profile, electronics

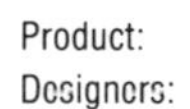

Product: Automated Rodent Trap
Designers: Henry Keck, Cecil Young, and Harold Ford
Design Firm: Keck-Craig Associates South Pasadena, California
Staff Design: Robert LaVoie, Mike Agron
Client: Ace Post Control, Culver City, California

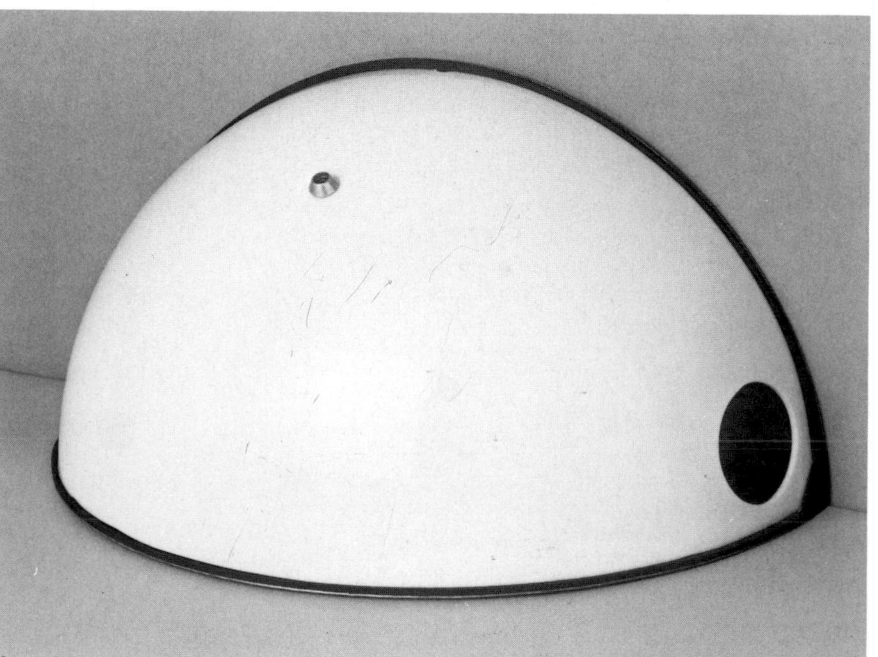

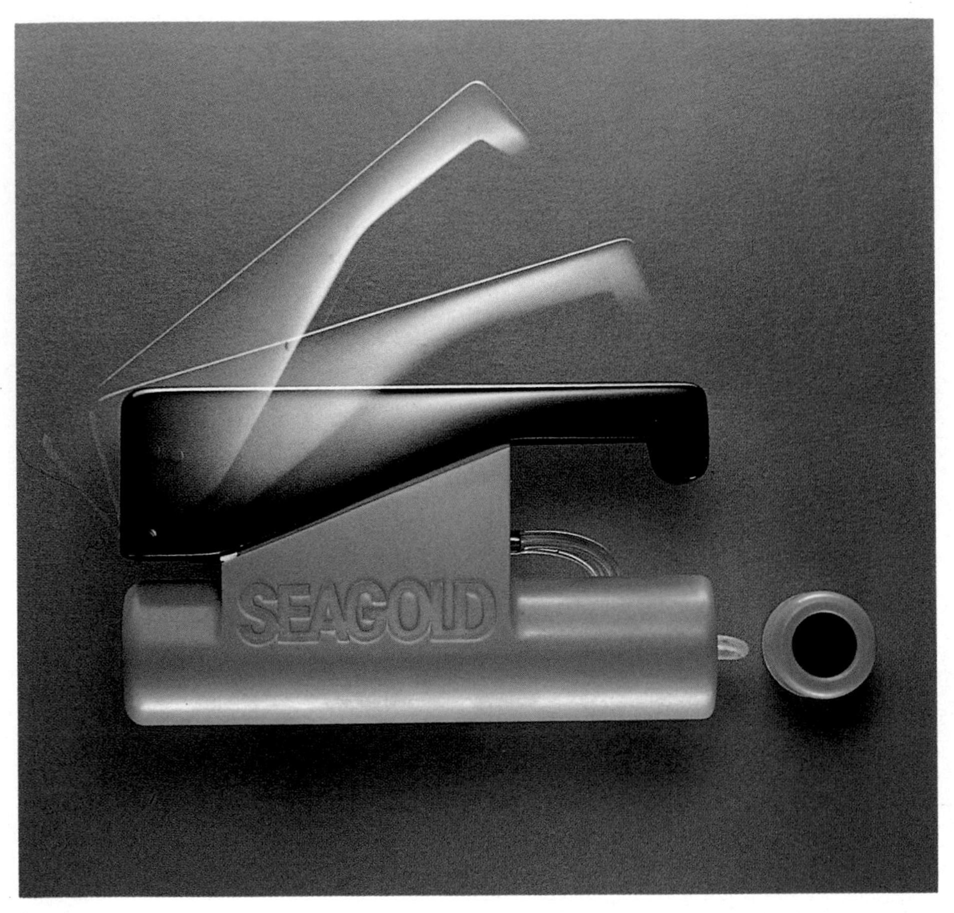

Product: Manual Desalinator
Designers: Jerry Adamson, Philip Poissant, and Derek Fenske
Design Firm: Adamson Industrial Design Inc. Toronto, Ontario, Canada
Staff Design: Frank Schrack
Client: Seagold Industries Ltd., Burnaby, British Columbia, Canada
Materials: Base molding: cast mica filled polyester; handle: compression molded glass filled polyester

Product: Orbitread 2001 Retread Machine
Design Firm: Keck-Craig Associates South Pasadena, California
Client: Retread Engineering, AMF Tire Equipment Division Santa Ana, California

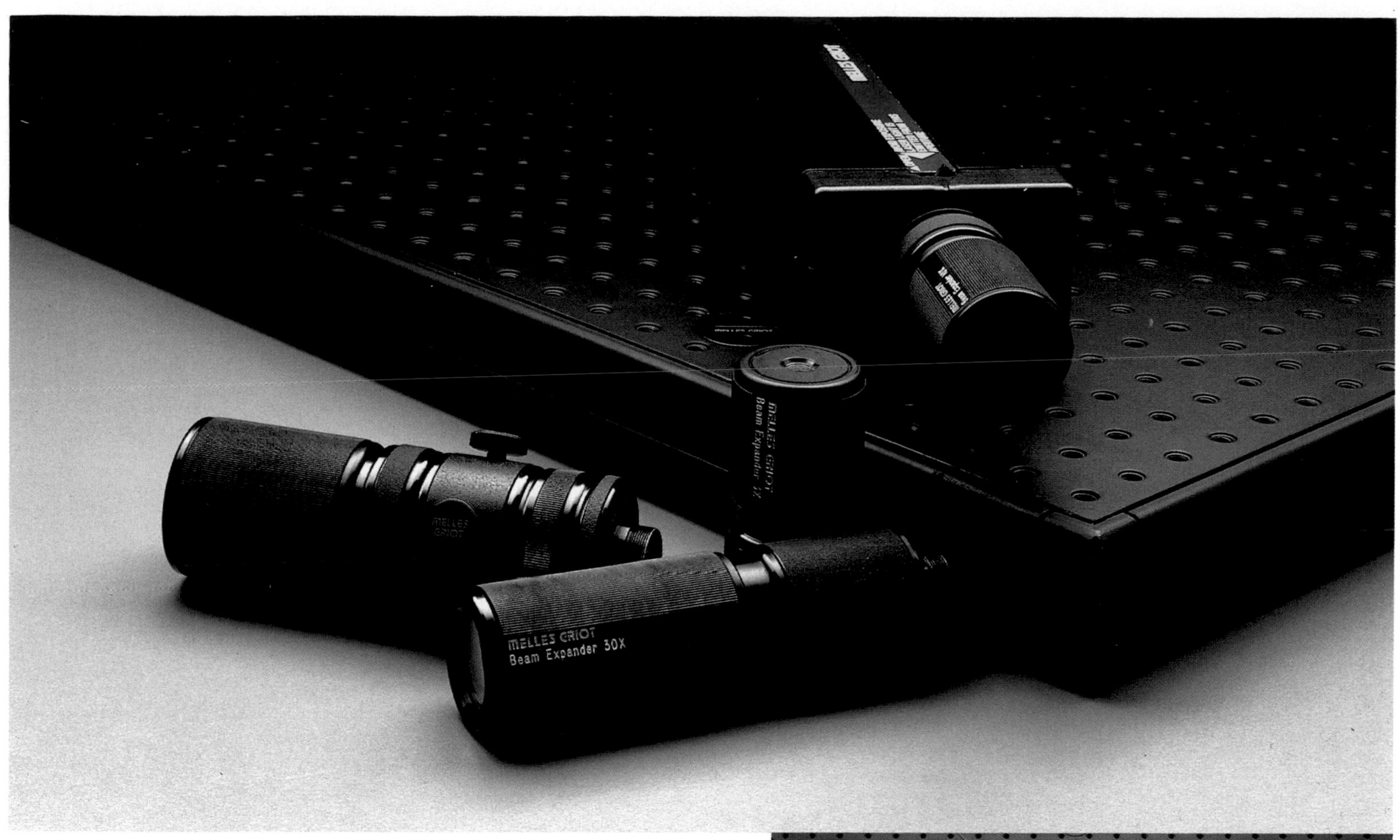

Product:	Self-Contained Helium Neon Laser
Designers:	Philippe Chretien, Robin Chu, and Bill Moggridge
Design Firm:	ID Two, San Francisco, California
Staff Design:	Scott Inman, Mitchell Enright, and Robert Flower
Client:	Melles-Griot, Irvine, California
Awards:	1984 *Industrial Design* magazine Design Review selection
Materials:	Aluminum extruded main body

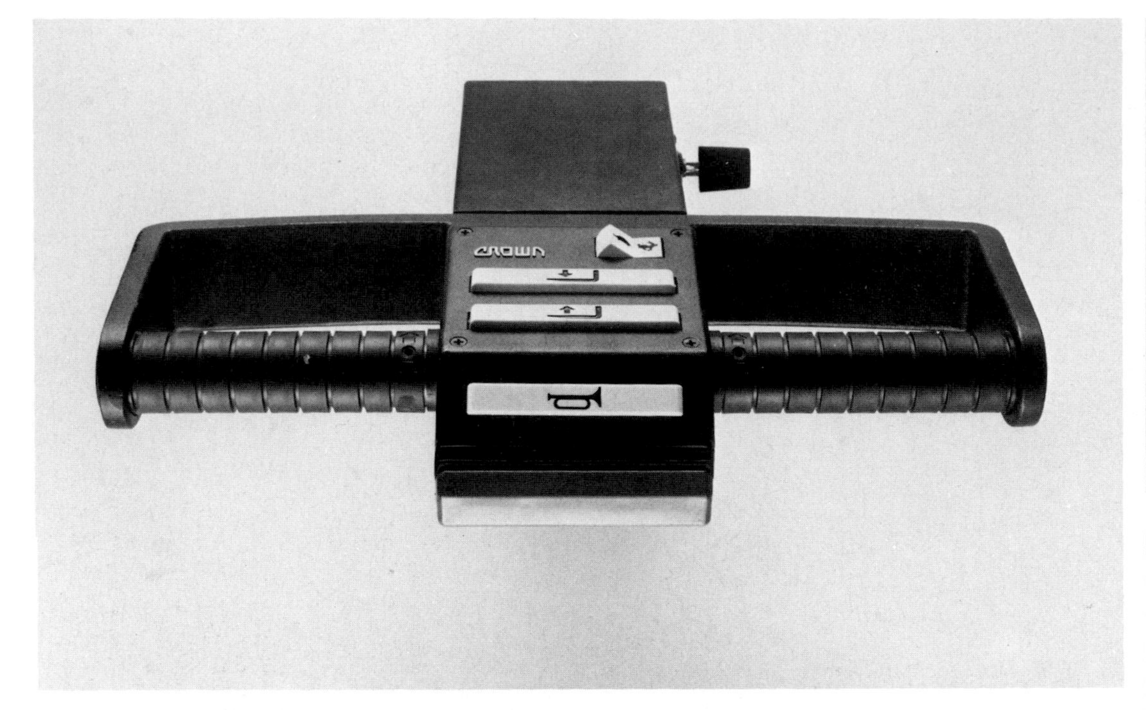

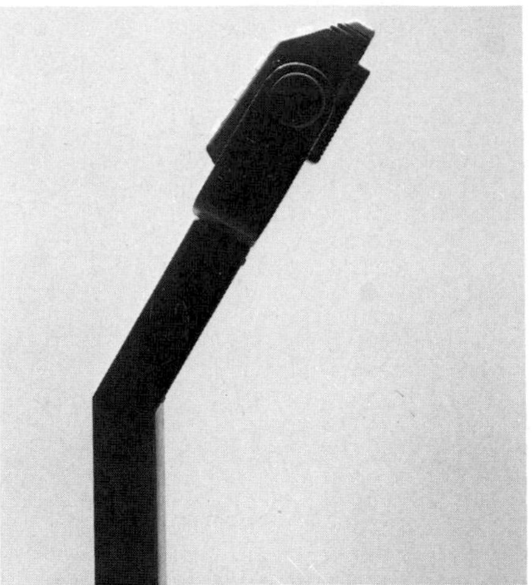

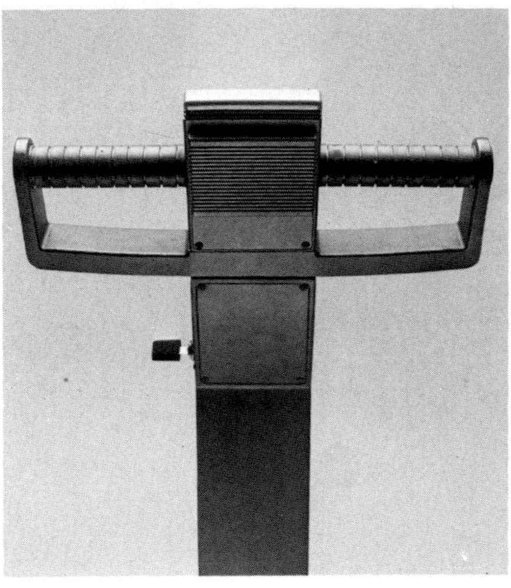

Product:	Crown Controls
Designers:	Keith Kresge, David Smith
Design Firm:	Richardson/Smith Inc. Worthington, Ohio
Staff Design:	Harold Stammen, Bob Eilerman, Guy Thornell, and Paul Leasor
Client:	Crown Controls Corporation, New Breman, Ohio
Materials:	Control tiller: sand-cast aluminum; control pod and cover: die-cast aluminum; protective yoke: sand-cast aluminum/magnesium alloy; rotating handle grip: high impact nylon; bellows: molded polyurethane; switch-bars: nylon with hot stamped information

Product:	Grundfos Submersible Sump Pump
Designer:	N. Due Jensen, Denmark
Client:	Grundfos A/S, Bjerringbro, Denmark
Awards:	The ID Prize 1985, Denmark

Product: Robot: The Merlin Flexible Manufacturing System

Designers: Alexander Bally, Chuck Kraeuter

Design Firm: Bally Designs Inc., Carnegie, Pennsylvania

Client: American Robot Corporation Pittsburgh, Pennsylvania

Awards: 1984 *Industrial Design* magazine Design Review selection; 1984 IDSA, Industrial Design Excellence Award

Materials: Structural parts: permanent mold, machined aluminum alloy; paint finish: Polene; covers: motor enclosure: thermo-formed royalite ABS; bellows: fabricated rubber

Product: Fiber Optic Draw Capstan and Winder
Designers: Eddie Machen, Charles Floyd
Design Firm: Machen Designs, Inc.
Charlotte, North Carolina
Staff Design: Earl Seagrave
Client: Walker Technical, Inc.
Charlotte, North Carolina
Materials: Winder/control frame: mild steel, rectangular tubing; textured, polyurethane, painted finish; face: aluminum, clear anodic finish; back: vacuum formed ABS; rollers: machined acetal; shafts: stainless steel
Capstan frame: aluminum, clear anodic finish; cover: sheet steel; textured, polyurethane, painted finish; rollers: stainless steel; shafts: stainless steel; belt: polyester/glass fiber composite

Product: Precision Implant 9000, ion implanter for production of semi-conductors
Designers: Barrie Weaver, Paul Canning, and Kerrin Lyons
Design Firm: Roberts Weaver, London, England
Client: Applied Materials, Inc., California
Materials: Housing: aluminum extrusions, aluminum board, and foamed polyurethane moldings

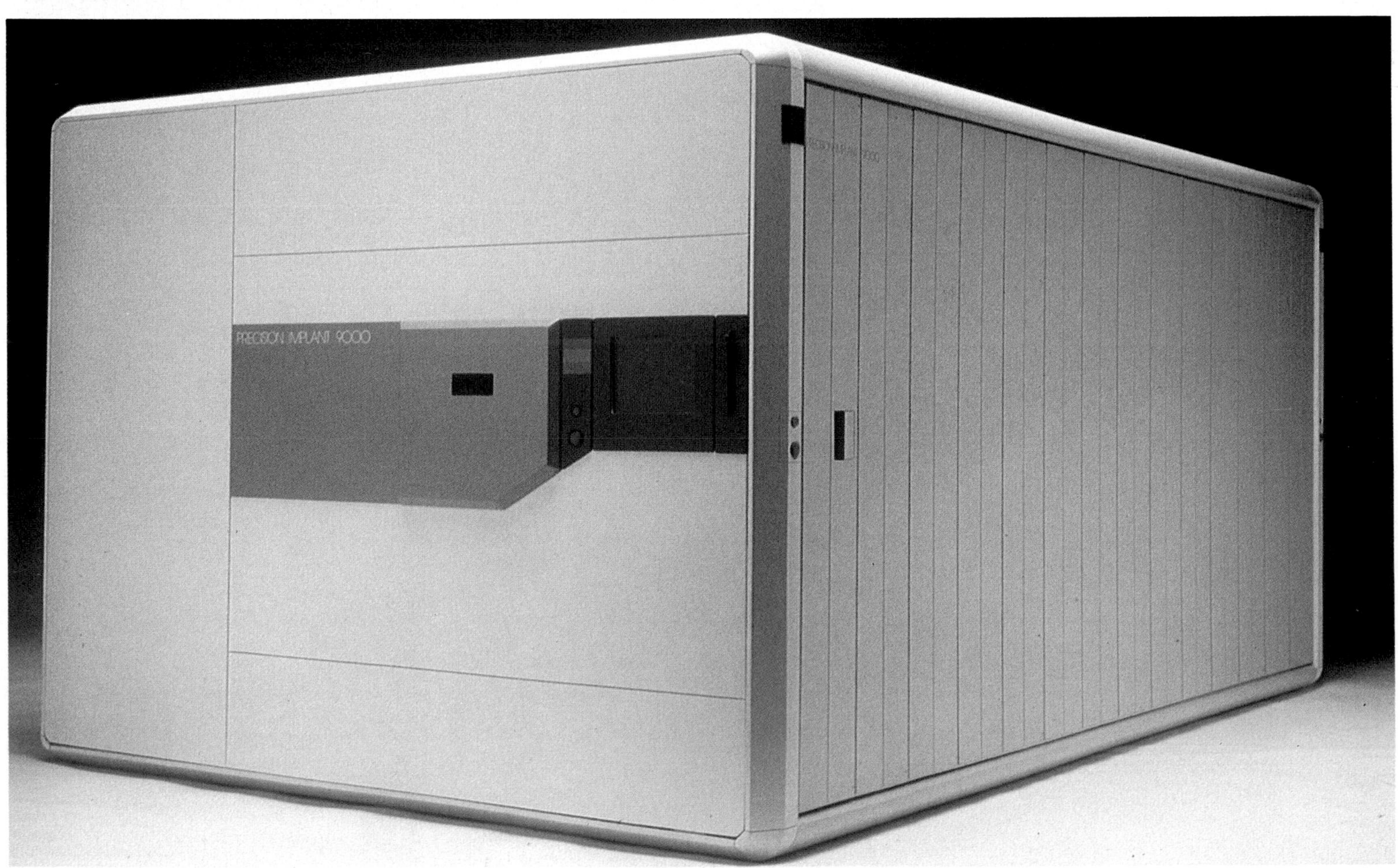

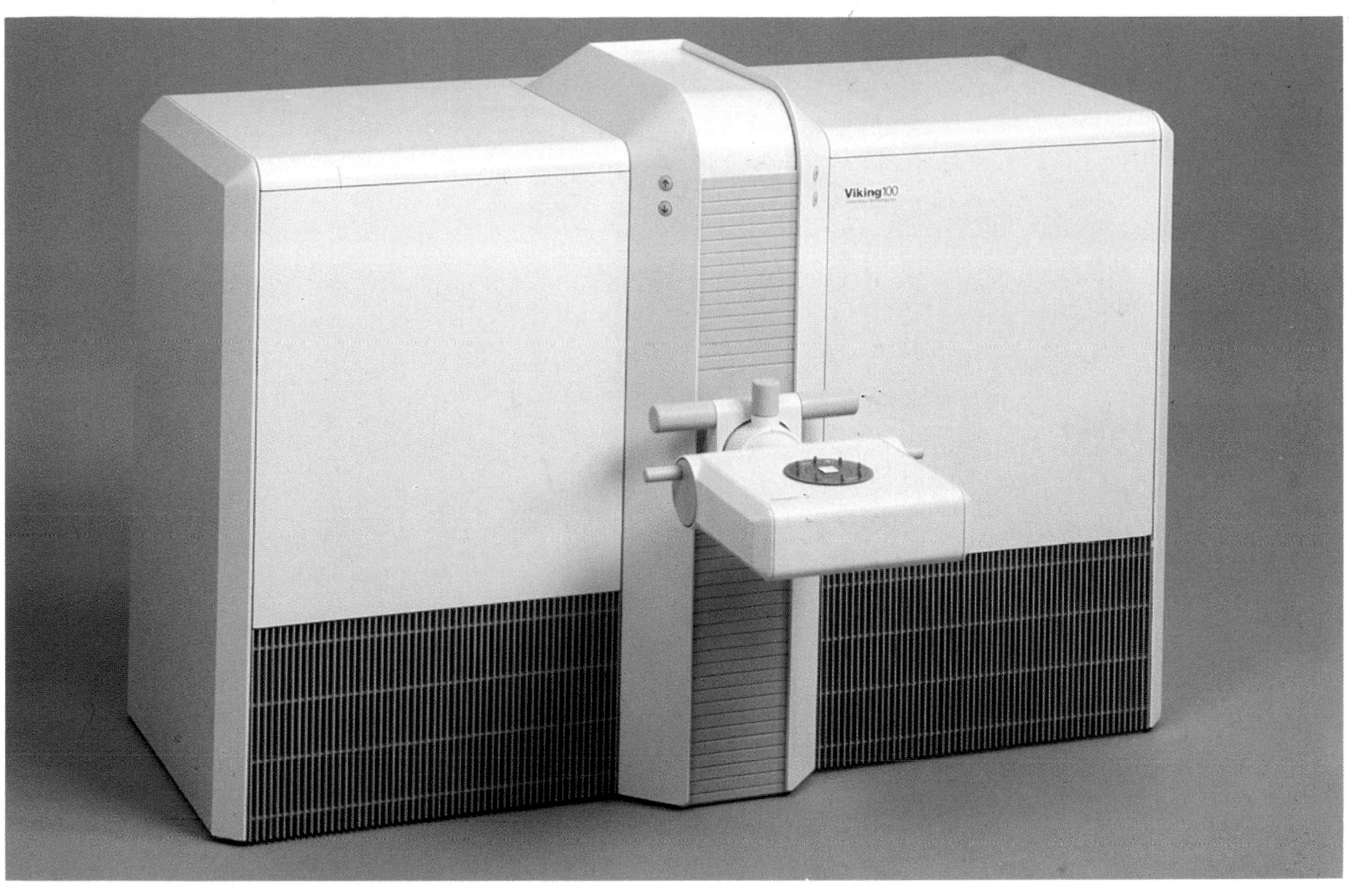

Product: CyberTek Viking 100 VLS1 Chip
Designer: Mike Nuttall
Design Firm: Matrix Product Design
Palo Alto, California
Staff Design: Charlie Fiorella, Bill Burnett
Client: Convergent Technologies
San Jose, California
Awards: 1984 *Industrial Design* magazine Design Review selection
Materials: Injection-molded ABS exterior; surface-mounted electronics

Product: LS1 and LS2, high intensity light sources for fibre optics
Designer: Barrie Weaver, London, England
Design Firm: Roberts Weaver, London, England
Client: Spectron Instruments, Oxford, England
Materials: Aluminum extrusions and folded sheet steel

Product: Industrial Carpet Cleaners
Client: K'A'RCHER, West Germany

Product: Clark GCS-GPS 20/30
Designers: Kent Brown, Dennis Lanci, Robert Kirby, and Jay Reinhart
Client: Clark Material Handling Products Company, Battle Creek, Michigan
Awards: 1985 *Industrial Design* magazine Design Review selection
Materials: Cast gray iron for counter weights, rear axle, and upright top tie bars; blanked, draw formed, and trimmed sheet metal for side door, cowl, valve cover, seat deck, and logo plate; flame cut and laser cut sheet stock, formed for frame; cut square tube and bar stock welded together for overhead guard; injection molded ABS for warning plate and valve lever knobs; aluminum shell cast for instrument cluster, and shift quadrant

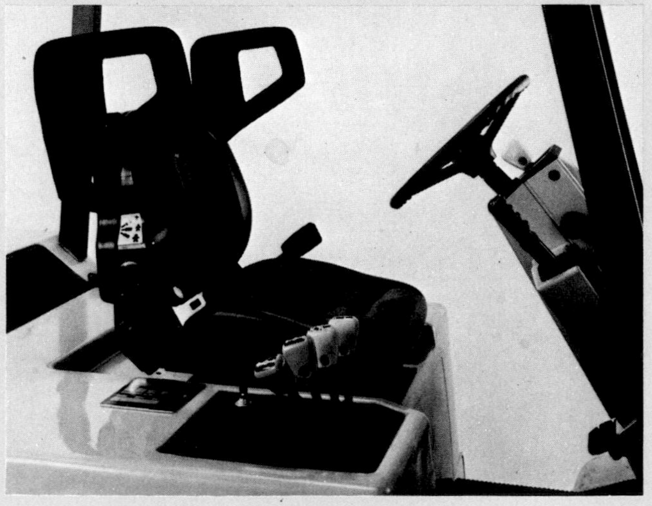

Product: ATM 500 Fuel Management Terminal
Designers: William Dalebout, Sohrab Vossoughi
Design Firm: ZIBA Associates, Portland, Oregon
Client: ATM Technologies, Inc., Beaverton, Oregon
Awards: 1984 *Industrial Design* magazine Design Review selection
Materials: Foamed polycarbonate; 1/8-inch formed aluminum; compressed urethane rubber gaskets; vacuum fluorescent display, painted with Polane-T, non-membrane, full travel keys

Product: Marley Dry Fix Rood
Designers: Chris Cooper, Geoff Quinell
Client: Marley Roof Tile Company, Ltd. England
Manufacturer: Marley Extrusions, England
Materials: Ventilated dry ridge, dry verge, uPVC fascia and ventilated soffit, and a comb eave filter
Awards: 1984 Design Council Award

Product: JCB 3CX Backhoe Loader
Client: JC Bamford Excavators Ltd.
England
Awards: 1984 Design Council Award

Product: Gasoline Dispenser
Designers: Allen Hawthorne, Gordon Bruce, and Arthur Nichols, IV
Design Firm: Eliot Noyes Industrial Design, Inc.
New Canaan, Connecticut
Client: Mobil Oil Corporation, Fairfax, Virginia
Materials: Painted, cold-rolled steel; brushed stainless steel; polycarbonate structural foam

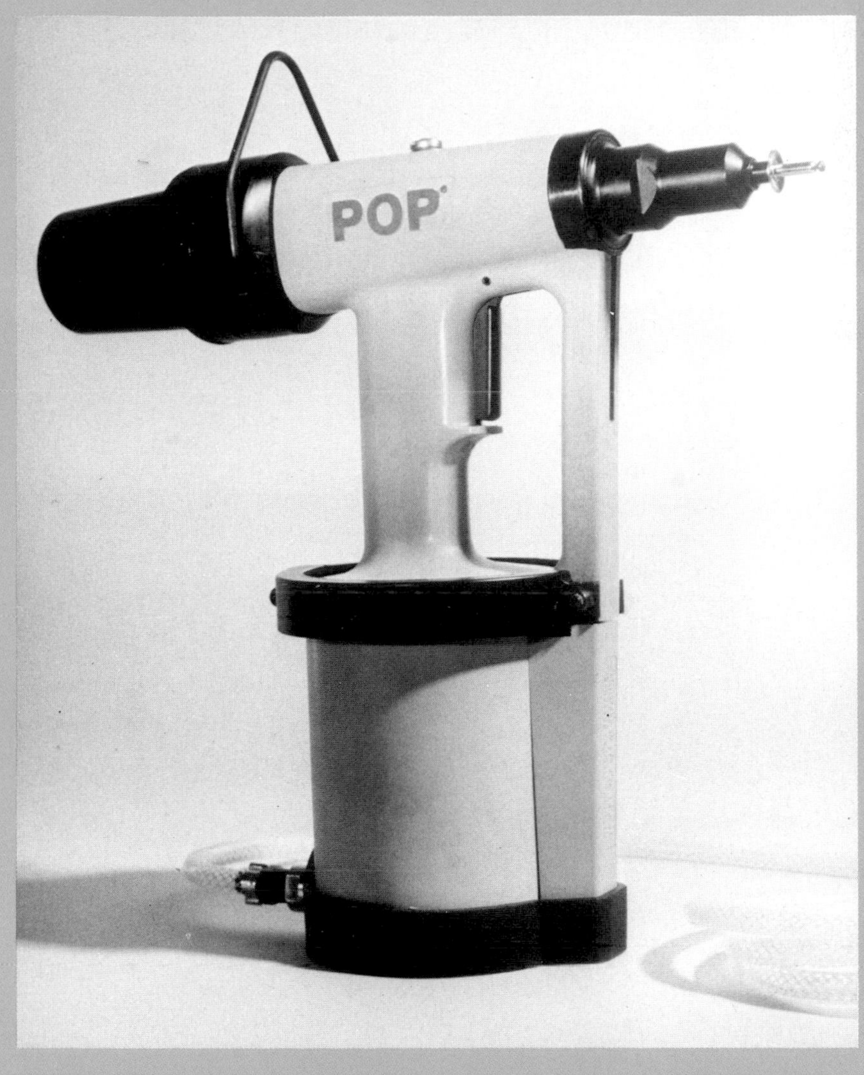

Product: 5500 Pop Rivet Tool
Designers: Richard H. Russell, R. Eric Anderson, David Kaiser, Thomas McLinden, and Rich O'Grady
Design Firm: ID Product Development Corporation, Farmington, Connecticut
Client: Pop Fasteners Division, Emhart Fastener Group, Shelton, Connecticut
Materials: Fiberglass reinforced polymer; internal working parts; all steel machined parts have an aircraft-quality alloy steel drivetrain

Product: Electronic Transmitter
Design Firm: Human Factors/Industrial Design, Inc., New York, New York
Client: Fisher Controls, Marshalltown, Iowa

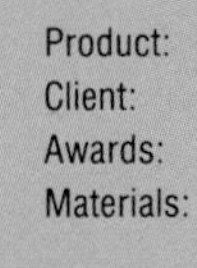
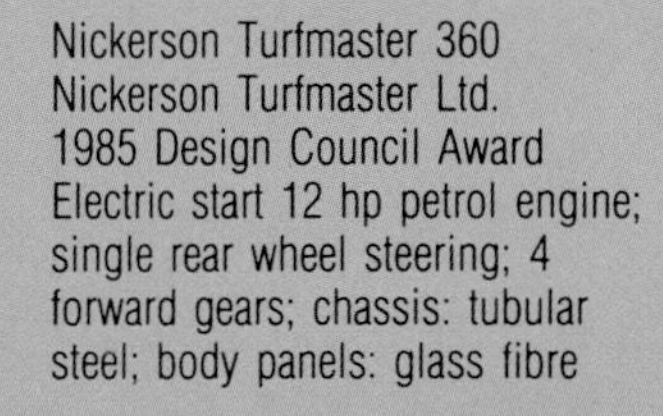

Product: Nickerson Turfmaster 360
Client: Nickerson Turfmaster Ltd.
Awards: 1985 Design Council Award
Materials: Electric start 12 hp petrol engine; single rear wheel steering; 4 forward gears; chassis: tubular steel; body panels: glass fibre

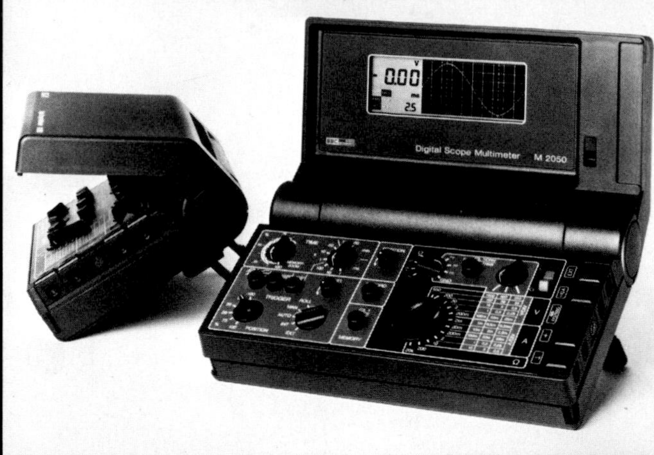

Product: Digital Scope Multimeter M 2050
Manufacturer: Metrawatt GmbH, Nürnberg, West Germany

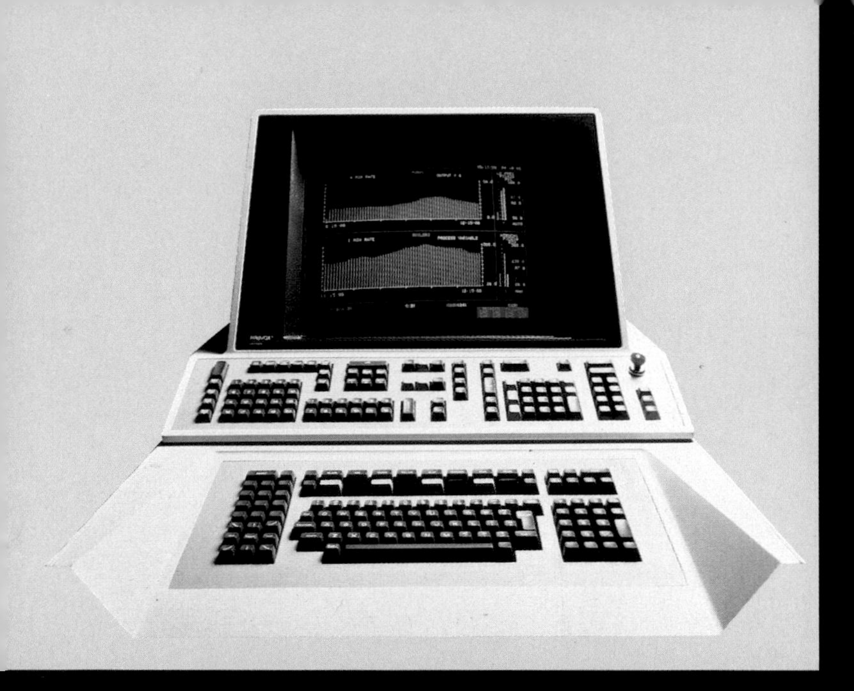

Product: Process Control Console
Design Firm: Human Factors/Industrial Design, Inc., New York, New York
Client: Fisher Controls, Marshalltown, Iowa

Product: Rear Tractor Wheels
Client: GKN Sankey, Ltd., England
Manufacturers: Karl Moller Nagbol, Denmark
Awards: 1985 Design Council Award

Product: Priestman VC15 Earth-Moving Machine
Client: Priestman Brothers Ltd.
Awards: 1984 Design Council Award

Product: Streetking 150 Suction Roa
Sweeper
Client: Schmidt Manufacturing & Equipment Ltd., England
Awards: 1984 Design Council Awarc

TRANSPORTATION

CHAPTER 11

''We don't style cars, we *design* them!'' So goes the tag line of the automotive industry. Marketing campaigns are capitalizing on the new public acceptance of design, and albeit unintentionally, correcting consumers' misconception of the development process. The designer is emerging from obscurity as slogans, finally, place credit where it is due.

Getting from here to there in the mid '80s can be accomplished in style . . . *whichever* one you may choose, from wit to elegance. Minimalist, fuel-efficient design is taken to its ultimate conclusion with ''Gashopper'' (the self-dubbed ''moped for the masses'') and, in the air, with the ultra-light planes. High-end producers are preserving their familiar, successful forms, while upgrading the details. Take, for example, the AMG-outfitted Mercedes 500 SEC.

Perhaps even more than the sleek, aerodynamic exteriors, interior materials and accessories define status. The Gulfstream's interior design, each seat equipped with amenities ranging from television to computers, rewrites the standards for executive and luxury air travel. On the other end of the spectrum, designers of mass transit have begun to apply the same notion. They realize there is a cost-effective logic. Using materials that communicate a sense of *worth,* along with durability, may well prove to be the most effective method for vandal-proofing their designs.

Yesterday's concept cars have become today's new line. To not only know *what is,* but to be able to predict with relative accuracy *what will be,* is the most exciting feature of this collection. We give you a glimpse of the future.

Product: Porsche 959
Manufacturer: Dr. ING. h.c. F. PORSCHE Inc.,
Porschestrasse, Stuttgart,
West Germany

Product: Ford Ghia Barchetta
Design: Design Center, Ford Motor Company, Dearborn,Michigan;
Ghia Bodyworks, Turin, Italy

Product: Mercedes Benz 500 SEC
Outfitted by: AMG, Westmonte, Illinois

Product: Honda Concept Car
Design Firm: Honda Motor Company, Ltd.
Pininfarina, Turin, Italy

Product: Probe V
Design Firm: Design Center, The Ford Motor Company, Dearborn, Michigan
Client: The Ford Motor Company
Dearborn, Michigan

Product: Pontiac Fiero
Designers: Ronald Hill, John Schinella, and William Scott
Design Firm: General Motors Corporation Warren, Michigan
Client: Pontiac Motor Division, Pontiac, Michigan
Awards: 1984 IDSA Industrial Design Excellence Award

Product: FireAero
Distributor: Industrial Design Research Inc. Laguna Beach, California
Client: American Honda, California
Materials: Fiberglass

Product: Buick Wildcat
Design: Buick Motor Division, General Motors Corporation, Flint, Michigan
Client: Buick Motor Division, Flint, Michigan

Product: Lotus, Mid-Engine Concept Car
Design Firm: Ital Design, Turin, Italy

Product: "TPC" Experimental Two Passenger Commuter Car
Client: General Motors Corporation Warren, Michigan

Product: Ford Ghia Trio 3-Passenger Car
Design: Design Center, Ford Motor Company, Dearborn, Michigan; Ghia Bodyworks, Turin, Italy

Product: Roger T2 cargo truck
Manufacturer: Ford Motor Company, Dearborn, Michigan

Product:	Vessa Trekka Micro-Car
Design:	Product Identity Limited, London, England; Crisp & Wilson; Lloyd Northover, London, England
Client:	Vessa Limited, Hampshire, England

Product:	London Transport 1990 Tube Stock
Design Firm:	DCA Design Consultants, Warwick, England

Product: Honda Gyro
Design Firm: Honda, Japan
Client: Honda, Gardena, California

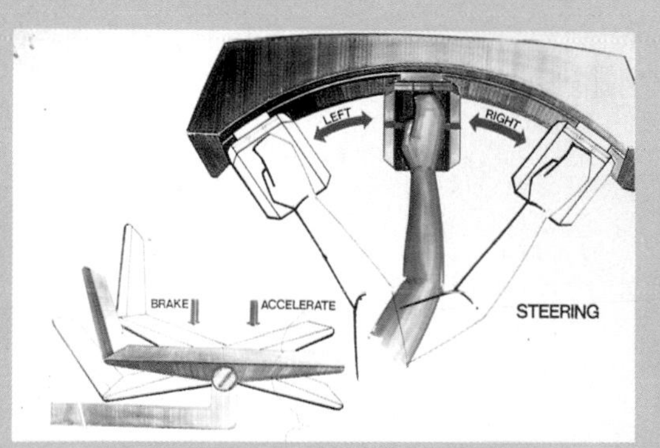

Product: Mock-Up Mini Van for Handicapped and Non-Handicapped Use
Designers: Mark Falanga, Jung-Hua Chang, and Mikael Backstrom
University of Illinois
Client: Easter Seals Corporation
Awards: 1985 RESNA award (Rehabilitation Engineering Society of North America)

Product: X-29
Client: Grumman, Bethpage, New York
Materials: Aeroplastic composite tailoring

Product: Maxair Drifter
Manufacturer: Maxair Aircraft Corporation
Glen Rock, Pennsylvania
Awards: 1984 Ultralight Reserve Grand Champion Award, Oshkosh, Wisconsin

Product: Laser 300
Client: OMAC, Inc., Reno, Nevada

Product: Edgley EA7 Optica Aircraft
Designers: John Edgley, Fiona Edgley
Design Firm: Edgley Aircraft Ltd.
Awards: 1984 Design Council Award

Product: Gulfstream Aerospace G-IV
Designers: Dave Ellies, Jim Grimes, and Terleski
Design Firm: Dave Ellies Industrial Design, Inc. Dallas, Texas
Manufacturer: Gulfstream Aerospace Corporation Savanna, Georgia

Product:	Program of Portholes
Design:	ninaber/peters/krouwel, industrial design, Delft, Netherlands
Client:	Boomsma B.V., Netherlands
Materials:	Aluminum extrusion and polycarbonate

Product:	"bobob," Child Safety Seat
Design:	ninaber/peters/krouwel, industrial design, Delft, Netherlands
Client:	Dremefa, B. V., Netherlands
Awards:	TNO award for innovative design in plastics
Materials:	Thermoplastic materials, polypropylene and ABS

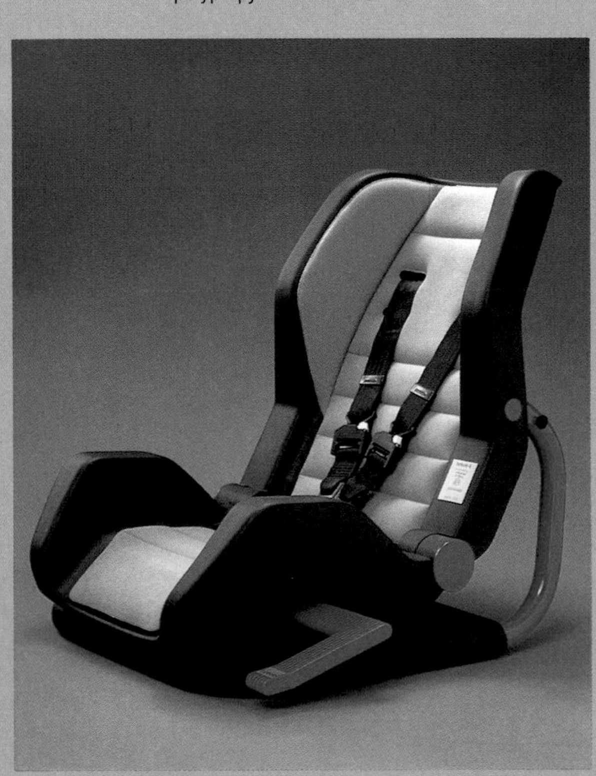

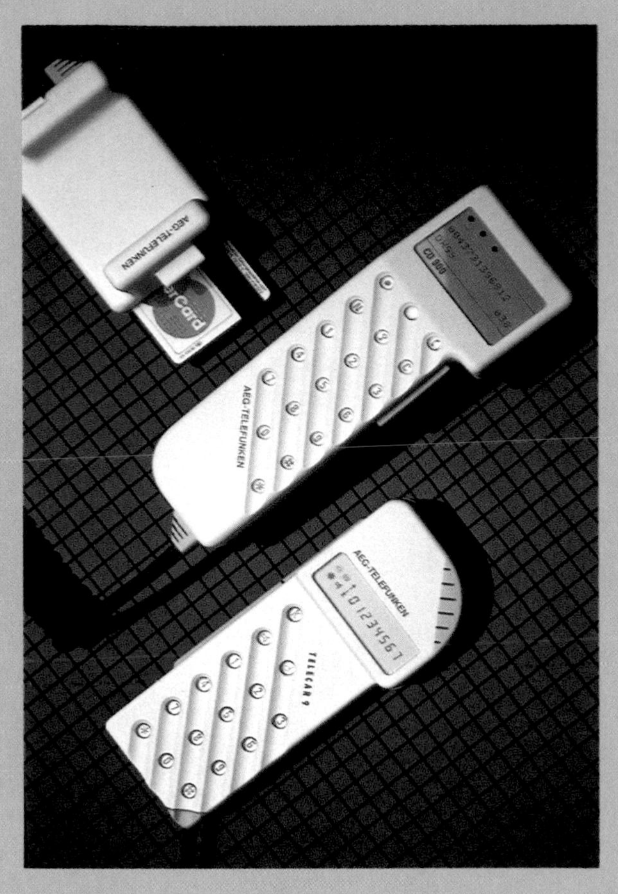

Product: Car Telephone
Design Firm: frogdesign, Campbell, California
Client: AEG-Telefunken, West Germany

Product: Mobile Telephone
Design Firm: Siemens Design Center, Iselin, New Jersey
Client: Siemens, Muenchen & Berlin West Germany
Materials: Noryl structural foam housing; Hosta foam push buttons

Product: Homofocal Headlamp
Design Firm: Lucas Electrical
Manufacturer: Lucas Electrical
Award: 1984 Design Council Award
Materials: DMC (Dough Molded Compound)

Product: Peugeot Headlights
Designers: Eugene Casey, Jr., David Miller, Douglas Smith, Robert Dawson, Thomas Pendleton, and Corbett Stone
Design Firm: King-Casey, Inc., New Canaan, Connecticut
Clients: Peugeot Motor of America, Inc. Lyndhurst, New Jersey; Sogedac Automobiles, Peugeot, Paris, France
Materials: Clear molded polycarbonate lens; two polycarbonate reflector housings; Sylvania plastic sealed beam (2B1 halogen-sealed)

Product: Sony Compact Disc Digital Audio Radio
Client: Sony Corporation of America
Park Ridge, New Jersey
Manufacturer: Sony Corporation, Tokyo, Japan

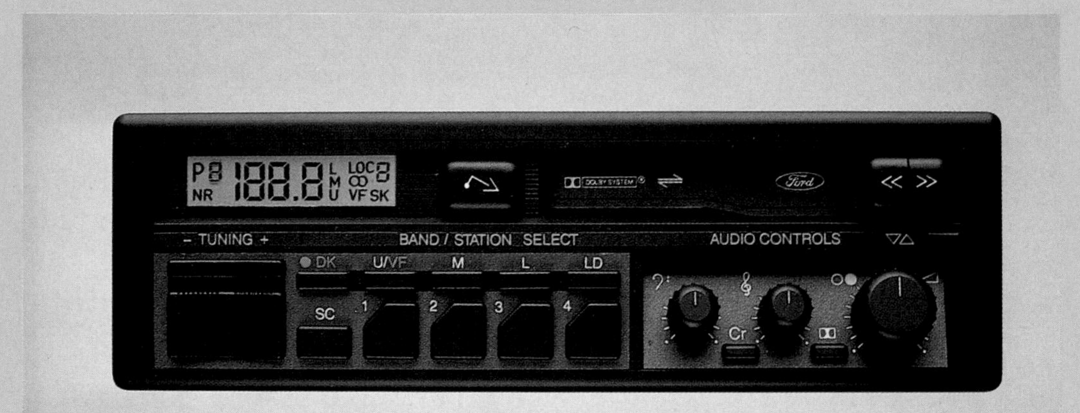

Product: Ford In-Car Audio
Designer: John Stoddard
Design Firm: ID Two, San Francisco, California
Client: The Ford Motor Company
Dearborn, Michigan

Product: Sony Discjockey
Design Firm: Sony Corporation, Tokyo, Japan
Client: Sony Corporation of America
Park Ridge, New Jersey

Product: ETAK Navigator Console
Design Firm: Steinhilber, Deutsch and Gard, Inc.
San Francisco, California
Client: ETAK

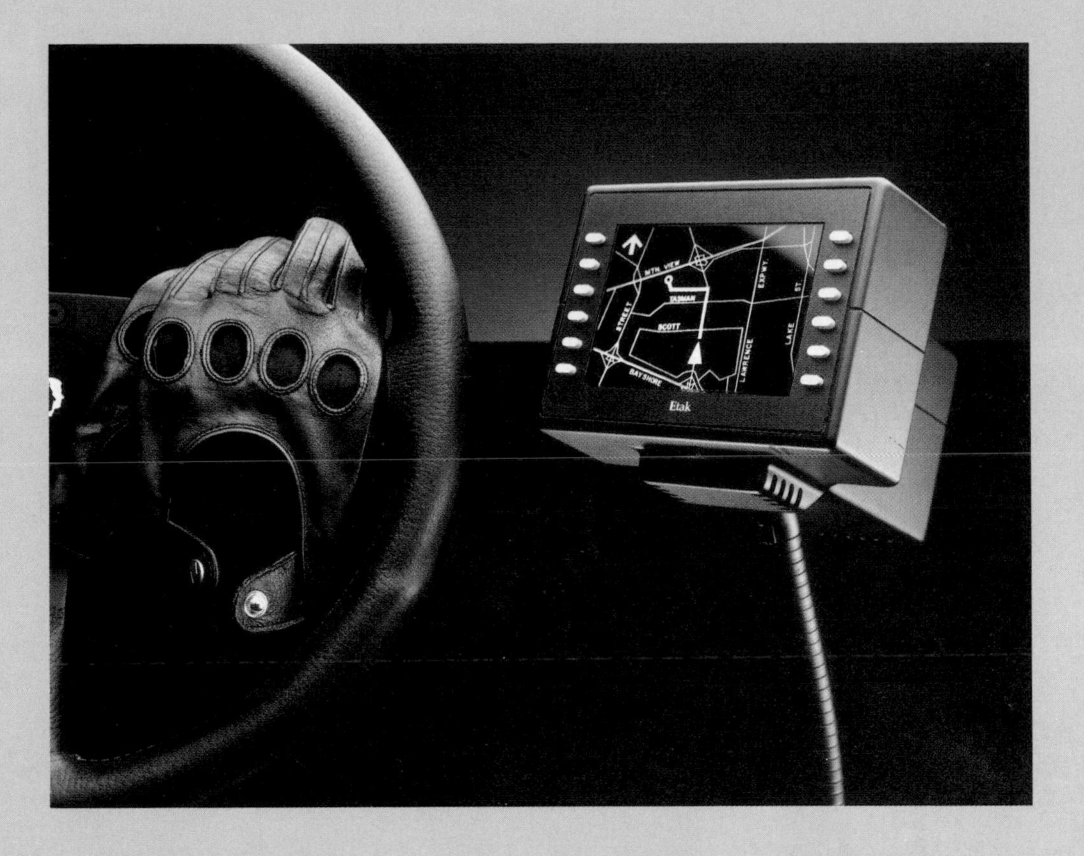

Product: Boston Acoustics C751 Automotive Loudspeaker System
Designer: Charles Rozier, New York, New York
Design Firm: Charles Rozier Design, New York, New York
Client: Boston Acoustics, Inc., Peabody, Massachusetts
Materials: Grille frames: molded ABS, painted matte black; grille: stamped perforated steel, painted glossy black; tweeter housing: molded ABS, painted matte black; logo plate: molded ABS, warm red and white silkscreen

SPORTS, FITNESS, AND RECREATIONAL EQUIPMENT

CHAPTER

Physical fitness has gone high style these days, and designers of exercise equipment have responded accordingly. These machines are the sleek, slim images of the bodies we hope to achieve (or, for the lucky few, maintain). Equally consistent is the vocabulary we use to describe these designs: strong, flexible, compact.

The health craze has expanded beyond the gymnasium and invaded the home, a move which has redefined the design criteria for exercise equipment. Diminished space dictates that home machines be easily stored. Perhaps this accounts for the fact that rowing machines have shown the strongest increase in retail sales of all home equiment, with models such as Precor M6.4 folding small enough to fit under a bed or flat against a wall. If not quite so collapsible, equipment must then be beautiful enough to serve as ''furniture'' for today's studio apartment dwellers. Pro Form's ''Aerobot'' comes remarkably close to fulfilling this rather extreme design requirement.

Whether for the pain of exercise or for capturing the pleasure of a moment, from bikes to cameras, these designs for the leisure world are also outstanding in the number of user-friendly features they offer. High-tech gadgets monitor everything from pulses to mileage to light, and if that's not enough, some then make any necessary adjustments for the assessed condition. A few even talk to you in the process. Machines that do the exercise *for you*?? Not this time around.

Product: Joe Lunch Box & Accessories
Designer: Winfried Scheuer
Design Firm: ID Two, San Francisco, California
Client: Joe, Inc., Washington, D.C.

Product: Hot and Cold Canteens
Design Firm: Heller Designs, Inc., New York, New York
Designer: Alan H. Heller, New York, New York
Materials: Plastic non-slip body; polyurethane insulation

Product: Deflector
Designers: Bob Johnston, Norm Widdis, and Len Clement
Design Firm: Cooper Canada Limited, Toronto, Ontario, Canada
Client: Cooper Canada Limited, Toronto, Ontario, Canada
Materials: Cross-linked polyethylene foam and high-density polyethylene sheet, which is thermo-formed to produce a sandwiched pad; molded arm pads are inserted into a lightweight lycra shell harness with an injection molded, quick release fastener

Product: A2050 Pro Staff Baseball Glove
Design Firm: KDA Consultants, Addison, Illinois
Client: Wilson Sporting Goods River Grove, Illinois
Awards: 1985 *Industrial Design* magazine Design Review selection
Materials: Patented Strata-loc web that uses rings of leather to form a pocket around the ball for sure catches and quick releases; a flexible back, adjustable wrist strap and gridded palm are added advantages

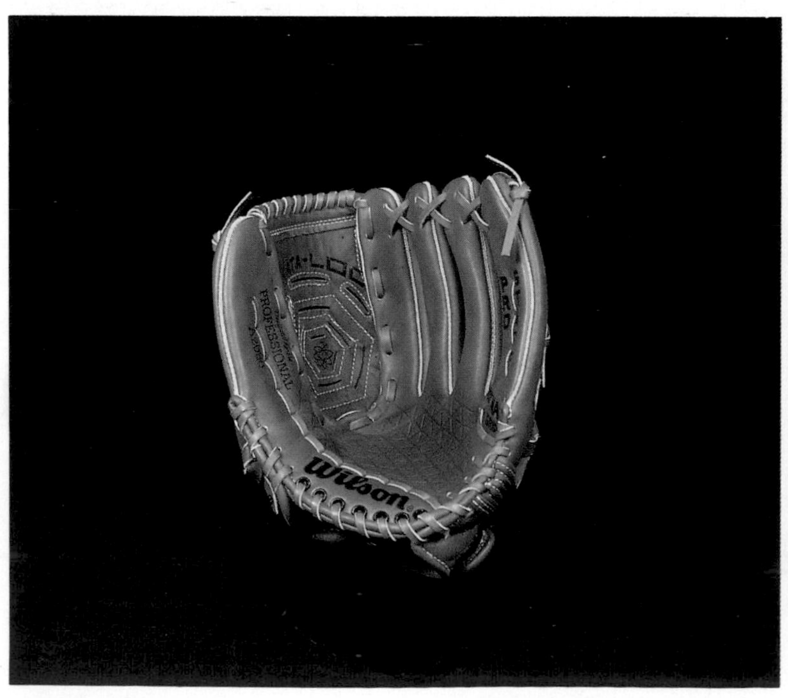

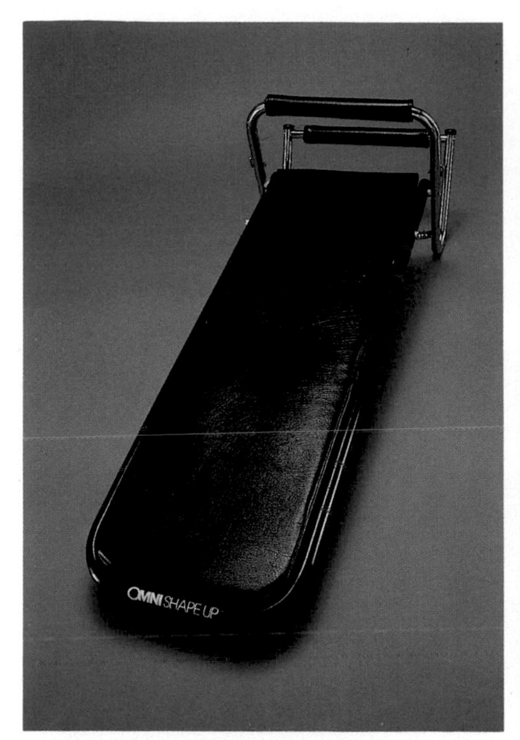

Product: Omni Shapeup
Designer: Gordon Randall Perry
Design Firm: Gordon Randall Perry Design, Inc., New York, New York
Manufacturer: MacLevy Products, Elmhurst, New York

Product: Golf Car
Design Firm:: Gregory Fossella Associates Boston, Massachusetts
Manufacturer: Pezepel, Miclec, Poland
Distributor: Melex, Raleigh, North Carolina
Materials: Light-weight, rust resistant steel and plastic construction; movable cup holders; a sizable molded dash with storage space; and a large bag well

Product: Aerobot
Designers: Bill Dalebout, Loarn Robertson, and Sohrab Vossoughi
Design Firm: ZIBA Design, Portland, Oregon
Client: Pro Form Inc., Beaverton, Oregon
Materials: Frame and levers: bent steel tubing with blue epoxy powder coating; seat: polypropelene, formed plywood, and molded urethane foam; resistance modules: UHMW polypropelene friction discs, powdered metal rotor; other parts: injection molded plastics

Product: M8.5 Stationary Bicycle
Designer: David Smith
Client: Precor, Redmond, Washington

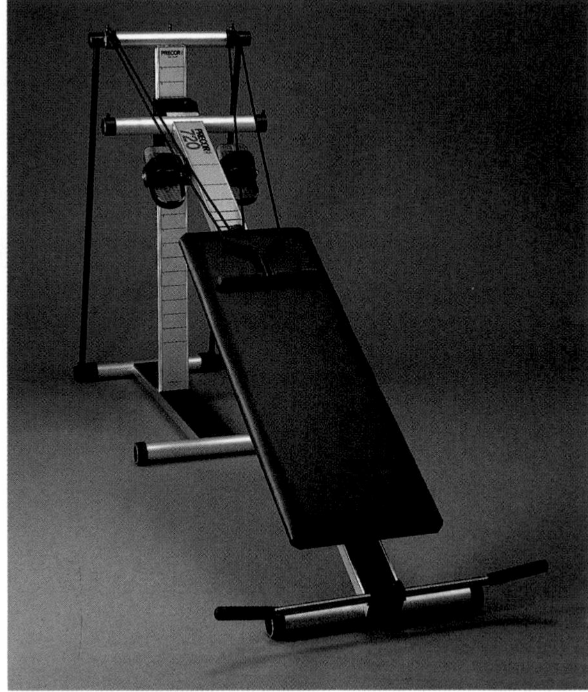

Product: Precor 720
Designer: David Smith
Client: Precor, Redmond, Washington

Product: Benchmark 920 Rower
Designers: Andrew Kostanecki, Carl Thompson, Robert Brainard, and Glen Walter
Design Firm: Andrew T. Kostanecki, Inc. New Canaan, Connecticut
Client: AMF American Athletic, Jefferson, Iowa
Materials: Padded seat, telescoping slide bar, foam-covered handgrips, and adjustable heel straps

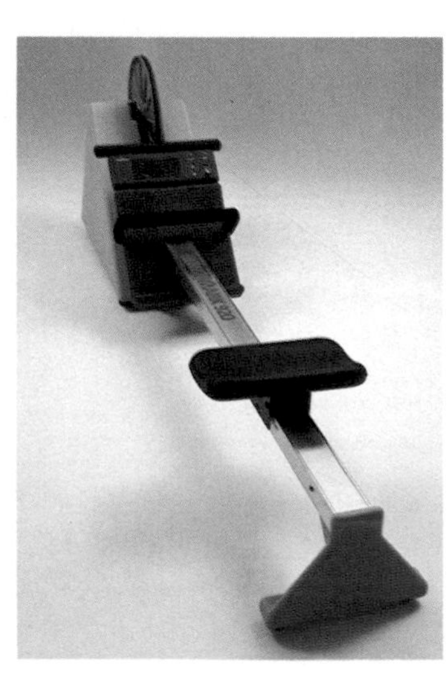

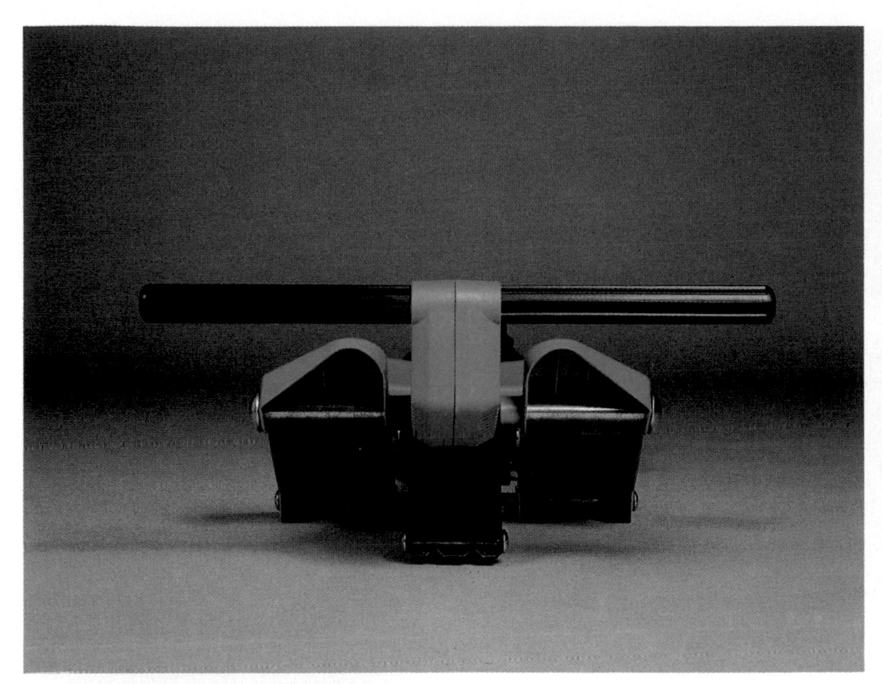

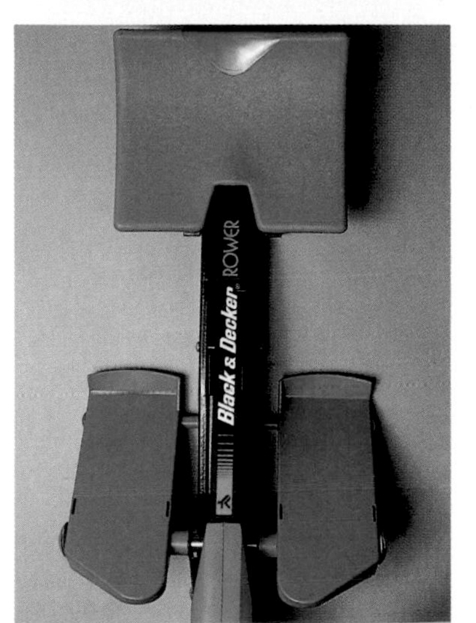

Product: Home Exercisers
Design Firm: Crisp & Wilson, Ashland Place, London, England
Client: Black & Decker, Maidenhead, Berkshire, England
Materials: Painted steel, polypropylene

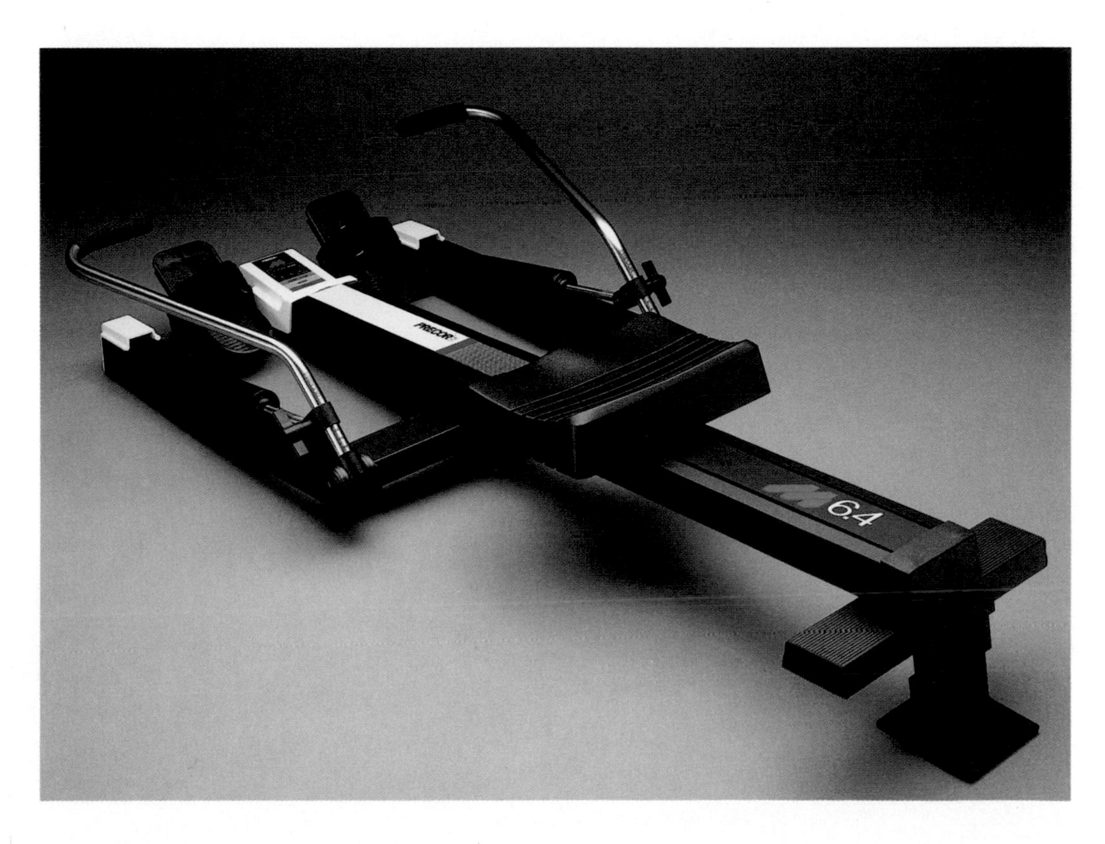

Product: M6.4 Rower
Designer: David Smith
Client: Precor, Redmond, Washington

Product: Thermos
Manufacturer: Bodum, Inc., Horsham, Pennsylvania

Product: Avant 1 Cross-Country Ski Binding
Design Firm: Alan Brownlie Design, Skaneateles, New York
Client: DMC, Canastota, New York
Materials: Its wide under-toe pivot platform offers the entry level skier a confidence-building package of stability, releasibility, and step-in entry.

Product: CS420 Advanced Cross-County Racing Ski Shoe
Design Firm: Schlagheck & Schultes, Munich, West Germany
Client: Trak, Ward Hill, Massachusetts

Product: Heavy Hands 866, Training Tool
Design: Equipment Division, AMF American Athletic
Manufacturer: AMF, Tyrolia-Freizeitgeräte-Ges. m.b.H. & Co., Austria

Product: Baby Swing
Distributor: Children's Playgrounds Inc. Cambridge, Massachusetts

Product: Timex Triathlon Watch
Designers: Gary Grimes, John T. Houlihan
Client: Timex, Waterbury, Connecticut
Materials: Case and push button: polycarbonate resin; strap: polyurethane; lens: mineral glass; caseback: stainless steel

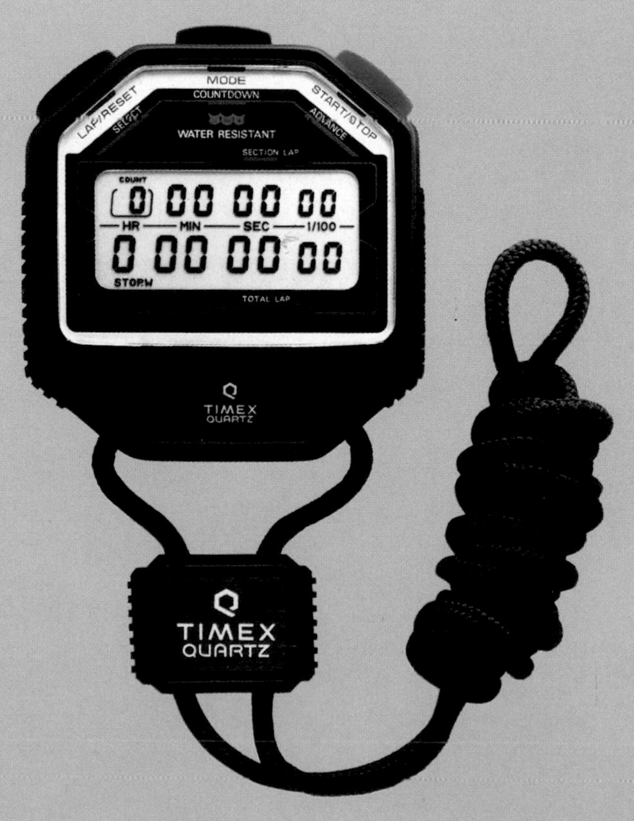

Product: Sure-Grip Hand-Held Stopwatch
Client: Timex, Middlebury, Connecticut
Materials: 14-digit display, 22-in. adjustable black nylon cord, and a 10-hour countdown timer

Product: 7/21 Compact Binoculars
Staff Design: Richard Blanchard
Manufacturer: J.C. Penney Company, Inc., New York, New York

Product: N2000 Camera
Distributor: Nikon Inc., Garden City, New York

Product: Minolta Talker
Manufacturer: Minolta Camera Company Asaka, Japan
Distributor: Minolta Corporation, Ramsey, New Jersey

Product: Vivitar Series 1 450mm f/4.5 Catadioptric Telephoto Lens
Designer: Steven Shull, Santa Monica, California
Client: Vivitar Corporation, Santa Monica, California
Manufacturer: U.S. Precision Lens, Taichung, Taiwan
Materials: Lens jacket and sunshade: compression molded silicon rubber; front lens barrel: screw machined aluminum; rear lens barrel: injection molded glass-filled polycarbonate; focusing collar: injection molded ABS with Tampo type

Product: Olympus XA camera
Design Firm: Olympus Optical Company Ltd. Tokyo, Japan
Distributor: Olympus Camera Corporation, Consumer Products Group Woodbury, New York

Product: Pentax Auto Sport
Manufacturer: Pentax Corporation a subsidiary of Asahai Optical Company Ltd. of Japan
Distributor: Pentax, Englewood, Colorado

Product: Avatar 2000
Design Firm: FOMAC, Inc., Wilmington, Massachusetts
Photo Credit: Chet Bukowski

Product: Peugeot's Take-A-Part Bicycle
Client: Peugeot, Carlstadt, New Jersey

Product: Spalding LA26
Design: International Industrial Design Inc.
Manufacturer: Miyata Industry Co., Ltd., Japan
Awards: Japan Good Design Δ Award

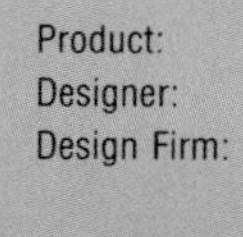

Product: The Minicruiser
Designer: Morton L. Heilig
Design Firm: Supercruiser Inc. Santa Monica, California

Product: The Supercruiser Scooter
Designer: Morton L. Heilig
Design Firm: Supercruiser Inc., Santa Monica, California

Product: Flickstand
Designers: Dixon Newbold, Ned Levine
Manufacturer: Rhode Gear USA, Providence, Rhode Island
Materials: Zytel™ band; stainless steel tubes with stamped depressions; Buttonhead hex screws; stainless steel wire

Product: Little Carrier
Designer: Björn Alskog
Client: Playsam Activity Toys, Division of Kalmarsunds-Gruppen, Kalmar, Sweden
Awards: "Utmärkt Svensk Form", Swedish Design Council Award
Materials: Epoxy-lacquered steel tubing; waterproof plywood; solid rubber tires with ball-bearings in front and nylon-bearings in rear

Product:	"Cyclotronic" Electric Speedometer for Bicycle
Design Firm:	ninaber/peters/krouwel, industrial design, Delft, Netherlands
Client:	Industrie Koot B.V., Netherlands
Materials:	Thermoplastic, polycarbonate

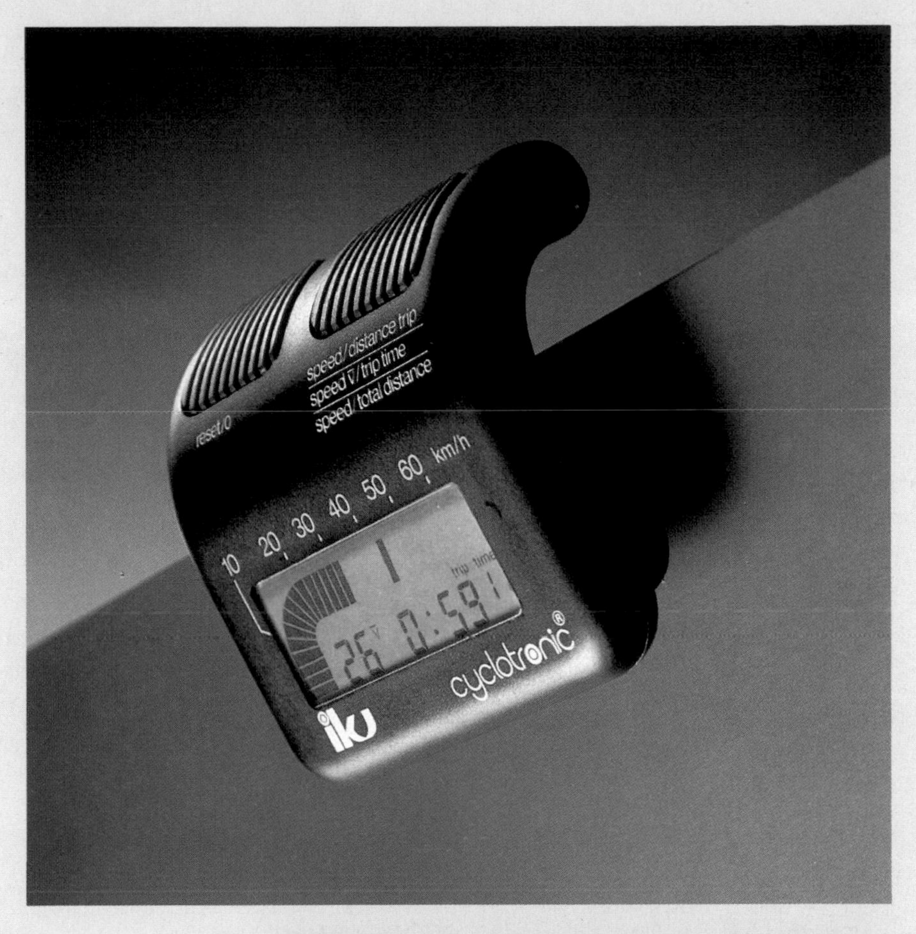

Product:	Bicycle Locking System
Designer:	Denis Bertuzzo, Weston, Ontario, Canada
Materials:	Durable flexible nylon tubing; 2 1/2-in. diameter tubing with rubberized epoxy finish

DESIGN AWARDS PROGRAMS

American Craft Museum Design Award
American Craft Council
40 West 53rd Street
New York, New York 10019
USA

ASID International Product Design Competition
American Society of Interior Designers
1430 Broadway
New York, New York 10018
USA

The Australian Design Award
Industrial Design Council of Australia
37 Little Collins Street
Melbourne 3000
Australia

Braun Prize for Technical Competition
Braun AG
Informationsabteilung
Postfach 1120
6242 Kronberg
West Germany

Canada Awards
Awards & Design Directorate
c/o Association of Canadian Industrial Designers
Humber College
205 Humber College Blvd.
Rexdale, Ontario
Canada

Canada Awards for Excellence In Design
Government of Canada
c/o National Design Council
235 Queen Street
Ottawa K1A OH5
Canada

Compasso d'Oro
Associazione per il Disegno Industriale + Municipality of Milan
Via Montenapoleone 18
20121 Milan
Italy

The Danish Design Council Award
The Danish Design Council
H.C. Andersens Blvd., 18
DK–1553 Copenhagen V
Denmark

Design Council Awards
The Design Council
28 Haymarket
London SW1Y 4SU
England

Dunlopillo Design Award
Dunlop Limited
Dunlop House
Ryder Street
London SW1Y 6PX
England

Good Design Prize/G–Mark Products
Japan Industrial Design Promotion
Organization (JIDPO)
P.O. Box 101, World Trade Center
Tokyo, Japan

Haus Industrieform Essen
Haus Industrieform Essen
Kennedyplatz 7,
D–4300 Essen 1
West Germany

IALD Awards Program
International Association of
Lighting Designers
30 West 22nd Street
New York, New York 10010
USA

IBD Product Design Competition
Institute of Business Designers
1155 Merchandise Mart
Chicago, Illinois 60654
USA

ICSID Philips Award
Philips Gloeilampenqabrieken
Building SX.,
Glaslan Einhoven
The Netherlands

ID Annual Design Review
Industrial Design magazine
330 West 42nd Street
New York, New York 10036
USA

ID Prize
The Danish Design Council
H.C. Andersens Blvd., 18
DK–1553 Copenhagen V
Denmark

IDEA Industrial Design Excellence Award
Industrial Designers Society of America
1360 Beverly Road
McLean, Virginia 22101
USA

International Design Competition
Japan Design Foundation
Semba Center Bldg. No. 4
Higashi–ku, Osaka 541
Japan

Pradikat if Die gute Industrieform
Die gute Industrieform
Hannover e. V.
Messegelände
3000 Hannover 82
West Germany

Progressive Architecture International
Conceptual Furniture Competition
Progressive Architecture Magazine
600 Summer Street, P.O. Box 1361
Stamford, Connecticut 06904
USA

Roscoe Annual Product Design Award
The Resources Council Inc.
979 Third Avenue
Room 902, North
New York, New York 10022
USA

The SCAN Prize
The Danish Design Council
H.C. Andersens Blvd., 18
DK–1553 Copenhagen V
Denmark

Signe D'Or Exposition
Design Centre asbi
Galerie Ravenstein 51
1000 Bruxelles
Belgium

SMAU Industrial Design Award
Corso Venezia 49
Milan, Italy

STAFF (Design and Light)
Staff Leuchtenwerke Design Center
Stuttgart,
Landesgewerbeamt
Baden–Württemberg
STAFF Preis "Design und Light,"
Kienestrasse 18, D–7000 Stuttgart 1
West Germany

Stuttgart Design Selection
Design Center Stuttgart
Landesgewerbeamt
Baden–Württemberg
Kienastrasse 18
7000 Stuttgart 1
West Germany

Svensk Form
Utmärkt Svensk Form
Foreningen Svensk Form
Box 7404, S–103 91 Stockholm,
Sweden

DESIGNERS

CLIENTS/ MANUFACTURERS